The Everlasting Covenant

Books by Robyn Carr

Chelynne
The Blue Falcon
The Bellerose Bargain
The Braeswood Tapestry
The Troubadour's Romance
By Right of Arms
The Everlasting Covenant

The Everlasting Covenant

by
Robyn Carr

BOSTON LITTLE, BROWN AND COMPANY TORONTO

FIRST EDITION

Library of Congress Cataloging-in-Publication Data

Carr, Robyn.
The everlasting covenant.

1. Great Britain — History — Wars of the Roses,
1455–1485 — Fiction. I. Title.
PS3553.A76334E94   1987   813'.54   86-33771
ISBN 0-316-12979-8

RRD VA

Published simultaneously in Canada
by Little, Brown & Company (Canada) Limited

PRINTED IN THE UNITED STATES OF AMERICA

For my mother, Bette Crandall Henrichs
— with love

The Everlasting Covenant

PART I

April 12, 1460

Chapter One

THERE WERE real battles going on elsewhere in England and across the world while Anne watched the contest of arms from her parents' pavilion Lord Shay of Wymount Castle, a bountiful estate north by only a short distance from Pontefract Castle, the king's residence, hosted this tournament. It was the first one Anne had ever seen, and it was the most exciting day of her life. The challenges had been many, the knights were magnificent, and the fighting was at fever pitch. If her family knew who had captured her heart, she would be stripped and flogged, and this caused her sly, secret smile.

In fact, if it were known that Anne had cast her heart at all, secretly or otherwise, she would probably be punished. She would not even have been allowed to attend the tournament, but her father, Lord Gifford, had insisted. "Let her see a bit of the world before she goes into seclusion," Ferris Gifford had insisted. It was assumed that Anne Gifford would go to the convent when an appropriate one could be found. Thankfully, such negotiations took time, and her family was busy.

Anne jumped and cheered as two opponents crashed together and were immediately unhorsed. These two, mercenaries from

Burgundy, came to fight and collect prizes, and they resumed the battle on foot with broadswords.

"Madam, their horses are being readied."

Anne's head turned as she heard her father alert her mother, Marcella. But she did not look in the direction of the Gifford knights who were preparing to ride in the melee. Rather, she cautiously stole a glance toward the deFrayne troop. And she saw him. Yet she had to quickly move her eyes away, looking toward the opposite end of the field where her father's troop, led by her oldest brother, Sir Quentin, were mounting their steeds. Color marked her cheeks, for Dylan had *looked* at her! He was so bold and foolish. Although it made her heart sail, she was sometimes afraid of the risks he was willing to take.

But Dylan had said, "They do not watch us or think of us, my love. You are the second-born daughter and I am the third son. We are the babies of these arguing lords and when we flee together, no one will even know we're gone."

Out of the corner of her eye she observed Marcella. Her mother had not noticed the direction of Anne's gaze, for Marcella was eyeing the deFrayne pavilion with cold contempt. Nothing would be said here, but words were hardly necessary. The deFraynes had slain Marcella's father, a knight of the Gifford house, in a battle some years past, just as Giffords had slain deFrayne knights when there was an opportunity. There had been no killing for fifteen years, but the blood lay fresh in the minds of each family and Marcella seemed to hate them the most fiercely, especially Daphne, Lady deFrayne. Lady Daphne's three sons were not only older than the Gifford sons, they were achieving more fame as knights. The jealousy Marcella felt was deep.

Anne looked toward Divina, her older sister. She was standing, waving, and blowing kisses toward the Gifford troop. It was understood that Divina, though nineteen and past her prime, should do whatever necessary to attract a husband. A betrothal, Lady Gifford specifically advised, that would not cost the Gifford family too much in dowry but would substantially improve their influence at court. Anne nearly laughed when considering the instructions; such an order would be difficult for even a comely maid to fulfill, and Divina was not very pretty.

She glanced at her father and her heart nearly stopped as she met his eyes. He focused on her face; his intense brown eyes were fluid and knowing. She was almost frightened; for a moment she wondered if her father could read her mind. But Ferris Gifford looked away and slowly exhaled.

Somehow I must make him stop such madness, Anne thought. Their families had been enemies since her great-grandfather's time, and whenever they met there was a fight. Tension had not eased over the years, and as their families grew in size the battles became larger. Marriages were arranged according to loyalties, to lend more soldiers and knights to the volatile feud. When a man pledged to the Gifford family, he swore his arms to aid them against the deFraynes. And this had begun many years ago, when Henry of Bolingbroke, son of John of Gaunt, the Duke of Lancaster, was engaged in usurping King Richard II. Therefore, it was the fault of the deFrayne family, since they supported the Lancaster usurpers, while the Gifford family had sworn fealty to King Richard.

Or was it the fault of the Giffords, who had not truly supported a king in just over sixty years, since the Lancaster rule began? Anne shook her head. She was never quite sure. But one of the great-grandfathers had killed the other, and so she must not love Dylan. In fact, she must love no man. She must satisfy the needs of the church, as one member of every noble family should. She suspected that this plan would save the family time and money, for the convent's dowry requirements were modest and there would be one less Gifford maiden to have wed. Her mother had said as much. And Anne did not think that Marcella would sacrifice a son to the church even if she had borne only boys. She had plans for her sons that included earning wealth and prestige.

The clarions sounded as the field was cleared and the deFraynes prepared to go against the Giffords. The spectators were hushed in expectation, for this never failed to be an exciting match. The horses churned up the dirt as they charged and the field became a confusing press of horses and men, a dozen on each side, some still astride, some felled, and all who were watching began to cheer. Anne rose that she might see, but it was difficult to place Dylan. The green of Gifford paired off with the blue of deFrayne, but with helms in place and horses being hurriedly removed from the field by pages and squires, there was only the mesh of blue and green, like an angry sea, amidst the crashing of metal and the clashing of broadswords.

Soon the combatants gave themselves room as they broke off into individual contests. Everywhere there was a couple; blue and green, green and blue. To the delight of the crowd the center of the field was taken by the eldest Gifford, Quentin, and the eldest deFrayne, Wayland. Anne looked hard for a peacock feather, difficult to find at such a distance, but finally she spied Dylan. He was engaged against one of the Gifford men-at-arms, but thank God, not one of her brothers. Ah, he fought beautifully. His movements were graceful and swift, his arm mighty. The Gifford man fell to one knee quickly, and Anne knew none of her father's knights was weak. It was a proud moment for Dylan.

There was a gasp from her mother, and Anne turned toward Quentin and Wayland. A knight in green livery struck Wayland's back. Sir Wayland swirled abruptly, not crushed by the blow but angered indeed, and began a battle with the second Gifford son, Bart. Sir Quentin paused, lowering his broadsword either to keep the contest fair or in stunned surprise. But even Quentin's pause could not rescind Bart's unchivalrous attack.

"The deFrayne bastard tricked them," Marcella snarled. Anne stared at her mother in startled wonder. Had she not seen? It was Bart who dishonored himself; Bart, who was not as large and strong as either Quentin or any of the deFrayne sons. Marcella should be mortified by her son's public disgrace; how could she defend him? How could she possibly fault a deFrayne? But the judge did not share Marcella's prejudice and was riding onto the field to call the point against Bart and keep the contest fair. "They will not interfere! My lord, rise and protest the interference," Marcella demanded of her husband.

But there was no need to protest, for Dylan had beaten his man and ran full speed to the mismatch of contestants and quickly took on Quentin, the larger and stronger of the two. Broadswords, sheathed so that there would be no death at this match, clattered and sang as the warriors fought. The deFrayne men were gaining, beating down the Giffords, and Anne felt her heart in her throat. She rose again, unconscious of her movements, her hands clutching the sheer veil that covered her long, unbound hair. Tears gathered in her eyes against her will. She had never before been so frightened. She chewed her lip, and a tear slid down her cheek. But Quentin fell. He fell and could not rise.

Anne suddenly realized she was standing and nervously twisting the cloth of her veil. She sat down abruptly and looked around guiltily. Again she met Ferris's eyes. But what was that glowing there? Pain and sympathy? Anger? She flinched as he reached across Marcella's skirts to squeeze his youngest daughter's hand. "You need not fear for your brothers, *petite*. They will not be hurt." His voice was gentle and soft.

"I am not afraid, Papa," she said. "But for a moment I forgot it is only a contest."

"Aye, little one. Only a contest."

"Papa . . . Bart —"

"Bart only went to his brother's defense, which is as it should be," Lady Gifford snapped, her icy blue eyes full of hate.

Lord Gifford sat in stony silence, staring at his wife. Then he turned his eyes back to the field, where the contest was being awarded to the deFrayne family. Sir Dylan, one of the youngest combatants on the field, stretched out a hand toward Sir Quentin to help him rise, but the gesture was refused. Without looking at Marcella, Ferris spoke. "Perhaps you should speak to your son about his honorable defense of his brother . . . since he does not often listen to me."

Lady Gifford neither replied nor looked at her husband, but her jaw worked and her eyes were narrowed toward the deFrayne pavilion, where Dylan's mother stood, smiling and waving at her victorious sons. Lady deFrayne was a slim beauty, still vivacious. Anne suddenly wondered if her mother was mostly jealous over Lady deFrayne's good looks.

All the Giffords were silent through the remainder of the jousts. It was as if they acknowledged, though they could not admit, that at least one in their troop had fought without honor. A late challenge pitted Sir Quentin against Sir Wayland, and in this joust Quentin won fairly, restoring some of the prestige to the Giffords and lessening the weight of the losses that would have to be paid to the deFraynes. But Anne felt no relief, for she saw how strong was her mother's hatred for that family. And her mother, more than her father, seemed to rule the house.

A huge feast followed, the victors seated above the salt and the defeated taking their lesser stations at tables far back in the grand hall. Torches were lit, acrobats and jugglers roved through the keep, minstrels crooned, dancing ensued, and food enough to feed all of London was spread about the trestle tables in the hall and yard. Friend and foe raised wine-filled hanaps in celebration, merrymaking ensued, and the tension of the day was eased. Still, it was not the gaiety that caused Anne's enlivened spirits. It was the sparkle in Dylan's eyes from across the crowded room that filled her with happiness. Neither fight nor feast could divert her attention from her chosen knight.

Anne Gifford was a new face among the crowd, and her fresh young beauty drew stares. There were whispers among young knights and older lords. She wore her best gown, a rose-colored velvet with silver trim, and a transparent veil of the same hue drew attention to her lustrous dark hair. Her cheeks glowed with excitement, and her eyes, dark and luminous, were filled with mystery and allure. Since no one in her family had ever made much of her looks, she did not realize that she was comely. To some who looked at her and wondered about her name, she was also very desirable.

As darkness surrounded the festivities and the men fell into their cups, Anne was aware of a scuffle. She backed around a stone stairwell in the common room just out of the way of two angry knights.

"The insult will be well met on the field," she heard Bart cry.

Peeking around the corner, she saw that her brother had pushed Cameron deFrayne, who was larger and stronger, against the wall.

"Insult?" Cameron returned, and by the sound of the reply, the men had indulged in equal amounts of wine and ale. "Truth, Gifford, you are a coward!"

"We shall see who is a coward when we test the matter with blades," Bart challenged.

The argument was quickly noticed by other men, who backed away from the two combatants. To judge by the eyes of the spectators, they hoped for a fight. Gifford against deFrayne always made an interesting fray, whether in a legitimate tournament or like this.

"Hah, as if you could lift a blade," Cameron flung back.

Bart lifted his arm as if to deliver a punch, but Sir Quentin pushed his way through the crowd and grasped Bart's raised arm at the wrist, pulling his brother away.

"Wine makes men brave," Quentin blustered. "Drink makes for clumsy contests. Let us meet at dawn, refreshed, and consider whether we need to prove ourselves further. Our host deserves better than a ruined hall."

Bart, temporarily subdued, glared at Cameron. "In the morning then," Cameron said.

Quentin, firmly holding his younger brother's arm, pulled him aside and through the gathered revelers. Anne pulled back into the stairwell. Quentin pushed Bart up against the wall within earshot and gave him a tongue-lashing.

"Fool," she heard her eldest brother say in a fierce whisper. "Is it not enough to act like an idiot on the field in front of hundreds of people? Must you goad them the more?"

"They were awarded their points at my misjudgment," Bart argued. "Why then need they insult me further? Is not payment for our losses enough?"

"When the cups are full a wise knight turns his back on nonsense. I'm sure you said your share."

"How can you take their side?"

"There is no side. But I tell you this, little brother, if you

[9]

dishonor this family in such a way again, you will meet *me* on the field. Go find some woman to appreciate your loose tongue. I've had enough of battles for one day."

Anne leaned against the stone wall. Like Quentin, she had had enough for one day. If it had had any advantage, the argument had taken attention from her. She found her parents in discussion with Quentin and Bart and curtsied before them, asking to be retired with her nurse, Minerva.

Old Minerva was relieved when she was excused, and Anne, being Minerva's favorite, brought a large chalice of heavily spiced wine to their closet for the servant. Despite the noise that echoed through the keep, it was only moments before Minerva's snores rivaled the shouts from below. And Anne quietly rose, fixing her quilts in a comfortable mound on her pallet. She pulled her dress over her shift, put her heavy chopines on her feet, and ran her fingers through her raven black hair.

Lifting her skirts, she fled through the upper halls, down the backstairs, winding down, down, and down. This was a route discovered in daylight, but she held her breath the whole way, for these stairs were dangerously steep and dark and there was but one torch lit at the bottom. She went through the buttery where kegs of ale and casks of wine were stored, the sour aroma penetrating the room and causing her to wrinkle her nose. The rear door, used only for bringing in supplies and food, was locked from within, but it opened easily and the squeaking could not be heard above the din in the common room and courtyard. The moon was high and full and her way was well lit. The stable was dark and foul and the door to the back room creaked as she opened it, causing her to tremble anew.

His arm came around her from behind and the moment she turned, his lips took hers. Her surprise lasted only a moment, and to her benefit, for her gasp left her lips parted and Dylan savored in the wine-sweet taste of her mouth. She pressed herself against him, holding him fiercely, holding him forever. Finally he released her mouth, but only to gather greedy fistfuls of her hair and roam the softness of her neck and shoulder with his lips.

"Anne, my love, my beautiful angel . . ."

"Dylan, this is such madness. We will both be killed for it." But her protest was breathless, and she had come as he requested as she always did. "How did this begin, Dylan? Where does it end?"

He held her back a bit and smiled down at her. He touched her nose with his lips. "It began when you snubbed me at the Lincoln fair, minx. And the next year, when the rain separated you from old Minerva, you were at my mercy in the gardener's pavilion."

Anne's eyes were moist with frustration and sadness. "A year has come and gone, Dylan, and a dozen times I have crept away from my family on some excuse to be with you. What is to become of us? I have never been so afraid as I was today."

"Afraid that I would win? Afraid that I would lose?"

She began to cry as emotion spilled down her cheeks, although she wished to be strong and brave. When their moment finally arrived and her lips could touch his, the fear that she might never be in his arms again came instantly.

Dylan held her gently, stroking her back, letting the tears come. He knew this was too much for her, but he could not abstain. Each time he saw her the longing became more intense within him; each time he touched her, he wanted more of her. And the poor little demoiselle, so in love with him, could not refuse these dangerous encounters. He wanted better for her, better for himself. But for now, this was all they had.

"Please, Dylan, have pity on me. Take me away now . . . tonight."

He chuckled ruefully and touched the graceful curve of her cheek. "Now? Carry you away from the tournament grounds? Do you think there are quite enough knights to come after us? Ah, my love, Lord Gifford would sound the alarm and every knight would mount up at the first call. A maiden, stolen from the lists . . ."

"Then soon, Dylan."

"Soon, my sweet love."

"Ah," she sighed, leaning her head against his chest. "I curse our grandfathers, Dylan. I would go into hell to curse them."

Dylan groaned sadly. There was a heaviness in his breast, like a boulder on his heart. "It has little to do with our grandfathers now," he said quietly. "The curse of the late-born son is to hear too much, too soon. But I think I have good news. It may come to nothing, but we do have one sympathetic ear. Daphne, my mother."

Anne's head snapped back and she stared into his eyes, stricken for a moment. "You've told her?"

"No, but Daphne has the eyes of a hawk, and, praise God, the heart of an angel. She has seen me watch you. She told me she understands . . . and if there is a way to help me without defying my father, she will do so."

Disappointed, Anne let her head drop to his chest again. "Oh, Dylan, there is no way for you to claim me with your father's good will. If I go to the deFraynes as your wife, my family will only start more battles against your house. We must both leave our families. There's no help for it."

"Then we shall." He lifted her chin with a finger. "If that is what must be, we shall leave them to their stupid war. I am a good fighter; I will do well anywhere. The inheritance my father has in mind for me will be nothing to dismiss . . . he would be pleased to add it to Wayland's or Cam's small fortune. Your dowry cannot be rich, little second-born lass . . . what do they have that we cannot win in a few months from Burgundy or Calais? We mean nothing to the families. Do not lose heart, sweet, for we will have each other one day soon. All that delays us now is the best moment to flee."

She giggled suddenly. "My *dowry*? Oh Dylan, I am to go to the convent. Have you never suspected? It was decided at my birth. Twas not for my sweet disposition that they promised to send me to the church, for I was a horrid child. My mother near lost her life birthing me, and then the midwives could not keep me from crying. Poor Lord Gifford . . . three sons to train and two daughters to see wed."

A rich, handsome smile broke over Dylan's face. "You? In a cloister? *Mon dieu*, the sisters would be outraged. You are the

[12]

most beautiful and the most passionate woman in Christendom."
He kissed her again, deeply, and her response to his touch gave
lie to a life as a nun. He chuckled again. "You, a bride of Christ?
Impossible! I am hard pressed not to spoil you, and all this time
Lady Gifford thinks of you as a nun."

"Oh, Dylan, I know you love me. And I will never be a sister.
I will be your wife. Or your mistress. I will only be with you."

"It is just as well, this plan they have. At least I shall never
lose you to another man. And perhaps it will be easier to steal
you from the convent than from your father's house."

"Do you promise, Dylan, my love?"

"I swear. Even though I wish it otherwise for both our sakes,
it is you I love, Anne. I fear I always will."

The fair at Lincoln was a fall festival attended by noble and
common families, knights, merchants, and monks. That of two
years past was etched in Anne's memory for all time. She was
with her sister; he was with his brothers. Anne was allowed to
go because she had argued and begged fiercely. She was three
and ten Dylan had a score of years. The streets were narrow
and crowded, and as they came upon a leathermonger's cart,
Divina slowed her pace and turned to Anne, directly behind
her. "They are deFraynes. Do not look at them."

This was said loudly enough so that the eldest deFrayne man
turned from the leathermonger's wares and snorted in the direction of the women, making some uncomplimentary comment
about their ugliness. Had they been Gifford men passing de-
Frayne men, no doubt there would have been a fight. It had
happened often over more than fifty years.

But on this occasion, there was something rare in the crisp
fall air. Wayland deFrayne ignored Divina Gifford as she lifted
her nose and her hem to pass quickly, but his younger brother,
Sir Cameron, watched her haughtily and with disdain. This
induced the youngest deFrayne to turn his head.

Divina glided past with a superior air, Anne close behind.
But Anne could not ape her sister's manner, though she tried.
She had never seen a deFrayne, and she had heard a lifetime of

wild and horrible tales about this wretched family who had cost hers so much. She glanced at them curiously, amazed to find them without fangs or horns. It was Sir Cameron who made her blush.

"The little one has great mettle. Someday I will capture her and bait the Gifford bastards to come and fetch her."

"If you touch her, I will kill you," another voice said. Anne, young and only curious about these evil men, looked directly at Dylan's beautiful face. He was a handsome youth, the most handsome she had ever seen. His eyes sparkled like jewels, turquoise and deep, his lips parted to reveal bright, even teeth, and his thick hair was wheat and rye, touched by the fire of the sun. "She is an angel," he said in a voice that was both playful and seductive at once.

Anne had smiled spontaneously. She met his eyes for only an instant, and in that first instant she was so filled with him, her life would be changed forever.

"She is only a Gifford brat," Cameron remarked.

"Nay. She was stolen as a baby and only awaits rescue," Dylan replied. "Look, she sports not the pale and gold of her sister and mother, but the ebony locks of the raven. She is not one of them. She is an angel."

"*Anne!*"

Divina had broken the spell, brief though it was, when she realized that her younger sister was transfixed by their banter. Anne instantly lifted her nose, tried to copy Divina's regal bearing, and followed. But she looked over her shoulder to find Dylan smiling at her. Later, she was lectured and disciplined for pausing before any member of the deFrayne household, and Bart offered to kill the deFrayne bastard who had dared to insult her. Bart would have been doubly distressed had he known that Anne's heart still beat wildly, excitedly, every time she thought of her brief pause to receive a smile from Dylan deFrayne.

A year exactly passed and it was again the Lincoln fair when a sudden downpour sent everyone fleeing to shelter. Anne's arm was grasped by a young courtier who would help, and she was pulled under the cover of a gardener's pavilion. Standing there amidst the hoes, scythes, and pots for over an hour of dreadful rain, she became acquainted with Dylan, her would-be arch-enemy.

Anne was only fourteen during her second harvest fair, but behind her was a full year of arousing imaginings that revolved around a dangerous intrigue with this handsome young man. He was exciting and forbidden, and little more was required to inspire a maiden's curiosity. That, and closer attention to her family's discussion of the Gifford-deFrayne feud, had begun to mature her. Her little-girl daydreams were changing into a woman's desire.

Had Dylan been his family's spokesman, he'd have laid the long-running feud to rest in an hour, for he won her heart in less time. He was kind, witty, charming, and courteous. He cared nothing about the old aches and accusations that had separated their households, and he was not even quite sure who had begun the dispute or how. "Perhaps I would feel differently if I were the eldest son, as does Sir Wayland, my brother. He has been schooled all his life on protecting Heathwick from the wicked Giffords. But I am unimportant and have not been reared with this hatred as the older boys have."

"It is said that your great-grandfather killed my great-grand-father," Anne pointed out.

Dylan laughed handsomely. "At my home, your great-grand-father killed mine. But if, indeed, it is the other way around, I apologize," he had said with a deep bow.

"And I accept," she giggled, giving him a curtsy, equally deep.

They enjoyed an hour, but the rain would give them no more. As the downpour lightened enough so that the other side of the street could be seen, Dylan grew more serious. "I have thought about you for a year," he told her.

"Have you? I can't guess why. . . ."

"Have you thought about me?" he asked.

"Once or twice," she lied, her cheeks pinkening.

"Do not tell your family you have spent the hour with me, *petite*. Your brothers will hunt me down and have me hanged."

"Would they?"

"It is a pact of honor. My brothers would do the same. Let us deny their battles, *chérie*. Will you? With me?"

Excitement filled her and her heart began to pound. To think that her own family would begrudge her this charming friend was deplorable. "If they knew you, Dylan, they would . . ."

He shook his head and his eyes hardened. "They will not sheath their swords long enough to know me, Anne. I have risked much. Do not tell them, I pray."

"Will you tell your brothers?"

He laughed suddenly. "No, *petite*, but not because they would harm you. The only honorable thing between our families is that the men do not abuse the women of their enemies. But they would take you from me and boast of the feat. You must not trust them either."

"I will not tell, Dylan."

He grasped her suddenly by the upper arms and covered her lips, kissing her deeply. "I must see you again."

"It is impossible!"

"I will think of a way. Keep our secret, sweet angel. Until next I find you — and I will find you, Anne — I will dream of you." And he had dashed away, disappearing into the sheet of rain, leaving her alone in the little shelter until the sky cleared and Minerva came frantically searching for her lost ward.

Good to his word, Dylan had found her again. She had gone with her mother on a pilgrimage to a nearby convent, escorted by a few men-at-arms. As their horses were taken, the handsome stableboy glanced her way, his turquoise eyes twinkling with mischief. She almost gasped aloud, but quickly realized that she alone recognized him. As her mother slept, she crept from their loft and went to the stable, although his only invitation had been his brief grin and shining eyes. "I am fortunate you are so young and innocent," he had said. "You have none of the teasing, wily ways of these noble dames and you do not make me beg a kind word."

"Were you any other man, Dylan deFrayne, I would make you come through my brothers to get the smallest smile, but, alas, you are my enemy and I cannot even practice all the clever allures I have watched other maids use. But how did you ever find me here?"

"I followed the troop from your home, traveling through the wood and keeping my distance. When your mother mentioned the convent to her escorts, I overheard and rode ahead to bribe the stablekeeper. A few silvers in his hand made the stable mine for the night." He had grinned brightly. "But at dawn I have to curry the horses."

"You are indecent; the sisters are shamed." Her tone, as she well remembered, had been teasing and bright, for she not only liked Dylan a great deal more than she should, but the sheer adventure of sneaking behind her mother's back to be with him was most exhilarating. Marcella was so caught up in the knightly accomplishments of her sons and a sound marriage for Divina, she had ignored Anne almost entirely.

Anne had been nursed by a servant and consigned to Minerva when she was weaned. Divina had followed her mother around the keep, while Anne remained closer to her nurse than her mother. It seemed to Anne, sometimes, that her mother looked at her as though she did not know who she was. She was all the more ripe for love when Dylan appeared

Although Anne believed she had loved Dylan from the first moment their eyes met, it was that night in the cloister stable that the adventure turned from the youthful games of naughty children to the torment of forbidden lovers. And Dylan had been the first to see it through grown-up eyes. He touched her cheek with his hand and his warm lips touched hers briefly, lightly. His lips trembled and his voice was soft. "I have fallen in love with you, Anne. And I am afraid I will ruin your life. Leave me quickly. Never come back to me again."

"Oh Dylan, nay. I *cannot!* I love you, too!"

He sighed deeply. "They may find a way to tear us apart, my Anne. Promise me that no matter what we have to endure, you will not let a beautiful love make you bitter and angry. Let it be your joy, even if it is a brief, secret joy."

A dozen times had been theirs since that rainstorm in Lincoln. Each encounter was more dangerous than the one before. That they had not been caught was one miracle, and that Dylan had not given in to temptation and compromised her virtue was another. The first miracle was nothing more than luck, and the second, a true test of his strength, for Anne was so in love with him that she could never have denied him anything. She wanted nothing so much as to be his in body and heart. A little girl on her first outing had smiled at him, a woman was molded in his arms.

Every night before she slept her head was filled with each small memory, brief moments they had stolen to be together. This night after the joust was no different. She had crept into the bower that she shared with Minerva and her sister. Minerva's snores were uninterrupted and Divina was peacefully dreaming of some knight who had flirted with her at the feast. Anne let her memories turn into dreams as she drifted off to sleep, the sun already struggling to rise as she laid down her head. This tournament was the finest thing God could give her, for five days would be spent here. And if she were clever and careful, each night she could spend precious moments in Dylan's arms.

Her eyes had barely closed when she was rudely jostled. "Anne, wake up. Wake up." The snappish demands could come only from her mother, and Anne opened her eyes slowly, the early morning light searing.

"Madam?" she questioned sleepily, confused. "Is it . . . have I missed mass?"

"No, silly wench, it is early. Dress yourself carefully and come to my chamber. Hurry now."

Anne sat up unsteadily. "Is something amiss? Is there some trouble?"

Marcella's brow was furrowed unhappily as she looked at her daughter, but her eyes were alive with intense concentration. Anne had seen this look in her mother's eyes before, for Marcella was adept at plotting. The fear that she was caught and in trouble fled while she wondered at her mother's new conspiracy and how it could possibly include her.

"Naught amiss for you, lass. It seems you've caught the eye of one or two contestants in the lists and it happens a man of some wealth who is a friend to the Duke of York is interested in you."

"Me? But —"

"I have already confirmed that it is not Divina he seeks. Hurry now. He will come to our chamber this morn and you will meet him."

Anne's eyes grew round. "Madam?"

Marcella rose above her pallet, her glittering eyes bearing down on her daughter, her smile strained. Anne tried to understand the expression. She assumed that the prospect of a marriage to this friend of the duke's pleased Marcella, but that the betrothed would be Anne and not Divina did not. "I said, dress yourself prettily. Your father has a suitor for you to meet."

"But madam, the convent! The sisters!"

"It appears you will be more useful as a bride. Now hurry. And do not be impudent. If all goes well, you will soon be married, and our family will profit by the match."

Chapter Two

FERRIS GIFFORD looked as though he had been dragged too early from his rest by the same impatient demands that had aroused Anne. Dark circles from a night of high revelry hung under his eyes and he slouched in his chair with a horn of cool ale to ease his head. He straightened slightly as Anne entered, and as he looked at his youngest child his eyes began to glow. He patted the stool beside him, and with a nervous smile she perched there.

"Could you have chosen no better gown?" Marcella questioned.

Anne looked down at the mauve velvet. A trousseau is not sewn for a girl preparing to enter the cloister, and the dress was a year old and tight-fitting. Her hem was too high and her breasts strained at the bodice. The sleeves rose above her wrists. "It is one of my best, madam," she said quietly.

"Could you have used one of Divina's, then?"

"But, madam, you told me never to touch her things. And she does not share them freely." A girl destined to the convent did not need fancy clothes, but a girl in search of a husband required a more elaborate wardrobe. Anne's wardrobe consisted of old dresses handed down from her sister and taken in to fit, for Divina was much larger; a new gown was rare.

"Well," Marcella huffed, "in this instance —"

"Leave the lass be," Ferris gruffly ordered. "There is no more beautiful woman in all the world, as the Earl of Ayliffe's notice will attest."

"The Earl of Ayliffe?" Anne whispered, looking at her father.

Marcella was busily searching through her coffer, her back to her husband and daughter, and Ferris's words were soft and almost consoling. "He is a rich man, *petite*. And powerful. It is fortunate that he has noticed you, but that does not a perfect husband make. He is also good and kind; a man I admire." With that final endorsement, Ferris squeezed her hand.

"But Father, the convent . . ."

"You are too good for the convent, Anne. And the earl's offer is too good for this family to be ignored."

"Then 'tis done?"

Ferris looked at her sympathetically. "Nearly done, lass. Your mother has been busy." His eyes drifted toward Marcella, and Anne could see that her father was unhappy. Marcella was accustomed to taking control whenever she pleased, and she often assumed tasks that should belong to her husband, though she had failed to completely control Ferris. Lord Gifford's influence was at test here, for Anne was the only one of their five children who did not hang on Marcella's every word. "Your mother did not consult me, but it is true that the earl's influence is important to us all."

Marcella rushed toward Anne and swiftly draped a gold necklace laden with diamonds around her neck. "At least you have a comely figure, if a little thin."

"She is not thin, madam. She is young. And the gown is too small for her growing bosom."

Anne flushed scarlet as a knock sounded at her parents' chamber door. Marcella lifted a brow as she considered Anne's chest, then grabbed the tight waist of Anne's gown and tugged it down with a sharp yank, exposing more of her breasts. Ferris's face slowly grew purple. Marcella turned to open the door, and

[21]

Ferris's rough fingers pinched the fabric of Anne's gown at her cleavage and yanked it up. Anne looked at her hands in her lap, helpless tears smarting in her eyes.

"Good morningtide, my lord," Marcella simpered, curtsying low, her wide velvet skirts lying in even pleats on the rushes.

"Madam," the earl returned.

Lord Gifford slowly stood up, and Anne cautiously glanced at the man whom her parents wished her to marry. She watched as the earl and her father approached each other in the small room, each bowing at the waist, wordless. Then the earl offered his hand. His lips curved in what seemed to be a shy smile.

Anne instantly saw what had excited her mother, and indeed, what might be the answer to the prayers of any other marriageable maiden. The earl was a stately man of well over forty years, his clothing rich and newly sewn, his neatly trimmed dark hair barely kissed by new silver at the temples, and his physique that of a much younger man. Anne was impressed, for money and power did not guarantee manners, cleanliness, nor handsomeness. But he was nearly as old as her father.

"And is this Anne, your lovely daughter?"

Ferris stepped aside that the earl could look at her. She saw his intention in his eyes. They turned from a hazy to a deep, smoldering blue as he looked at her. A smile slowly formed on his lips and he held out a hand. Anne cautiously put hers into his, and she felt him tremble. Or was it herself? He bowed low over her hand, gently brushing his lips on her cold flesh. "I am honored, *mademoiselle.*"

"The honor is mine, my lord," she said softly, nervously.

"Your parents have told you, I trust, that I am interested in a bride?"

She nodded weakly, looking into his eyes. He did not appear to be cruel; in fact, there was a certain gentleness in his demeanor. But just the same, her chin quivered. When she was in Dylan's arms, she felt beautiful. At this moment she felt like livestock at barter.

"Are you frightened of me, maid Anne?" he asked, his voice

soothing and kind. "Or is it the prospect of marriage that frightens you?"

"I . . . I was to go to the convent. . . ."

His complexion seemed to darken as he gave an embarrassed chuckle, and he squeezed her hand softly. "I realize that I do not have the appearance of a young swain, nor that of a saintly mother superior, but you needn't be afraid." The earl looked at Ferris. "The girl is breathtaking, yet sweet. I would be honored to take her to wife. But she is too young. Too skittish. I do not wish for her to be damaged by the prospect."

"But my lord, she will . . ."

The earl held up his hand to silence Marcella's interruption and continued speaking to Lord Gifford. "I think it is in the maiden's best interests to extend our courtship. If I can show that I can be trusted before we are wed, the marriage will be more pleasurable to us both. If it suits you, we can draw up betrothal contracts now and be married some months hence. During the next several months I must travel to attend to many affairs of state, during which time I can make an occasional visit to your family at Raedelle. We will become better acquainted. Anne will become assured that marriage to me will not be a fearsome ordeal."

"Fearsome ordeal, indeed," Marcella grumbled. "Lord Forbes, if you desire a bride this eventide, she will oblige. You needn't coddle her to this degree. She is a sturdy girl, though small. And she can read and speak French and Latin. She —"

Marcella stopped in midsentence when she saw Lord Forbes frowning. "My lady, I would expect you to be more sensitive to her age and inexperience than I. But never mind, a few months will serve us all."

Anne felt a smile come to her lips. She had never seen anyone manage Marcella so deftly. And he promised her time. The earl looked at her. "Does that meet with your approval, my dear?"

"You are very generous, my lord."

He reached for her hand again and this time she was more willing. "My name is Brennan Forbes, and you may use it freely.

Despite your youth, you have submitted to my sudden request to meet you with poise and elegance, Anne. I thank you. You will find my disposition generous and I hope you will be pleased with what I can offer you. Your servant, *mademoiselle*."

He turned to Marcella. "Call on me for any needs the girl may have. I will extend my purse to her clothing and travel costs." He then gave an abrupt nod to Lord and Lady Gifford and departed.

As Anne watched his aristocratic departure, she was sorry for him. He seemed a good and decent man, humble and polite for one who could, through money and power, be demanding and coarse if he so chose. He was handsome, kind, and sensitive. It was a shame that her heart was no longer hers to give.

Many young women were given to older men, for often women died in childbirth. Thus, a great number of wealthy men were twice and thrice widowed before they themselves died. Often a maid was wed only for the sake of money; it was rare that the man was also civil and handsome. Brennan Forbes would be considered among the finest looking and most courtly.

Yet Anne said a silent prayer of thanks that she had been given the gift of time. She would not be married to Brennan Forbes; she must tell Dylan at once. They must flee.

"Well, daughter?" Ferris asked.

Anne answered with a calmness that she did not feel. "I find it hard to believe he is interested in me. Surely I am too young for him; surely he could find a prettier maid."

Ferris shook his head, and Marcella frowned. Anne was the most beautiful woman in their household, and Ferris tended to think there was no greater beauty in all England. And her disposition was sweet. Her humility was a product of careless brothers who only teased her if they bothered with her at all. Trenton, the youngest boy at two years senior to Anne, had been her friend and playmate when they were younger, but lately achieving knighthood took precedence over attention to his little sister. The other boys had never been attached to her at all. And her older sister was as selfish with her kindness as she was with her gowns. Marcella had no time for Anne, except to pause to scold her occasionally, and Ferris was away from her more often than he liked. He knew that only he and old Minerva ever spoiled her.

Ferris had been bothered by more than one old lord about this pretty little maid, but had feared to tell his wife. Marcella seemed unconcerned with her children's feelings and might have swiftly married Anne to the first lucrative offer. And yet Anne had so many visible attributes that Ferris often wondered why his wife put so much energy into the marriage of their other daughter. It often seemed as though Marcella could not acknowledge their youngest except to push her aside. His wife's treatment of Anne hurt him deeply.

"I will walk with you to your bower, *petite*," Ferris said, holding out his hand to her.

Marcella grasped her to retrieve her jewelry. "Mind your manners, Anne, or you will be punished."

"Yes, madam," she said. Ferris frowned at his wife.

Anne walked down the dark gallery with her father. The hour was still early and few people were astir. When they had traveled some distance from Marcella's bedchamber, Ferris paused.

"Marriage to the earl is not the worst that could befall you, lass."

She smiled up at him. It pained her that her father, so kind and gentle, might suffer for trying to protect her. "I know, Father. The earl seems a good man."

"Then you will go to him willingly?"

"Yes, Father. If that is your desire."

Ferris sighed deeply, a troubled look coming into his eyes. "Anne . . . lass . . . you must not . . . ahem, you must let these matters of marriage rest with your parents. Do not give your love to a young swain of your choice. One whom . . . we cannot approve for you."

"No, Father," she said, looking down at the floor.

"Do not pin your hopes on things that can never be."

Her cheeks grew warm and she stared at the floor. Could he know? But, if he knew, he would punish her. Ferris Gifford might be the least passionate where the feud was concerned, but he had never hidden the fact that he despised Lord deFrayne.

Ferris lifted her chin with a finger, forcing her to look into his eyes. "We do not always love wisely, child. I must tell you this, this one time only. If it occurs to you to give your heart to the wrong man, you do not face only a life of ruin for yourself, but you well could ruin the family who has reared you and the family that will follow as your heirs. Much ill can come from such a mistake, Anne — pain, fighting, poverty, even death. Marriage to Brennan Forbes will keep you well, make you rich, and, I trust, he will do everything in his power to make you happy."

"If you wish me to marry him, I shall, my lord," she said, knowing it was a lie and knowing, too, that Ferris Gifford must have seen Dylan smile at her.

"I wish it, lass. He is the duke's man and the Duke of York will wear the crown of England one day. Perhaps soon."

"Papa," she said in a surprised whisper, touching his hand. "Do you plot against the —"

"Hush, child," Ferris warned. "Let us just say that your marriage to the earl and other matters of negotiation will restore this family to its former wealth and importance, if all goes well. Now, if you hurry, you can still get to mass. Very few will rise for mass this morning," he said, his tone secretive. "No one else from our family will be seen there." He bent to kiss her forehead. "May I trust you, Anne, to do right by your old father now?"

She rose on her toes to kiss his cheek, saddened by his request. Was it a plea to resist Dylan's affection and go placidly to the earl's marriage bed? "I love you, Papa," she said, turning from him to go directly to the chapel.

Her throat ached and tears threatened. Her father would be crushed by her betrayal, but betray him she must, for she could never love any man as she loved Dylan; not her father, and certainly not Lord Forbes, however kind and decent he was. Nothing could make her turn her heart from Dylan now. For a year, through so much danger and risk, all she had thought of was the moment she could finally belong to him. Such determined vision in a young woman could not be easily dispelled.

[26]

And Ferris knew, she was sure of it. He had asked, in his own cautious way, that she forsake Dylan's love and do what was right. He had even directed her to go alone to mass, a place where she might find Dylan without any members of her family looking on.

Oh Father, forgive me, for I am a bad daughter, an ill bride, and I sin and lie for the want of one love.

She kept her head bowed, seated far back behind the few who had risen for mass. She heard the sound of armor behind her, and her heart began to beat wildly. As the priest prayed she stole a look and saw Dylan, outfitted in chain mail and breastplate, his plumed helm in the crook of his arm. Why was he armored? There were no jousts today.

When the mass was complete, she rose, keeping her head bowed, crossed herself, and moved as quietly as a nun out of the church. She swiftly glided around the side, through the gardens and toward the concealing coppice. There was a narrow path that led to a clearing beside a stream. At dawn and again at dusk one could meet many a castle servant on this path, for it led from the town to the hall, but at this hour she hoped it was private.

She turned and saw that he was close behind her and his face was troubled.

"We depart, my sweet love. I have made the family tardy since I could not be found in my bed." He shrugged. "They assume I warmed some castle wench's pallet elsewhere. Except, perhaps, Lady Daphne, whose eyes were filled with pain. She sent me to mass to atone, and Daphne generally ignores her sons' wenching. The pain in my mother's eyes, I trust, is for you, Anne."

"Dylan, why? Where do you go?"

"There is a plot against King Henry. The Duke, Richard of York, gathers armies. If King Henry falls to some conspiracy, my family will fall with him."

She rushed to him, his armor crushing her. Tears slid down her cheeks in yet another fearful moment. "Dylan, everything has changed. We must flee quickly. My mother has found an earl who wishes to make me his bride . . . and my father plots with the Duke of York. Oh please, let us be done with this!"

"There are kings and plotting dukes in every country, *ma belle*."

Anne was confused by the political conspiracies that engulfed noble families. She did not know who was right or wrong. The all too frequent plots and bloody battles made only one impression on her — this futile and carnal waste of life kept her from Dylan. "But different dukes and kings. . . . Oh, Dylan, we can serve the same one if we make haste away from here."

"Anne . . ." Agony seemed to draw out her name.

She stepped backward abruptly. For the first time since their eyes met, she heard hesitation in Dylan's voice. She had committed every dream to their day. She would not dream lies; she was too proud to lie to herself. With wisdom that was rare in one so young, she questioned him quickly and purposefully. "Our promise, our oath that we *will* be together, is it no more? Do you have me wed this earl while you go to King Henry's aid? Dylan, speak now."

His features softened and he moved near. He grasped her upper arms and pulled her into his embrace, gently rubbing his cheek against hers.

"If you want me no more, Dylan, you must tell me now. We have made a promise that there is but one way; we both deny our families or not at all. If I defy my father, I cannot go to your family and present my new loyalties. 'Tis both or not at all."

"Anne, my love . . ."

"If you cannot, I will not judge you. But your word, Dylan. Now. Today. There is little time."

"I cannot live without you, my sweet love."

"There is no longer a convent to protect me, Dylan. The Earl of Ayliffe gives me some months —"

"Ayliffe? Good God!"

"Do you know of him?"

Dylan laughed ruefully. "I am amazed that you do not run to him. He is . . . he has more than I will ever be able to offer."

She touched his cheek. "But I love you, Dylan. And I know

there are rich brides that can give you more than I. Do we
doubt now, after all we have dared?"

"Nay, darling. I will come for you. It may take a little
while . . . but I will come."

"And I will wait."

"Trust me, Anne. Trust me."

She kissed him, again fearing it would be their last kiss. "Stay
here and let me depart alone. If I see your face as I mount with
my parents and brothers, my eyes will betray me." And so he
left her alone by the stream. She shivered at the memory of
that moment of cold dread when she feared Dylan had given
up on their dream. In the end he was true, but that alone would
not keep the pain of parting from bringing its inevitable tears.
She sank onto the grassy bank and wept.

Anne's tears dried, yet she remained seated on the bank of
the stream. The spring morning was uplifting, the sky was clear
and blue, the birds melodious. Pain was replaced with hope,
for soon she could escape with Dylan. She plucked at early
spring flowers and her eyes fell on the scar on her hand. She
had passed it off as an accident in the weaving room, but it was
wrought of a blade. It had happened on a dark, moonless night
in the wood outside the Giffords' ancestral home, Raedelle Keep,
when she had crept from her bed and Dylan had spread his
mantle on the grass for them.

At fifteen she came to know the woman's ways of her body.
She longed for Dylan's lovemaking and offered her virginity,
but Dylan was the one to deny her. He would not spoil her
and by some merciless act of fate leave her violated, or pregnant,
and punished by her family. "If they discover we have been
together, it will be hard enough for us, but should it ever be
learned that we have shared our bodies, I dare not think of the
price we will pay, and you more than I. But lie close to me,
and give me your promise we will be together one day."

She had pulled his knife from his belt and before he could
protest, she ran the sharp blade across the back of her hand,
drawing an immediate swell of crimson blood. "In blood, if it

[29]

pleases you," she said. His horrified eyes roved from her hand to her face. " 'Tis virgin's blood, Dylan. I will never forsake you. I will love you till I die."

It took him a moment to recover his senses and reckon with the courage of her act. She had not winced or shuddered, but had cut her flesh swiftly and deftly. He took the blade and made an identical cut on his own hand. He smiled sheepishly as he held the bloodied hands together. "This is a pact most often made between men."

"I'm certain that lovers of old have done this and more," she said.

"Then I pledge, my love, that we *will* be together one day. For more than a stolen moment, for all time."

These promises were the ones that bound them still. It would be wrong, they decided, for only one of them to forsake a family. It would only strengthen the feud between the two families, for with such an act there would be a boastful victor and a shamed loser.

For many years, ever since Henry of Bolingbroke had usurped the throne from his cousin, King Richard II, the earls of Heathwick and Raedelle, Lords deFrayne and Gifford, had supported opposite sides. But they had once been good friends. Lord Gifford, Anne's great-grandfather, sent a message to his friend after Richard had been captured and imprisoned. DeFrayne responded, offering Lord Gifford amnesty for his arms. The Gifford family still possessed that old letter from Lord deFrayne, their proof that the Giffords were wronged, betrayed, for the story went that when Lord Gifford went to the meeting place to surrender, he was ambushed and slain. Family wars ensued and there was much bloodshed. Then Henry V, the second Lancaster king, Bolingbroke's son, ordered an end to the fighting with the added threat that the lands of both the victor and the vanquished would be confiscated. The Giffords, reduced to a barony and still suffering under heavy attainder for their part in support of Richard II, could not risk any further action against them from the king. And the deFraynes, who had become wealthy and influential by route of conquest, were unwilling to test the king's order. Thus, open warfare had stilled, but the animosity continued. Now the Giffords hoped to steal the crown away from King Henry VI, another Lancaster, and give it to Richard, Duke of York.

While the families argued over diverse politics, Anne and Dylan had been free. They had love; what need had they for the arguments of dukes and kings? But then she had seen Dylan at mass in chain mail. It was not for the tourney this time, but for a real conflict. He spoke as though his support had been commissioned and the political animosity, once so distant, crept closer, edging its way into the hopes and dreams of young love.

For a moment she thought Dylan might forsake their love for a cause. She would have freed him tearlessly had he asked it of her. Not painlessly, she knew, but Anne was stronger and more brave than she realized. And she would do anything for Dylan's sake. But in the end he had pledged himself anew, true to their plans. Anne continued to push the plots and wars far from her mind, thinking only of Dylan's embrace, his kiss, oblivious to how closely threatened she really was. Anne had absolutely no idea of the kind of life she might have to endure in exile at Dylan's side, and Dylan had only a vague notion.

" 'Tis an unseemly place for a maid to hide."

She jumped at the masculine voice and looked up to see the Earl of Ayliffe towering above her. Her cheeks flamed, as if he could read her mind.

"Do you not worry about your safety, Anne? What if some man happened down this path and spied you?"

"It appears, my lord, that a man has done exactly that. Need I be afraid?"

He smiled and dropped down onto the grass near her, drawing up his knees. She was again struck by his youthful appearance; that he'd not grown paunchy or sloppy with age. At twenty he might have been as handsome as Dylan, and, indeed, he was handsome still.

"May we talk awhile, maid Anne?"

She cocked her head to one side. Her experience with men was severely limited, but an earl who asked permission to speak inspired her curiosity. "You are overly solicitous, my lord. Certainly you could assert your great power and wealth and have a young bride at your whim. You could have had your wedding done in my mother's bedchamber this morn, had you asked for it."

He laughed lightly. "I suppose I could. But, Anne, did it ever occur to you that that which is won by force is held only by hope? I would have you love me."

Her eyes widened and her cheeks grew hot again. She looked away from his face.

"I suppose it seems absurd to you now, for you are so young, and I am nearly as old as your father. But you will learn, *petite*, that age has little to do with it. Or perhaps it is a great advantage. Were I a young knight smitten by your beauty, I would be hard pressed to delay the marriage." He laughed pleasantly. "It would be most difficult to ignore the great opportunity of this private coppice. But I am no longer an impatient young man, and I respect your youth and your purity. And," he said, reaching out a finger to turn her face back toward him, "I wish for you to be as happy as I shall be."

"I do not deserve such kindness, my lord."

"And why not?" he asked with a laugh. "Because you have had your heart set on some young squire, or some arrogant and handsome young knight? I can assure you, demoiselle, I have traveled enough of this world to know the way of young hearts and young virgins. If you are an honest maid with good intentions, all you need is time. And I shall show you that marriage to me and your life as the Countess of Ayliffe will be pleasurable and happy. In time all the young knights who have filled your dreams will fade away and the love of a good and generous man will replace them." He shrugged. "In time, Anne, you will become a woman. And I plan for that to happen in my home, under my patient care."

She could not help but smile at him, for it was clear that he was a tender and kind man. If she had not known Dylan, she could love a man such as Brennan Forbes. "I thank you, my lord, for your uncommon goodness."

"My name, Anne. Please, use my name."

"Brennan," she tested, laughing.

"You need not thank me. I have been married, twice, and both times have been very fortunate to be loved by good women. I'm afraid I was not as good a husband as they were wives, but they both did their parts to refine me a bit. Gone are the barbs of a selfish, impatient young man, and I can be a good husband now. If you only let me, I can make you very happy."

"Your wives? They died?"

"Aye, the first over twenty years ago when I was but a lad. Childbed took her and my firstborn. I was a long time in getting over that loss. The second, a good woman, gave me a son who is now ten years old, and a fever took her two years past. I have missed her and, until very recently, I could not imagine that I would take a third bride."

"I am so sorry for your losses, Brennan," Anne said sincerely, "I cannot imagine losing a loved one. . . ." In even thinking of the possibility of losing Dylan, Anne felt the threat of tears.

"It was difficult, but there is always great risk in loving someone. I have known your parents and they mentioned their daughter, but . . ." His voice trailed off and he studied her face. "I was pleased to see you at the tournament. Otherwise, we might not have met."

"I have a sister. . . ."

"Yes. Divina."

"It was assumed that she would marry and I would go to the convent."

Brennan's shoulders moved in a rueful chuckle. "Lady Gifford seems more clever than to make such a dreadful mistake. Why has she kept you hidden until this tournament?"

Anne shrugged her shoulders as she thought of how she wished to have been hidden just a little longer. But the idea of Divina failing to meet this man's standards almost made her smile. With the energy her sister put toward finding a husband, and in that effort the accrual of many pretty dresses and trinkets that she selfishly hoarded, Divina had become filled with self-importance. Anne often felt that Divina had their mother's favor. She tried to console herself that it was their mother's obligation to see the older daughter wed first, but that explanation for her mother's inattentiveness seemed inadequate. Even though Anne felt no temptation toward Lord Forbes's prestigious offer of marriage, something inside her began to glow from the sheer vanity of being singled out. Divina would be deliciously scandalized.

"How long have you been sitting alone in the wood?"

"Since mass," she said absently.

"Worrying over what harsh demands would be made on you by an eager earl?"

"I was worried before. Until this morning, it was only the convent. . . ."

"I will protect you better than nuns, Anne."

She nodded, but looked down again.

"Do you come willingly, *ma chérie?*" he asked.

Again, she nodded. She looked into his eyes. "You are kind to me, Brennan. I would not have you think me ungrateful."

"But?" he asked. Anne chewed her lip. "Come, my love, let us not begin with lies between us. I have told you I can be understanding of your plight; I am aware of your youth. If you tell me the truth, perhaps I can help."

Anne knew better than to think there was any possible way Brennan Forbes could really accept the truth. She loved another and always would. But she boldly expressed one reservation she felt, if only to see the extent of the man's professed understanding. "You are kind and polite, and handsome as well. Indeed, all the things a maid would wish to have in a husband. Perhaps too kind, Brennan. You almost seem — " she paused, her eyes lightly closed, and took a deep breath before finishing — "like a father."

Only silence answered her. She cautiously opened her eyes and found him smiling at her. He slowly rose and held out a hand to help her to her feet. He tucked her hand in the crook of his arm and began to lead her out of the copse, down the path toward the gardens.

"Are you angry with me, my lord?" she asked as they walked.

"No, my sweet. Some of those things you expect from a father will certainly be yours as my wife. You will have protection and a strong arm as you achieve your full womanhood. You will have the generosity of my purse, as if you were a favored daughter. You will lend dignity to my name, as you have given your father's name greater worth while you lived under his roof."

He paused on the path crowded by trees and looked down into her eyes. "But there will come a time, my love, when the ways of men and women will be ours, and then you must see me as a husband and lover, not as a parent to guide you into your adulthood." He gave her forehead a light kiss. "There is time enough for you to adjust yourself to seeing me in a diferent light. When the time has come, you will have no doubt — my affection for you is not fatherly in nature."

"Mother will not *allow* it," Divina shrieked. "It is *unheard* of!"

Anne stared at her sister in wide-eye wonder. Had she really looked forward to this? Divina had sullenly held her peace until the family had returned to Raedelle, and then the feathers began to fly. Anne had followed Divina up the stairs to the room they had shared all these years, only to watch Divina angrily throw all of her gowns out on the bed to remove them from their common bower.

"Divina, it was not of my doing. I'm sorry you are jealous."

"Jealous? I am not jealous but outraged! What did you do to attract him? What did you promise?"

"Nothing," Anne cried. "I had never even seen him before."

"He has been about. You have seen him."

"*You* have seen him, Divina. He has seen you. I have never gone to a tournament before."

"I will not stay here in this room with you another day. You lie! You did something sinful to attract him to you!" The door to their bedchamber slowly swung open, and Marcella stood to her full and menacing height, frowning at her daughters. "Mother, tell her that you will not allow it, this betrothal. It is not fair."

Marcella looked from Divina to Anne, then back to Divina. "It is done. The Earl of Ayliffe has requested the hand of your sister and would consider no other."

"But *why?*" Divina wailed.

"His fancy," Marcella shrugged, smiling rather deviously. "He is rich and was not enticed by her dowry. Understanding his fancy is not my concern; an alliance with his influence is."

"But Mother —"

"Lower your voice, Divina. I will not listen to this shrieking."

"I will not go to the convent in her stead. I will *not!*"

"It is not too late to find you a suitable marriage. I was almost twenty when I was wed. And . . . we have invested a goodly sum in that effort already. Your clothes will do you no good with the sisters." She glanced at Anne and frowned. She had not considered Anne to be good marriageable stock; she was small, thin, and had always preferred playing with the boys to learning the management of a castle. Divina, hearty and determined to copy her mother's behavior, seemed more logical in a wifely role. Yet Anne had captured a rich earl in her simple, ill-fitting frocks, saying nothing encouraging, smiling shyly. It was beyond Marcella's comprehension. Beside Divina, Anne appeared frail.

Marcella pinched her eyes closed. Like Daphne. Anne was more like Daphne than she had realized. Perhaps it made men feel powerful and strong when facing frail and timid women.

She had never looked at Anne as an eligible nobleman might. But she would gladly accept the earl's influence in any case.

"I will not stay in this room with her any longer," Divina cried. "I will not!"

Marcella ground her teeth. "Do not make the convent seem a preferable place for you to live, Divina."

"How could you allow it, madam? You should have refused his offer. Refused it outright."

"It would have been much as refusing an open chest filled with gold," she said, failing to mention that it had also been a favorable match, that the earl would make an exemplary mate, and that he had approached the Giffords, not the other way around.

"Madam, tell her not to hate me so," Anne entreated. "Tell her it was not of my doing. I did nothing to entice the —"

"You have been a great deal of trouble," Marcella said. "Try not to goad the rest of us with your good fortune, which was little of your own making." She turned to Divina. "Find another room if you wish, but do not make me listen to any more of your tantrums. I have a great deal on my mind."

Anne watched as Divina finished dividing her belongings from Anne's.

"I would give you this betrothal if I could," Anne said quietly.

Divina glared at her. "Perhaps that will happen yet," Divina replied icily.

·Chapter Three

$\mathcal{S}$UMMER CAME and was gone. The days shortened and grew cold and the candles and torches burned until late at night at Raedelle Castle, for the Giffords were busy with secret meetings, the gathering of arms and funds, and many messages were being sent and received. The Duke of York was preparing to take London by siege, if necessary, and at his right hand would be the Gifford family. Marcella's energy was high and ran rampant through the castle as her demands increased, her temper shortened, and a flush of excitement brightened her cheeks.

The Gifford sons and the men-at-arms suited daily for possible call to battle, laying out their accouterments and keeping their squires and pages fleet and ready. Horses were curried and exercised with dubious intent. At the first call to arms, they would ride.

During this time Anne heard nothing from Dylan. Only her memories kept her warm as the days grew colder. Word had come that the deFraynes rode with the forces of Henry's queen, Margaret of Anjou. Anne prayed each night that Dylan was not with them, but she knew he must be. She had waited for over five months to see that twinkling eye emerge from behind a thick-trunked oak, or that playful smile sparkle from within a group of traveling monks. Never before had so many months passed without a surprise appearance. He had promised he would come, yet nothing happened.

The Earl of Ayliffe journeyed to Raedelle five times in five months. Each visit stretched out longer than the last, and each time Anne pitied him more. His eyes grew velvety soft with desire, his words deep and resonant with longing. And all Anne could accord him was respect and a mien of obedience. For all his claims to have put aside the impatience of youth, his mannerisms betrayed him as a man who chafed at delay and grew eager for a bride. His extended courtship had won him only a young woman who admired him, but did not want him for a husband.

Brennan Forbes had stolen a kiss on his last visit. Oh, it was not a theft, as Anne recalled. He *desired* to be kissed. And so she allowed, closing her eyes and tilting her chin. He had moved over her mouth with hunger, but she met him with indifference. She wept that night for shame, for nothing in her was stirred, and he deserved better. He *was* a good man. "There is no lacking within you, Brennan," she had said. " 'Tis I. I fear I will not please you."

It was the truth, for she had begun to curse her inability to accept such good fortune. There was not a man in the land who would make a better husband than Brennan Forbes. Even Dylan, she well knew, could not offer so much. His temper was shorter, his passion for all things was not only quicker, but richer and deeper, and he would not be a docile mate. Sometimes frivolous, sometimes deadly serious, she wondered if a life of flight and hiding would cause him to one day resent her. It would take strength to share Dylan's pallet, when all Brennan wished to do was spoil and pamper her. However, Dylan was the man she loved. It was then that the realization came to her as it had earlier come to Dylan — this was not a love they willingly struggled to keep alive, as in those first early days. It was a love neither of them could deny. She hoped it would not lead to their doom.

Yet Dylan did not come, and Brennan visited regularly. And in the month of October old Minerva, Anne's nurse since birth, fell ill and bedridden. The lonely days stretched out longer as Anne sat vigil by Minerva's bed while the rest of her family plotted wars and reigns.

Minerva had lived in Raedelle all of her sixty-seven years. She had taken Ferris from the womb and nursed him, and she had tended others of the Gifford house, and each of Ferris's children. Of the entire family, it was only Anne and Ferris who suffered when she fell ill. From her rasping breath and fevered form, they knew death was imminent.

Ferris placed his hand on his daughter's shoulder and looked down at his dying nurse. "Go on, lass," he said softly. "I'll sit here for a time with my old love."

"She is no better, Papa," Anne whispered. "Her fever does not break and she can barely breathe. The midwife and the leech know of nothing more to do."

"I know that, lass. She has had a long life. You have been a faithful ward. You alone sit with old Minerva."

Tears began to gather in Anne's eyes. She knew that her beloved servant would die. This woman, not her own mother, brought her through childhood with love and tenderness. There were few enough remedies for serious illness; none for old age. And it hurt her deeply that none of the other children nor their mother, all of whom Minerva had served so faithfully, paid homage in this sickroom.

There was a faint stirring in the bed, and Minerva opened her eyes. For a moment her stare was blank as she looked at Ferris and Anne, and then recognition cleared her gaze. A weak smile touched her lips. "Ferris, my boy," she whispered. "Get this sweet child from this foul place."

Anne picked up Minerva's hot bony hand and rubbed it against her cheek. "I would stay with you, my dear."

"Death is unpleasant enough, without being seen by one with

such life," the old nurse said. "Let me talk to my boy. Come back in an hour."

Anne exchanged troubled glances with her father.

"Walk about in the cool air, lass. Clear your head of this sickroom and come back later. She'll be here."

Anne left as she was told, wandering about Raedelle Castle absentmindedly. She paused briefly to watch as Quentin practiced arms in the courtyard in front of the hall with other knights. Quentin would be the next baron of Raedelle, and she had no trouble imagining him in that role. Though he strongly resembled their mother, his temperament was more even than Marcella's. Quentin loved soldiering, and he loved Raedelle. He was not soft, but sometimes kind. Quentin was usually fairminded, as was borne out when he reprimanded Bart at the feast following the tournament. Quentin was large, thick, and somber. He excelled at knightly arts, mostly because of his natural bulk and strength. But he was not ambitious. He would inherit Raedelle and there was little reason to wish for more.

She spied, or rather heard, Bart as he snapped orders at a group of squires who had not yet won his approval. Bart strongly resembled Quentin in looks, but not size. Not as tall, not as broad, Bart had to work twice as hard to do half as well as Quentin in the contests. And Bart was quick-tempered and ambitious, as was often the case with the second son. He longed for wealth and power, but Raedelle was Quentin's, and Bart's fortunes must be earned another way. It was becoming apparent that he was not going to get his due through soldiering, but through clever association. She had noticed that when he looked at her of late his eyes would slowly traverse her slight form from nose to toes and back again, as if trying to account for the fact that she had lured an earl into their midst. Sometimes the gleam in his eye made her shiver. She knew, without being told, that Bart had plans revolving around this proposed marriage.

And Trenton, who was busy examining the battle gear that lay in shining rows in the courtyard, turned and smiled at her. He was a gentle lad at seventeen, too young for all this conspiracy, too young to go to battle. But he was without choice and must follow his brothers or be labeled as a weakling and coward. He was not, of course. He would be as large as Quentin, and with good training just as strong, but Trenton was kind and good through and through. He was neither conniving nor ambitious.

Anne and Trenton had been playmates until Trenton was sent to another keep for training as a squire. Upon his return he had cast aside playful games and concentrated on his knightly skills — a third-born son had much challenge ahead to even cover his head. Their fondness for each other had not really waned. Precious were the evening hours when Trenton sang sweet troubadours' songs in their common hall. Trenton alone shared the raven locks and dark eyes of their common sire. She greatly feared losing him to a senseless war, and if there was one sibling she could tell about Dylan, it might be him. But, like his brothers, he had been strictly taught to suspect and despise all deFraynes. And it was Trenton, not Bart, she would have asked the earl to see to, if indeed she were to marry him, which she would not.

The busyness of the courtyard changed her mind about a stroll there, and she went back into the hall and through the galleries and cookery toward the rear of the castle. She paused to watch Divina, who had taken over Marcella's duties in the cookery, since Marcella was so occupied with letters. Divina's command was no lighter than their mother's, and possibly harsher. She barked orders at the maids and matrons like a seasoned baroness, though she was only nineteen. She yelled about the many hungry knights, chided and ridiculed them for laziness, though it looked as though they worked feverishly. Divina tried hard to live up to their mother's standards, mimicking Marcella, and Anne was suddenly filled with pity. For so long she had envied Divina's apparent closeness to their mother, but now she could see the true value. Divina was neither betrothed nor happy and was busy with Marcella's chores.

Raedelle's wall had been built thick and tall two centuries ago, and the gates were opened for the passage of troops and villagers. The town lay to the south, a hill stood at the back of the castle, and the bastions and parapets were stocked with both new guns and ready archers. There was a strong feeling of impending war. Anne frowned in confusion and disappointment, for she could not think of any amount of money or power that could make war so appealing, causing people to forget family loyalty. Minerva lay forgotten, quietly dying. Yet, her family, with the exception of Divina, was happier and more excited than she had ever seen them. There were whisperings of duchies, once the power had been won for York. And laughter over the monkish, impotent King Henry, whose wife, they said, had cuckolded him with the Duke of Somerset. The prince, they gossiped, was wrought of Somerset's loins, for the king was too often at poetry and prayer.

She wandered into the gardens, but there was much astir there as castlewomen clipped late-blooming herbs for poultices and lotions for warriors at roost here. Troops must be tended after battle. Large groups of calves, piglets, and lambs were being led to slaughter, for there were many mouths to feed; soldiers needed meat for strength. And the stable was no help, for an army that could not be housed in the main hall had found refuge there. In the weaving rooms the women frantically spun their yarn for cloth for gambesons, banners, and standards for the house of York, or of Gifford green. Finally, the church proved the only quiet place, and Anne knelt to pray for Minerva . . . and Dylan.

She did not raise her head for what she perceived to be an hour and shared the church only with a peasant from the village who knelt behind her. He had undoubtedly sinned worse than she, for his capped head was bowed the whole while. When she reasoned it was time to return to Minerva, she lifted her head. She rose to leave and turned to depart the chapel. The peasant finished his prayers and lifted his bright turquoise eyes to meet hers. Her heart nearly stopped. Dylan! Inside Raedelle walls!

She stood numbly, terrified. She could not speak to him here, for the priest might come out of an ambry and catch them together. She lowered her eyes and with head bowed, fled swiftly with small steps, knowing he would follow. But where?

All of Raedelle was astir with the commotion of building an army for a subversive cause. There was no nook in all of the castle and town that would be safe. And Dylan was at risk inside Raedelle grounds.

She considered his costume, his peasant rags and straw hat. He sat unbothered in the church because . . . because Raedelle was so astir with preparations for war that no one paid attention to another serf. She walked on, trying to keep her steps short and her manner relaxed, through the portcullis of the inner bailey and through the town to the gate. And there she saw what she had seen for weeks — knights and squires and pages and peasants roving through the opened gates as if a Mayday fair was taking place within Raedelle's walls. Women carried baskets, carts laden with supplies were coming in, empty carts moved out. Farmers gathered the last remnants of their crops from the fields, corralled their stock, and destriers were being led about as pages exercised them for the knights. Outside the walls she could hear the shouts from men who practiced arms in the fields.

"Where are you bound, maid Anne?" the knight who kept the gate asked.

"I have been through a long morning at the bedside of my nurse, old Minerva. She is dying." She brushed at a tear. "I need a space away from her illness and this mania of knights. I will return to her directly."

"You should not wander far," he advised.

"There are more knights within hearing of my screams than ever before, sir. I mean only to circle the outer wall once to loosen these stiff limbs. Worry not."

The protection lining the walls was more than adequate, and so the gate keeper did not argue or detain her. Anne did not dare look over her shoulder to see if Dylan followed. She did in fact walk around the outer wall, to the rear of the keep, a trip that took the half of an hour. There, where the castle was built into the side of a hill, was a shallow coppice of no more than a dozen trees. It was the only place that could not be seen from the wall or tower. Anyone fleeing over the hill could be spotted, or troops converging on the castle from the far side of the hill could be seen. But this little place where the wall met the hill was hidden. And this was the place where Dylan had spread his mantle on the grass for her once before.

When she entered the little shelter, she turned expectantly, but it was many long moments before he arrived. In his hand was a scythe. He dropped it instantly to take her in his arms.

"Dylan, my God, you came inside Raedelle's walls," she gasped, holding his face in her hands and covering him with kisses.

"There is no time, my love. A troop of a dozen men awaits us. Come with me now."

"Now? How?"

"If we can make the wood there are two horses tethered. Anne, there may never be another chance."

"Oh Dylan, why did you come inside?"

"I have roved this fair countryside for some weeks, but the Raedelle gate is stout at night, for the Giffords conspire to unseat King Henry. Coming inside by daylight appeared to be the only way."

Joy penetrated through tears of fear and Anne laughed. He had come! "As a peasant man with a crooked back. Oh, Dylan!"

"You were so long at your prayers, I thought I would die." He kissed her mouth hungrily, his wildly beating heart pressed against hers. He grasped her hand and covered her palm and fingers with kisses. And then he held her so tightly she was nearly crushed.

"I was afraid you would never come," she whispered against his ear. "I have never been so afraid."

"Listen to me, my love. We must flee by the light of day. I have watched your house, and there is no way for you to escape after the sun is set. It is a long way to the wood. We will have to run. Can you come now?"

"Now, yes," she said, kissing him again. His arms tightened about her waist, holding her so near she felt almost a part of him. Finally they would be as one.

"Are you afraid?" he asked her.

"No, Dylan. I am only afraid of losing you."

"Let me hold you, just for a moment, before we —"

"Old Minerva," she said suddenly, stiffening. "Dylan, Minerva lies dying."

"There is no time, Anne. It must be *now!*"

"Wait, Dylan, wait. The guard saw me leave the wall and my dress is a bright color. An hour, my love. Stay here, where you are safe, and let me return to Minerva. I will only kiss her brow, that is all. I will take a dark, poor gown and one of her old shawls and leave Raedelle just as you have come. Less notice will be taken of a peasant leading an old hag down the road than if we run for the wood."

He frowned slightly. "I do not want to let go of you again. I fear I will never have another chance. There is war on the land. Anne, at any moment our chance to flee could be lost."

"But Dylan, for a year and a half we have awaited this. An hour. Please."

He held her head against his chest and stroked the silky length of her hair. "It is so close," he said breathlessly. "You have no idea how terrible it is, the war that is coming."

"We will be far away from it, my love."

"God help us, I hope so. I do not think Henry's army can hold them back." He lifted her chin. "Anne, if we fail . . ."

"Dylan, hush! I have never walked through Raedelle's gate more easily. They are so upset with their conspiracy, they notice me less than ever. I will take a shawl in a basket and tell the guard I am returning to cut wild flowers for old Minerva."

As she looked into his eyes she saw a fear and intensity that she had never before seen. In a panicked breath he whispered, "Anne, come *now!*"

She was afraid for him, never before seeing that look of panic etched into his handsome face. "Less than an hour, Dylan. It will be safer. Wait here." She kissed his lips. "I love you."

It was difficult to keep from skipping back to the gate. Anne had to keep her head slightly bowed so that no one would see the smile she could not hide, the flush of her cheeks. At last. There was not the slightest tugging at her heart for the betrayal her family would feel, for she hated what they were doing. They were moved to depose a king for want of power and money, not for a higher principle; not for England's good.

She fled through the town, her feet carrying her swiftly, her breath coming in labored gasps from the combination of exertion and anticipation. She raced through the keep, ignoring all the activity in her path, and ran up the back stairs to the chamber that was Minerva's.

Ferris slumped against the closed door, a tear tracing its way down his ruddy cheek. He lifted his head as Anne's foot touched the top step. "She is dead," he said.

"No," she said in a breath, shaking her head.

Ferris grasped her by the upper arms and kissed her brow. "It is almost as if she chose to die while you were away. She loved you so." He looked into her eyes. "Prepare her, my sweet. Her body needs to be readied by loving hands, and yours are the only ones I know."

"Oh Papa, I cannot," she cried, panicked. Ferris held her away and looked into her eyes. "Not Minerva," she said, the tears flowing freely, tears that to her shame were not for her old nurse, but for the cursed delay. She should have fled with Dylan instantly.

"You would not do this for Minerva?" he asked, frowning through the pain in his eyes.

"Papa, I . . ." It was on her lips to tell him. There was a fleeting hope that he would understand her, even help her. Although Ferris was committed to his cause for the Duke of York and had admitted hatred for Lord deFrayne, he did not encourage his sons to take up the feud. She knew he disliked the continued animosity between the two families. But Ferris, even as the lord of Raedelle, could not control the hatred of the others. And he could not betray the family honor. If he knew Dylan was here for his daughter, he might stand aside as the others captured a deFrayne. She was still afraid to confide in him.

"I will do it, Papa. Go to church for me; buy a prayer for her soul and tell the priest."

Ferris nodded and walked wearily down the stairs. Anne entered the sickroom and looked down at the peaceful face of her nurse and lifelong friend. Minerva was old and had worked hard. In death, she had rest and peace. It was almost as if she smiled. Anne bent over the bed and kissed Minerva's brow. "Forgive me, my love," she whispered, a fresh tear dropping onto the wrinkled face.

Then she whirled, grasped a shawl from the coffer at the foot of the bed, and raced down the back stairs through the gallery to her own chamber. She stripped off her bright rose-colored gown and donned a dull tan working apron and tucked her hair under a cap. She dug through her small jewel chest and stuffed her few trinkets into her pockets; things that could be sold for money if Dylan had little. She pushed Minerva's shawl into a basket and scurried again toward the back stair. Though the passage was longer, she would leave the keep through the cookery to avoid passing her brothers in the courtyard. She hoped no one would notice her. She could be taken for any village wench.

The tower horn sounded and Anne stopped short. She lowered her eyes again and resumed walking, aware of running all around her. *Oh dear God, no* her heart screamed. *Oh dear God, give me flight, and I will never ask another thing.*

Afraid of the truth, she walked swiftly. Her cheeks drained of color and her eyes glazed over. Her heart beat wildly and her stomach churned miserably. The knights armed themselves and began to run. At the wall the men were clumsily struggling to arm the new bronze cannon. Quentin, already astride, held his prancing steed in wait for the opening of the gate. *Wings, dear Father in heaven. Give me wings to clear the wall.*

"A deFrayne troop," she heard a man shout. She lifted her eyes. Twenty or more knights cleared the gates with destriers, spears, and lances, and the mighty oaken portal was closing behind them. "A deFrayne troop is being engaged by our riders on the south Driscoll cross."

"No," she said in a breath, shaking her head. "Oh please, let it not be so!"

Archers lined the walls, bows ready and quivers in place. She looked around, turning full circle, her hair slipping from under the cap and falling to her shoulders. A choking sob escaped her and she covered her mouth. She could not get out, she could not go to him. Was he safe? Would he be killed? The troop who had waited to escort them to safety was being attacked by Gifford riders. But Dylan was not with them. He was in the trees against the wall.

"From the wall. Archers ready."

"No," she screamed, but to no avail. There was commotion and a flurry of arrows. She knew that Dylan must be running for the tethered horses in the wood. "No," she screamed again, fearing she would go mad. Peasant clothes, no armor, no weapon save the scythe he had taken.

"Is it a deFrayne?"

"No colors, my lord. It could be anyone, but he flees and so he dies."

"He's crossing the field! Bowman! Draw!"

"Too late. He's in the trees. Send riders."

Anne's fists pressed against her mouth and she shook with terror. Her pockets were stuffed with her minor jewels, her disguise was in her basket, and tears flowed down her pale cheeks. Anyone who looked closely might guess that she was prepared for flight. Suddenly, a hand, heavy and strong, rested on her shoulder and turned her around. She looked into the angry eyes of her father.

"My God," Ferris said in a breath. "'Tis true. You would betray us!"

"Betray you?" She shouted in hurt, furious pain. "Betray what? Your war against your king? Your foul, senseless hatred? What, Father, do I betray? Not my heart! Never!"

Ferris looked into the eyes of his daughter, eyes filled with agony and terror and hopelessness. He knew he was too late. "Had you made away, you might have been killed," he whispered, shaking her.

A high shriek of hysteria escaped her. She had lost her chance. Death seemed no worse than what she felt now. "I don't care," she cried. "I love him!"

"Oh my sweet Anne, how I prayed you would not . . ."

"*Father*," she cried, dropping the basket and falling into his embrace in anguish she had never before known. Ferris lifted her into his arms, her head against his chest, and carried her toward the hall. She clung to him in her misery, no longer caring who knew, no longer caring if they chose to strip her to naked flesh and nail her to the gate. She sobbed, her insides tearing at her. Despite her father's strong arms capably bearing her to the hall, she never felt so alone. She wished to die.

"What is the matter with *her*?" Marcella's sharp voice inquired as Anne was carried into the common room.

"Minerva has died. The lass is in despair."

"Well, tell the girl to gather her wits. We've more than old Minerva to worry about. There are deFraynes at our gate."

"Leave the child be," Ferris said, ignoring her passion and continuing to the stair.

"Ferris, God above, put that wench down and get to your horse. DeFrayne blood is at hand. Isn't that more important than an old woman's death?"

"*Marcella*," he shouted, his face nearly turning purple. "You have no mercy in your heart." He shook his head in denial. "Leave my daughter *alone*!"

Ten days passed after the battle at the cross between the deFrayne troop and Gifford riders. Anne's deep despair and unrelenting tears were passed off as grief over Minerva's death. Ferris did not speak of the true reason and looked at his daughter with pity. And he watched her very closely.

Four bodies wearing the deFrayne livery were brought to Raedelle, but Dylan was not among the dead. While there was some relief in his spared life, there was little hope, for the guard was tripled and the Raedelle demesne was kept well cleared of any strangers for ten leagues in circumference.

Anne covered her head and picked up her basket, walking through the town and to the gate. The October air cut like a knife, but she did not feel the cold. Her cheeks were chafed from the flowing tears, her eyes red and swollen. Dylan would never again be able to come to her in time; he had been swept away in the gathering storm. A civil war in England was brewing. Her heart cried out for him, but he was gone.

"No one is to leave the keep, maid Anne."

"I wish to gather late flowers from the wood for Minerva's grave," she told the gatekeeper angrily, with determination. "Those were her favorite."

"But, maid Anne . . ."

"Leave the girl alone," Ferris's rough voice instructed. She met her father's eyes briefly. He knew she could not run away; she would be returned by her father's men. Dylan could not come for her; no one could get through the heavy Raedelle guard. Ferris would do nothing to help her, but he would not see her hurt any further.

Anne went into the wood near the road. She stooped to break a few blossoms from around the foot of a tree, but before she could do even that much, she began to weep again. She looked into the thick trees. Her lips moved over his name. Dylan, my love. Dylan, my love. If only he would appear, turn from the side of a thick-trunked tree and take her into his arms. If only she could recall the day and run with him, holding his hand, through the field to the wood where the horses awaited them. If only she could see his bright eyes, his smile, his sandy hair, just once more. . . .

She wept, which was all she could do. And prayed, *Dear God, was that truly my only chance for Dylan? Will he never come again? Must we live apart and abide their foolish wars? Is it over? So soon?*

She did not hear the horse approach, nor was she aware of his presence until she felt the gentle touch of his hand on her back and heard his voice.

"Oh, my poor lass, do you hurt so badly?"

She turned to look at Brennan. Sympathy drew his soft eyes deep and clear. He knelt close behind her, his horse grazing just a short distance away. He smiled consolingly and opened his arms to her. She leaned toward him, filled with gloom yet grateful for any strong arm that would help her bear her lonely burden. As she wept against his costly, impeccable tabard, he gently stroked her back and crooned words of consolation.

"Oh Brennan, I have never felt such loss," she cried.

"I know, my sweet love. I, too, have felt the pain of loss, and there is little another can do to shield us from it. Even knowing something of what you must feel, I cannot drive your misery away. But if you let me, I will hold you fast and keep you safe until your grief is done."

"Sweet Jesus, why is it so hard?"

"We have pain and joy, dear Anne, each in its time. It is a wonder, I think, that we live so long, when the misery can be so deep."

The grief was so intense, robbing her of appetite and sleep, that she thought she might die of it. But each morning she awoke, realizing that life, stubborn and thorny, was winning. She accepted his solace and let him hold her until the tears dried and she was exhausted. At least two hours passed as a mighty lord of lands sat upon the grass near the wood, holding an anguished maiden. Then, as the afternoon sun was fading, he mounted his steed, lifted her onto his lap and drew his mantle around her, directing his mount toward Raedelle's gates.

Anne was listless and spent, but grateful for Brennan's attention. Though he was unaware of whose loss she was mourning, his kindness was deep and his love for her was pure. They did not speak through the whole of the afternoon, nor even as they rode through Raedelle's gates. He only gave his devotion, asking nothing in return. Had she the strength, she would have been sorry that a man so good could not be rewarded with her unfailing love.

Anne relied on the support of his strong arm as they walked into the hall. He paused at the foot of the stair, ready to send her to her chamber with a final word when Marcella descended. "Jesu, does the wench still lament her nurse? I have never witnessed such indulgence as this," Marcella said.

Brennan frowned and looked at Marcella with distaste. "Madam, you have a heart so cold I find it difficult to believe you have borne one so gentle." He looked down at Anne. "Eat something that will not upset and take a full goblet of wine. Food and rest will cure most of this ill, and what else, time will heal." He touched his lips to her brow. "Go on, love. I will be near."

Anne stole a look at her mother. There was anger in Marcella's eyes and the hostility seemed to be toward Anne. She had become so accustomed to her mother's indifference that she could not understand the hostility she saw. Could you hate someone you never noticed? But it occurred to her for the first time that her mother hated her. She could not remember ever hurting her mother, not in her worst mischief as a child. Yet there was no mistaking the cold contempt in those icy blue eyes. She shuddered with revulsion and fear.

"Do not leave me soon, Brennan," she said, feeling he was her only friend just now.

"I will be near, until you are better," he said. His eyes appeared brighter, as if grateful that she should need him.

"Thank you," she whispered. She passed her mother on the stair, but could not look at her again. She followed Brennan's instructions, ate and drank what she could, and slept deeply. And, much to her relief, dreamlessly.

Chapter Four

ANNE MIGHT NOT have recovered from her severe melancholia had it not been for the tender encouragement of Lord Forbes. Brennan's patient understanding and steadfast presence eased her through the weeks following Dylan's departure. She grew attached to him and depended heavily on his loyal support. She began, in a way, to love him. It was impossible to be indifferent to a man so kind and devoted. She knew it was not the love of a bride; absent was the fierce tension of longing, the heat of desire. She also knew that she did not display the passion and yearning Brennan would have liked in return. Nonetheless, Brennan Forbes had earned a small place in the heart of young Anne Gifford.

Brennan stayed at Raedelle for a fortnight following his promise to stay near to Anne, and then he reluctantly departed. He hurried through his own business of establishing forces and funds for the Duke of York's armies, and returned to Raedelle a few days before Christmas. He came laden with gifts. Many of the gifts were chosen specifically for Anne, but the entire Gifford family was remembered generously by the rich and powerful earl.

Anne greeted Brennan warmly, surprised and genuinely pleased by his return. She had assumed he would be occupied during the Christmas celebration, if not by his politics, then with his son. Until he arrived, she had been very lonely, for there was no one for her. Minerva was gone, and Trenton, who in quieter times would talk to her and sing his songs, had been caught up in the excitement of building forces. There was good reason she would be happy to welcome a friend. In her happiness, she served him promptly, made him comfortable in the common room before a blazing hearth and in the company of many of her family members, and excused herself to change into a better gown. She returned quickly, her dark hair still unbound and shimmering down her back, wearing her best rose-colored velvet.

Brennan had brought a special gift for Anne. It was the marriage ring that had been his mother's and had been retrieved from the fingers of his two dead wives. As he sensed her growing acceptance of him, he became impatient to impress her, to hurry her. And he couldn't wait to see the look in her eyes when she spied the magnificent diamond marriage ring.

He invited her to sit beside him and presented the small package for her to open. When she was near and eagerly unfastening the ribbons, he noticed that her gown was frayed at the hem and shiny on the elbows. It was not unbecoming, and Anne could be ravishing in the simplest rag, but he frowned, knowing the dress had either been passed on from her older sister, or had been Anne's for a very long time. He doubted the latter, for she had grown taller since the previous summer. Taller, fuller, and more beautiful.

"Oh Brennan," she sighed, her eyes rounding when she spied the ring. "It is so beautiful. I have never seen anything more beautiful"

The family crest of dark green beryl that Marcella wore shrank and burned on her finger. Her greatest jewels could not compare to this. Although Brennan had arrived with gifts for the entire Gifford family, Marcella forgot herself as jealousy engulfed her. The earl obviously was not negotiating a family pact for honor and power; he was simply smitten with the lass. "God's blood, but you'll spoil the wench, my lord. How do you expect her to serve you, weighted with such trinkets?"

Lord Forbes's head snapped around in Marcella's direction, and he glared at her. The gem was hardly a trinket; the future Countess of Ayliffe was not a wench. "Someone should spoil her, madam. Certainly you do not."

"My lord?" she questioned, insulted. Marcella drew herself to her impressive full height, her hands clasped in front of her.

Brennan had felt disquiet; but now he was suddenly incensed. "Did I not lend my purse to a trousseau? I gave you monies to outfit the lass, yet she descends from her chamber in a dress worn for two winters before this. Is this, madam, the attire befitting a countess?"

Marcella scowled, but upon noticing his changed mood, she checked her response. "Your pardon, Lord Forbes, but our family has been beset with a great many obligations; serious matters of state have lately taken precedence over the attire of my youngest child."

"Anne, is this the finest gown you possess?" Brennan asked her, his anger straining to find full bloom.

"Brennan, please," she softly begged. "It is of no matter. I have other gowns, finer gowns. Please."

The pleading in her eyes only further convinced him. As he looked at Marcella, he saw standing behind her a scowling Divina, wearing a very beautiful deep green velvet gown, with a fancy and valuable necklace sparkling on her throat. They treated Anne more like a servant than a daughter. Comparing the two daughters, Brennan was even more confused. Little was required to enhance Anne's beauty, but much money and attention had seemed poorly placed on Divina. What confusion clouded Lady Gifford's judgment? How had this woman consigned her beautiful lastborn child to a life of misery among the spoils? Why had they considered the convent for the sweetest, the most desirable of their daughters?

"Affairs of state," he snorted. "It is usually the lord who handles soldiers and politics, madam. It is to Lord Gifford's credit that he has one so efficient to endorse letters on his behalf, but I ask you, madam, who cares for the wants of your children? You willingly accept a rich betrothal contract for this young woman, yet you take no pains to make her presentable?" Marcella took a step toward the Earl of Ayliffe, but he held up a hand to ward her off, shaking his head impatiently. "Never mind. Since I am displeased, I will pleasure myself by having clothing made for her; clothing that I find suitable for a countess. And never, madam, *ever* refer to my future wife as a wench again." He took a deep breath. "Guard this precious jewel carefully, Lady Gifford, as though your very life depends on it."

Lord Gifford did not defend his wife, but watched the Earl of Ayliffe with admiration and gratitude. He had earlier resented Marcella's interference in this marriage arrangement, but now he was quite pleased. He was inwardly delighted by Marcella's shocked expression; his wife resented her lost control. Ferris knew, as he had never known before, that Anne would be safe. If ever there was a man capable of loving her as was her due, and perhaps even drawing her desires away from the deFrayne fugitive, it was Brennan Forbes. Ferris Gifford gave a slight, almost imperceptible nod of approval.

Brennan held a hand out toward Anne. "Come, my dear. Come with me for a moment."

She placed her hand in Brennan's, some confusion shining in her eyes and her brow slightly furrowed, but she went with him willingly as he led her toward the stair. She found herself in her own chamber, stripped down to her shift and standing behind a screen while Brennan lounged in a chair on the opposite side. A maid knotted cords around Anne's waist, chest, down her arms, from her hips to the floor, and across her shoulders, while the manservant who had accompanied Brennan sat at a table in the room and translated the knotted cords into measurements to be taken to a tailor. The brisk efficiency left her breathless; awed. Brennan dictated his desires to his scribe; the number of dresses, the ells required for each so that no train or full skirt would be slight, the colors, the styles, slippers to match, furs, cloaks, undergarments, bedgowns, wrappers, wimples, hennins, barbarettes, and caps.

The process took two hours. When Anne finally came out from behind the screen, her gown was still unfastened in the back and she held it on her shoulders. She looked at her future husband sheepishly. "Brennan, you needn't go to so much trouble. I do not need —"

He cut her off brusquely, still somewhat angry that he had found her appearance as he had, so many months after assigning Marcella this duty on his behalf. Without letting her finish, he turned to his man. "Travel to London immediately to have these items fashioned for Lady Anne. They should be delivered here posthaste. I'm certain my seal will afford good credit. And explain the matter as urgent." Then he looked at Anne. "Lady Anne," he said, his poor humor finally dissipating since he had rectified the matter to his satisfaction, "it suits you. You will wear the title well."

"Brennan," she said, shaking her head, "you should not have exchanged such angry words with my lady mother."

"Lady Gifford needs be chastened, my dear. She has not withheld the slightest frock from your mule-faced sister, yet there is no question that Divina does not appreciate her mother's generosity. God knows, she needs the attention; she is ugly and poor-tempered." Anne could not help but smile because of Brennan's criticism. Divina had been so hard on her that it felt rather good to hear her maligned. "Why in the world would Lady Gifford favor her? It is obvious she does."

"Oh Brennan, you must understand. Divina and I are so different. I could not even be nursed by my own mother. My birth made madam very ill and I was a horrid child; she often says so. I was raised by old Minerva, while my older sister, so much less of a problem, followed madam about, copying all her manners and habits. I did the same with old Minerva. Truly, we were raised by different women and it goes hard on Divina now, for it is almost as if I have stolen something from her — our mother is more mindful of me because of you. All this attention and fuss was to be for Divina." She smiled sweetly. "She is not as lucky as I."

Brennan gave a huff of disapproval. "You are too forgiving. As she wiggles the entire Gifford clan nearer the Duke, Lady Gifford should remember that my friendship comes in deference to my desire to have you as my wife, not because I admire her politics. I would expect this family to pledge their arms where they see fit, regardless of betrothals." He frowned slightly as he looked at his young bride-to-be, knowing that Marcella had made Anne a pawn in a play for power. "I tell you this, Lady Anne; your family will not show you due respect before you demand it of them. Before we are wed, and after, they will use you for as long as you allow. Now, I will not say more at the risk of offending you. But the new gowns, Anne, will please me. You must allow."

She smiled in happy exasperation. She was not entirely sure that he wasn't an angel sent to help ease her through this painful and frightening time of her life. "I do not think the subject will arise again. Madam surely knows that you have a quick temper."

"Only where I perceive injustice. Now, where is that ring?" he asked. She held out her clenched fist and slowly opened it, exposing the glittering gem. He took the ring and placed it on her finger and kissed her brow. "I hope you will wear it with pride, my love, and know how highly I value you."

Her eyes were transfixed by the sparkling diamond. Tears began to swell. This very fine man should give his ring to a more deserving woman. In her heart she knew she could never return his affection as he deserved, that she would be happier accepting a copper band presented by Dylan. If she were stronger, she would tell him the truth; that she could not love him as passionately as he should be loved. But she was afraid and lonely. Brennan Forbes was the only kindness in her life.

He lifted her chin with a finger. "I love you, Anne. I cannot wait for you much longer."

"Oh Brennan," she said, choking on a sob and embracing him

suddenly. "I am so afraid that I will fail you. You should have a perfect woman, a perfect wife. I'm sure I cannot be all that you expect me to be."

He held her for a moment and then looked tenderly into her eyes. "You are the woman I want, and if you let me love you, you cannot possibly fail me."

She was awestruck that he did not ask for her love in return, nor did he extract any promises from her but that she receive his devotion willingly. If he asked her, she would not be able to conceal the lie: the love she held in her heart was for another. This was not her choice, but her burden. The love she did feel for Brennan was the deep love of a daughter; of fondness, respect, and gratitude. It was the love one felt for a dear and treasured friend.

"You are a rare man, Brennan Forbes. You do me great honor; I will strive to bring only dignity to your house, your name."

"I have never felt what I feel for you. I never thought it possible. But I cannot change it now. I only pray that someday you will feel it, too."

She almost sighed that she hoped so as well, but instead she rested her head on his chest, her arms around him. She was grateful to have this strong arm to lean on, and silently she prayed for forgiveness, for she knew Brennan would be hurt by her love for Dylan. "I will try to make you proud of me, Brennan. I will try to be deserving of your love," she said.

"That is a good place to begin," he said.

The threat of impending war eased during the Christmas season. There were more than the usual number of knights, squires, and pages present, which called for more castle servants. Raedelle was splitting at the seams with people, but the mood was gayer than it had been in the fall. The gates were stoutly closed and the daily practice of arms ceased because of the snow and cold and feasting in the hall. Trenton sang again, his beautiful voice filling the evening hours. Quentin discussed politics with the earl, but his main concern rested on preserving Raedelle, his inheritance. Bart edged into their conversations, eager for some recognition or appointment, but he was cautious and polite. Even Marcella seemed to relax a bit, although her favorite topic of conversation was still politics. She wrote fewer letters since there were fewer couriers, and therefore she concentrated more on household and family matters.

Divina, somewhat encouraged by gifts the earl had given her, was careful not to insult Anne. In fact, she lavished attention on Brennan Forbes and occasionally smiled at Anne. Anne was no more fooled than Brennan — Divina would like to replace Anne in Brennan's regard, or, at the very least, accept a husband brought to her by the earl. But nothing was said. It was a relief to have Divina act decently.

Though the motives of her brothers and sister might be self-serving, Anne felt a sense of family for the first time in her memory. Her sister did not harass her, her mother treated her with cautious kindness, and her father, who was quiet even in turbulent times, appeared almost joyful. Bart and Quentin treated Anne with a brand new respect, for her womanly assets had brought a rich and powerful earl into their household, and their opportunity for recognition in the realm was finally at hand. Trenton was the only one unchanged, and with his war tools laid temporarily aside, she could enjoy their kinship once again.

Anne had been a forgotten child. She had not suffered, because Minerva and her father had loved her tenderly. But she had never known her value; she had never known how often her father sat bemused at how the others overlooked her. The most remarkable change due to the earl's attention came from Marcella, and her mother treated her with deference that was entirely new. It was Anne's first taste of power. She knew that if the earl suddenly vanished, she would be whisked away to the nuns without pause. "Little second-born lass," Dylan had said. The little lass was no more — she was soon to be a countess. Her countenance had not changed, her mind had not suddenly accepted great vision, yet her future would determine her family's destiny.

Anne could not deny a feeling of exhilaration her new position accorded her, but she was even more puzzled by her mother's lack of love. She did not know what she had done to fall so far from favor. Still a simple lass at heart, she would have preferred genuine family love in lieu of wealth and power. As the days of Christmas passed, Anne often stood in the tower to look out over the vast Raedelle demesne in search of tracks in the snow. She gazed longingly for a lone rider. When Brennan spoke of a wedding, she tried to delay it by persuading him that the beauty of late spring would be perfect. She hoped that Dylan would steal her away before then. While her sister envied the jewels and special clothes that would soon arrive, Anne longed to share a simple pallet behind a stable with the man she loved. Marcella and the others spoke excitedly of the Duke's coronation, when he had finally unseated King Henry and defeated Margaret of Anjou's forces. But Anne didn't care who was king. She wished for it to be over, and to be forgotten again. She wished to be with Dylan.

"Richard, Duke of York, has been ambushed and slain. He was attacked by surprise in Sandal Castle at Wakefield, and all who were in residence, including sons and knights, were either slain or captured."

Members of the Gifford family froze in silence on the stair, in the doorways, in front of the fire. A deep moan of disappointment left Marcella, and Divina began to quietly weep. The messenger had ridden hard to Raedelle to bring the news to the Earl of Ayliffe and the Gifford family. Anne stood paralyzed and examined the stricken faces that had once been so hopeful, as they fell in despair. Their hope was suddenly crushed.

"Who has survived the Duke?" Brennan asked.

"The Earl of March, young Edward, is the heir. He was not with his father. He had gone home to Ludlow to collect Welsh armies."

Brennan walked to the stair where Anne stood, her hand half raised toward him. "I hope you understand and forgive me, my love. I will return to you as quickly as possible."

She nodded numbly. She knew why he would ask forgiveness.

Although it was unspoken, they both realized that his presence kept her family at bay.

"I am for Edward," Brennan said to the room at large. "I cannot think one reason to delay."

"He is a *boy*," Marcella cried despairingly.

"His age is irrelevant, madam," the earl replied. "He is the heir." Edward, Earl of March, was now the Duke of York. And it was through the house of York that they placed the claim to the crown of England. Edward, at the age of nineteen, did not have a reputation as a strong knight. He had not yet fought in any significant battle. While Anne was struggling to understand how this tragedy affected her own life, she could not help but notice that Brennan was the only man on his feet; the only one of the Duke's vassals preparing to depart. Again, she saw the true colors of her family; they were anxious to attach themselves to power, to regain what had been lost. But their real loyalties were rooted in sand. While the Giffords vacillated, Brennan was for York.

The Giffords did not tarry long though, for they did not wish to lose the earl's favor. Lord Gifford assembled what seemed to Anne a mighty troop of one hundred knights and two hundred archers. Lord Forbes sent a courier to Ayliffe to assemble and move west one thousand plus two thousand, and sudden awareness of Brennan's capability, something she had not really considered before, impressed her. Soon a troop led by both Lord Gifford and the Earl of Ayliffe departed from Raedelle, and Marcella resumed her letters.

Through early January there were messengers through the gate on a regular basis, bringing word of the Giffords, and of others.

"The deFraynes have joined with the king's men, even after those men showed their courage by sneaking into the Duke's home to slay him," Marcella told her daughters. She read a letter from Quentin so that it appeared Marcella was only imparting news, but Anne had heard a lifetime of such commentary, drumming it into all the Gifford children that the deFraynes were evil, treacherous characters. "It is rumored that the soldiers dressed as women to gain entrance to the Duke's castle." Marcella's cheeks reddened; her eyes glittered. "How like the deFrayne bastards to be attracted to such a cowardly ruse."

Anne listened without reaction. She wished to know if all the deFrayne men had pledged to the Lancaster king. Did even Dylan choose politics and war over their love? But she was silent. There was nothing she could say. She listened as Marcella enthusiastically described the horrible treatment that would befall the Lancaster supporters, especially the deFraynes, when the assault was finished and they were caught.

Letters also arrived from Brennan, which Marcella snatched from Anne's hand the moment she had finished reading each one. However, Brennan did not write about political issues or military plans, and each letter that expressed his longing for his bride only depressed and disappointed Lady Gifford. "I had not thought the earl, at his maturity, could behave like a besotted fool. What lunacy is this lust? A man of power weds a dowry and a family of substantial arms. To read his dribble makes me think he cares naught for the allegiance of a mighty family."

Mighty? Anne wondered. Dowry? Brennan Forbes was already rich and influential. He did not need Marcella's nagging, nor the modest fighting skills of the Giffords. And, if Lord Forbes had offered a partnership toward a cause, he need not have included marriage to Anne. Marcella had greatly mistaken the value of her assets. But Anne could not dismiss what was happening, although the men were far away. The arguments of dukes and kings had never touched her so closely before. She knew that York was going hard against Lancaster. The Giffords hard against the deFraynes. Where was Dylan?

During the last half of January there came the final revelation. A cart driven by an elderly couple arrived with clothing sewn for Anne of Raedelle. Two large coffers and several carefully wrapped bundles were brought to her rooms. It was the old couple's son who owned a tailor shop, and they were en route to their daughter's home. Since it meant only a slight departure from their planned journey, they delivered the newly sewn clothing. While the man drank cold ale in the common room, the woman went with Anne to her chamber to inspect the goods.

This was the first time there had been such an event at Raedelle, and Anne could not hide her excitement. Divina, whose curiosity for once outpaced her hostility, went along to see the gowns. Marcella took only a cursory look and then quickly departed. The sight of such beautiful gowns brought her both jealousy and the memory of her indiscretion, and near blunder, with the earl.

The old woman stayed on and on, turning gowns inside out to show Anne the stitchery, going over each detail of the craftsmanship, displaying shawls and wimples and hennins with various gowns to show the versatility of the costumes. Anne was impressed with the wardrobe, but just as she felt the urge to giggle in happiness, she noticed her sister's tears.

"Divina," she began, attempting consolation.

"Do not," Divina said, struggling to maintain some dignity. "Just let me see," she said quietly, her cheeks damp. "Let me see how it might have been for me."

"You must believe me, Divina. I would not purposely do anything to hurt you."

"If I am sent to the convent," Divina said, "I will never forgive you. Never!"

Anne was left to watch the old woman's nervous presentation of clothing, her blasé reaction no longer a matter of choice. She was robbed of the happiness the new clothing brought by Divina's jealousy and pain. Anne wondered how Divina could ignore the irony. Anne was always expected to make do on lesser gowns, to accept her future as a nun, and to exist without companionship or sisterly affection. But Divina, hurt and jealous, was to be pitied. Anne grew tired of the old woman's chatter. She felt a sense of loss rather than the delight of acquisition. Anne did not value material possessions above her sister's love.

Finally, Divina departed, closing the chamber door, and Anne turned to put her belongings away. It was then that the old woman sighed wearily and withdrew a small, torn parchment from her deep apron pocket. "I worried we'd never be left alone, mum, and I've a secret something to pass along."

Anne took the parchment in bemused silence, opened it and read:

Anne, my love, please forgive me.

The hand was not Brennan's. She looked at the old woman. "Where did you come by this?" she questioned in a whisper.

"Just four leagues off your gates, mum. The lad said 'twas for your eyes alone, and he'd be killed were it known. Must have meant a great deal to him. He paid me a noble sum to pass it along."

"You were not told to help me examine these things, were you?"

"Nay, mum, but I knew no other way. I can't read, mum. Is it important, like the lad said?"

Anne caressed the parchment with her fingers, reading it over and over through moist eyes. The words blurred and ran together. The message was clear. "Did he say anything else?" she asked, her voice catching. "Anything at all?"

"That you would understand, mum," the woman said, shrugging her shoulders.

"He was astride?" she asked. "Dressed . . . dressed warmly?"

Anne felt a touch and saw the old woman's hand on her forearm. "Well kept, armored . . . safe astride a good horse, mum."

Anne looked at the old woman closely. Then she took the note directly to the hearth and dropped it in the flame. "You must forget the errand and never speak of it." Then she kissed the woman's old and withered cheek. "I thank you from my heart."

"I'm thinkin' it's young lovers you are."

"Please," Anne said in a weak whisper. She was filled with pain. He was so close, yet he could not reach her. He did not beg her to come to him. He did not ask her to wait. He did not promise that soon, after this conflict, they would have each other. Her eyes were luminous with loss and agony.

"I'll not hurt you, lass. But I saw the same in his eyes, I did. If it helps you to know that, I saw the same in his eyes."

Anne nodded and her chin quivered. He was not coming for her. Not ever. His family had snatched him into their war and he had made his choice. And her family had given her to Brennan for the same purpose — to form a war pact. Dylan must surely have decided that it was now forever hopeless. He had given up their oath.

The old woman touched her cheek with a sympathetic stroke and then quietly left the room.

Anne choked back painful tears and lifted an ermine-lined cloak from the new clothing spread across her bed. She went to the donjon and stood alongside a watchman, looking out over the Raedelle lands. She examined the forest's edge for any detail, for fresh tracks in the snow. If she caught the slightest glimpse of him, she would scale the wall with her bare hands and run to him. But there was nothing. He had been four leagues away when he passed the note to the old woman; he was now surely ten leagues gone.

Tears slowly slid down her cheeks, and the guard did not comment until she had stood there for over an hour. "My lady, you'll become ill of the cold if you do not descend." She shook her head, her cheeks chapped from the tears, the winter wind, the icy cold. A hundred desperate plans coursed through her mind: to dress like a soldier and pass through the gate on horseback, or as a monk, but there were no monks in Raedelle, or as an old woman, as she had first attempted. But the guards let no one pass now, since the successful surprise attack on the Duke of York. And Dylan was gone — he had made his choice.

The sun began to lower in the sky. "My lady," the tower guard whispered. "Please, why do you weep?"

"My betrothed," she said weakly, her voice catching on a sob. "We are at war."

"But mademoiselle, the earl is one of the very best; his army is strong and well known. You need not be afraid for him."

"Of course not," she said, letting her chin fall. She could not see as far now, for the sky had darkened. Around the parapets the archers were lighting cressets. She returned to her chamber with a heavy heart and tears continued to stain her reddened cheeks as she placed her clothes in coffers. She looked up at the sound of her opening chamber door. Marcella stood there, a frown on her lips.

"What ails you now?" she demanded.

"I . . . I am overcome by Lord Forbes's generosity," she stammered, wiping at her tears.

"As are we all. 'Twas unkind of him to laud his wealth over us in this way. Your sister has never had such good fortune and I am certain her pain is great. Divina weeps."

"Madam . . . Mother . . . I would gladly share my good fortune with . . ."

"Divina will not take your leavings, girl."

Anne stiffened. "I have taken hers often enough."

Marcella smiled tolerantly. "It has not taken you long to become haughty. You were not so vain before the earl took a fancy to you."

"I did not ask this of the earl, nor did I ask to be his bride. Am I at some fault here? Or is it only Divina's jealousy that makes you dislike my good fortune?" Anne's heart was breaking, and she shook her head sadly. "Why do you pity Divina, madam? Did you ever pity me when I was poorly gowned and destined to the convent? Why do you hate me? Mother?"

Marcella looked away and closed her eyes briefly. Anne saw a flicker of pain cross her mother's features.

"Because birthing me was hard? Because I was a horrid child?" She choked on a sob. "Was Divina so much better?"

Marcella looked back at Anne. Now Anne saw it again — hate. Pain had turned to hate. She did not understand. "You are mistaken if you think I favor your sister over you, though she tries much harder to please me than you ever have. She is older and should marry first, but somehow you have managed where she has failed. You must be careful, Anne, that you do not become vain."

"Oh madam, there is little chance of that," Anne said wearily, turning away. "You and my sister will surely put me in my place."

"Do you expect me to coddle you as does your mighty earl?" Marcella snapped in sudden fury. "I have raised five children — three of them great knights — and what does he choose to discuss? Not the power of the family that will support him, not the arms we lend to his cause, but the *frayed hem* on the gown of his young tart! Do not pretend innocence with me; you relish in his poor treatment of me!"

Anne felt as though she had been slapped. "Where have I failed you, madam? How is it you love me so little? Does a mother really forget to love a child whose birth was painful? I cannot imagine it."

"You have been very fortunate, Anne. And take special care that you do not misuse your new power."

Marcella turned and left the chamber. It was Anne's alone now, for Minerva was dead and Divina was gone. She did not join the family for the evening meal, and nothing was brought to her. She refused to go to the common room to dine with her mother and sister and face their jealous glares. Soon, they seemed to forget her again, for no one noticed that Anne continued to wear her old gowns. And that her mind was far, far away — to a place where there could be fighting, where there could be no winners. A battle between Dylan and Brennan.

How alike they are, she thought. These two men who wanted her, though on opposite sides, were both so proud, so hard in their convictions and steadfast in their loyalties. Both had asked for forgiveness when they had to abandon her to serve their leaders and lend arms to what they believed in. She had once thought Dylan unconcerned with the choice of king; that he did not care about those loyalties chosen for him by his family. But it could not be so. It was that other feud, the one between the Giffords and deFraynes, that did not interest him. When it came to his king, he was steadfast. Otherwise, he would not have asked her forgiveness. His secret note was his admission that he had joined the cause and had, by necessity, sacrificed his promises to her.

She knew the history of her country quite well, and she had not the faintest idea who was right, whose right it was to wear the crown. She knew that if Brennan was killed in some battle, her mother and sister would feast on her gowns and trinkets and send her away to a convent without delay. From the convent Dylan could rescue her. But she could not find it in her heart to wish for Brennan's death, even if that meant a chance to have Dylan. Brennan had become her only ally, and her generosity was sincere.

In her lonely room she sometimes longed for Trenton, but she knew his alliance would be less available as he grew older, practiced his knightly skills, and turned his gaze toward his future. She longed for the presence of her father, though he could not help her. Or Minerva, who had deflected Marcella's blows so deftly through Anne's childhood that it was not until the old nurse died that Anne realized how little Marcella loved her. Her tears for Minerva were painful as this final truth dawned.

She could not have her father or brother, bring her old nurse back, or recapture the moment when Dylan had urged her to *flee now*. She was alone with one defense: Brennan's power. It was a defense she was destined to learn to use.

On the first day of February, as Anne descended to the common room to partake of the evening meal, she found her mother and sister sitting before the fire. They were laughing together when they looked her way, and she was instantly envious. "I see you have learned your lesson well," Divina said with sarcasm. "If you wear your poorest threads, perhaps the earl will flog us all and purchase you even more."

"That is not why she dresses in threadbare working tunics," Marcella explained. "It is because she knows her place when the earl is not present to chastise us for her appearance. Even though I lend to his cause a husband, three sons, and their knights, it is only to bed my youngest that stirs his blood."

Anne felt the diamond marriage ring as she clenched her fists. "I thought to promote York was your cause as well, madam."

"Indeed, daughter, and my cause would be better served if the earl reckoned with all that this family can do to aid him. We send one hundred knights, a number to be proud of, but he hungers mostly for your proper attire, making no mention of our strong arms."

"He is more concerned with the condition of poor Anne's gown than with the men who might be killed in the fighting," Divina said angrily, as if Anne were responsible for this war.

"Then why did the men go?" Anne asked. "Surely not because the earl wishes to marry me and clothe me well."

"Surely not," Marcella said. "Yet his gratitude and gifts fall to you, as though you have performed some great task just by passing before his eyes. How *did* you manage to trap him?"

"I never met him before he asked for me," Anne cried defensively. "Please, I did nothing to slight either of you."

"Perhaps the wench did no more than smile at him from Father's pavilion . . . just before she bared her bosom."

Divina's remark cut like a knife. Anne glanced at her sister. Divina wore a costly gown that had been specially sewn to draw the eyes of eligible men to her generous bosom and narrow waist, for those were her most enviable assets. Divina, but a younger version of their mother, had a narrow face, sharp nose, weak chin, and pale, thin hair. Her voluptuous shape drew attention away from plain looks, but soon Divina would be worse than plain — her mouth had already begun to turn down in disappointment and anger as their mother's did.

"Shhh," Marcella cautioned. "We mustn't upset the future countess by calling her a wench. Please do not complain to the earl, my dear. Another lashing is not my desire."

Anne knew the moment had come. Brennan had warned her. Though she could not understand their reasons, the fact was simple — her mother and sister resented her, possibly hated her. And they would victimize her and use her until she refused to allow it.

"It is a pity you hate me so well," she said, her eyes dry and her posture proud. "You can be so cruel to me when Lord Forbes is absent that it will be impossible to be tricked by your courtesy when he returns. I thought I had a generous and forgiving heart until today, but I cannot find leniency now. I doubt I shall be able to forgive you." She turned away and took two steps toward the stair. She turned back. "And you are correct, Lord Forbes treasures me far more than I deserve. I shall be the Countess of Ayliffe. I do hope you have no needs, or a desire to visit. I will find it difficult to succor this family that so despises me."

They were silent as she slowly climbed the stairs. A young castlemaid was descending, and as she passed, Anne requested a tray of food and wine brought to her room. She had never before asked for any special treatment. It was plain that the only way she could exist among them was to play this role that had been assigned to her, a role she had never wanted.

She heard their whisperings as she approached her chamber. She pulled off her old gown and searched through her trunks for a new bedgown and chamber robe. She found satin slippers for her feet. And, although she had no appetite, she took her dinner in leisure at a small table before the fire. She did not rise as usual to her chores. The next day was Candlemas Day, and she dressed herself carefully in one of her new gowns.

Her mother came to her first, asking to be excused for her teasing remarks, asking Anne to remember her family. Anne could not possibly consider such hostile remarks as teasing, but excused her mother anyway. Marcella would be careful, if not kind, and she expected little more. Divina came next, appearing with reddened eyes and trembling lips. Her anguished apology came harder, but her fear of being abandoned by the earl's influence was greater. Divina was terrified that she would be sent to live out her life with nuns.

As Anne went to mass she heard a murmur run through the keep and found many looking up to the sky and shielding their eyes. There appeared to be three suns shining there, and panicked castlefolk began to run to their huts to pray or murmur incantations, or to burn incense. Anne felt a shudder of horror run through her. A pain in her chest caused her to wonder if the devil had come to earth to finish them all for their wicked ways.

She fled to the chapel and knelt in prayer. *O blessed Father in Heaven, Mother of God, though I have no right, I beg you keep them safe.*

Both of them. She stayed on her knees through the morning, afraid to look again at the sky, afraid she would see it bleed.

Not very far away, Edward, the Duke of York, also saw the three suns. His soldiers were frightened. But he quickly shouted across the masses of panicked men that it was the sign of the Trinity, and God supported them and they would be victorious. He then led them into battle. And the blood was not in the sky, but on the land.

Chapter Five

THE GIFFORD MEN returned to Raedelle with the high flush of victory on their cheeks. Edward's first battle for the crown took place at Mortimer's Cross, only a day's journey from the Gifford keep. The tower guard sent out the summons to open the gate to the returning soldiers when the standard of Gifford green was sighted. Their troop was reduced, but not by loss; they had left behind some of their best soldiers and knights with Ayliffe's and Edward's forces.

The women — Marcella, Divina, wives of knights, and servants — ran excitedly from the town and hall. Except for Anne; she lagged behind, looking at each man. Lord Gifford, who appeared tired and worn, but unhurt, slumped slightly in his saddle. Though he was just a bit older than Brennan, he appeared too old for such fighting; he seemed spent by the battle. Not so Sir Quentin, their mightiest, who sat high in his saddle, looking proud and elated. By his expression, he had finally proven himself in more than a contest. Bart, wearing a look of giddy excitement in addition to pride, must have also done well. But Trenton looked dazed. Perhaps, Anne thought, he is surprised that he survived.

While Anne stood back, Marcella and Divina ran to the men. She strained her eyes, but did not see Brennan. Behind the dismounting troop of two dozen knights, she noticed serfs or commoners seated on or lying across horses with their heads down. Prisoners. They were prisoners. Six of them, far to the rear of the troop. Ferris stood before her, looking down at her with distinct sadness in his eyes. She stared up at her father, afraid to breathe. Had it happened? "Brennan?" she asked in a whisper.

"In the best of health, child. A powerful soldier, Lord Forbes. Would that I had his strength, his cunning."

"Papa, where is he? Why has he not come?"

"He is with Edward, lass. Where we should be." Marcella's joyful shriek rose from the crowd of knights and horses as she threw her arms around Bart's neck and embraced him enthusiastically. Quentin, still astride, laughed at his mother's excitement. Trenton looked away. Anne glanced around her father's bulky form to see the object of such passionate joy.

"Edward was victorious?" she asked, still uncertain about what was happening all around her.

"Anne," Ferris said, frowning. "For his life, do not look at him! For his *life!* For yours!"

Perplexed, she studied her father's face, his anguished eyes.

"*DeFraynes!*" Marcella shouted with joy. "What better gift could you bring me?"

"Oh Father, no," Anne said, beginning to tremble.

"Have a care, child. His life, yours, and mine, all rest on caution now. If you give any secret away, he will only die faster and we will suffer greatly."

Terrified of her own feelings, Anne looked at the ground. She could feel the heat of blood rush to her head, covering her face to the roots of her hair; her heart began to pound. She clutched her shaking fingers together so that if anyone noticed her, they would think she hung her head in disappointment that her betrothed had not returned with the others. Fortunately, Marcella and the others were busy inspecting the catch. "What can be done?" Anne asked quietly.

"For now, very little. I have to think. I would not have allowed this much to happen, but I have little control over my sons now. And they knew how this would please their mother."

"And Brennan?" she asked weakly.

Ferris shook his head. "Lord Forbes is not opposed to the taking of hostages among the defeated, but this odd, personal zeal offends him. Edward called to spare the common soldiers and execute the lords. Few enough of Henry's nobles survived the battle. These men should have been restrained with Edward's forces, not brought here as prizes of war."

"Perhaps she will ransom them," Anne said hopefully.

"That possibility, though remote, is why I have returned with my sons. We should not have left Lord Forbes. Certainly not for this farce."

Anne warily looked up at her father. She felt the weakest hold on her control, but she longed to see Ferris's expression. "I would have thought you would bare my back for this sin."

A rueful smile spread across his face. "For the sin of being a woman? Of being good in your heart?" He placed a hand on her shoulder. "There is very little I can still do, Anne. Do not let anyone know what you feel. Not now. They do not understand."

"But you do, Father. How can it be so?"

"Do not question small mercies; I have never been in favor of senseless plunder. Fair battle will see me fight, otherwise will be dealt with otherwise. How did I fail to teach this to my sons?"

"Why do you have no better control over them? Why do they do this for madam?" she asked.

"Perhaps my sons think they do this thing for all of us, Anne," he said quietly. "When your mother has her mind set . . . ." He paused for a moment. "Anne, hear me, though this is difficult for you now. Lord Forbes is your single hope. He is the only one who can keep you safe. If, through some miracle, young Dylan can escape with his life, it is still only Lord Forbes who can save you. Do you understand?"

She nodded weakly. For her sake, for Dylan's, the only possible answer was marriage to the earl.

"Will Edward win his crown?" she asked.

"Almost certainly. King Henry is held hostage and Edward's armies are invincible."

Raedelle squires had begun to pull destriers from the returning knights, and a large group of laughing, ecstatic people who had been gathered around the captive hostages started to disperse. Bart passed by with two badly injured men wearing the deFrayne blue livery embroidered with red roses for the Lancaster house. These two unfortunates were lying on their bellies, across saddleless horses, their dangling hands tied at the wrists, stained with blood. He paused before his father and sister, his chin proudly jutted out, his chest full and high. Ferris squeezed Anne's arm as if to give strength. Bart grasped one captive man by the hair to lift his head and show his face. It was the eldest deFrayne, Sir Wayland, either dead or near dead. Bart smiled as if to take credit for finally besting the man whose back he had attacked at the tournament. He gave a sharp nod, then passed on.

"Put the deFraynes in the keep, tied, and stoutly locked in," Marcella instructed.

Next came Quentin, pulling the reins of two palfreys. These two captured soldiers were obviously of the deFrayne troop, but unknown to Anne. She could not tell if they were hurt. Their hands were tied behind them and they balanced precariously on the horses' backs. Quentin, though pleased, did not gloat. "Worry not, sister, your betrothed fared the battle well. He will arrive soon. He received the duke's honors for his skills."

She nodded at Quentin, attempting to smile, if not for his good wishes, then as a distraction. No one must suspect that the capture of these men distressed her.

Finally, Trenton, still a fuzzy-faced youth younger than Dylan by several years, pulled his two palfreys past. Dylan kept his eyes focused straight ahead. A large purple lump disfigured his forehead; dried blood from his nose stained his growth of blond beard. He did not so much as glance her way, and she felt Ferris squeeze her arm again. "Trenton?" she asked quietly. "You are unhurt?"

"Aye," he said, pausing before her. She tried to see Dylan from the corner of her eye while she focused on Trenton's face. "Lord Forbes was magnificent, Anne. He was commended by Edward and will hold a high place in his court. You would have been proud." He paused and a deep blush rose to his cheeks. "He lent me no small amount of aid."

"I am glad you were not hurt."

Trenton nodded, obviously relieved himself, then pulled the palfreys past. She glanced quickly at Dylan's hard eyes. She saw that blood from some wound stained his chausses on the thighs, marked his tied hands, soiled his tunic. It was dark and old. Whatever had bled had stopped. His blue eyes glittered with hatred; his jaw muscles tensed as he ground his teeth. She saw his courage, and the futility of it all.

Marcella followed the palfreys, snapping her orders. The captured soldiers could be tied in the stable, separated from their young lords by a substantial distance, for surely they would attempt to rescue the deFraynes. Wayland and Dylan were to be kept in the castle, tied, behind locked doors, guarded. A different sentry would be posted every several hours. Then they would be executed, quartered, and sent in pieces to Heathwick Castle. Anne listened and shuddered. Marcella laughed happily. Divina followed her mother, also laughing.

Soon the servants and others had also departed the courtyard and the steeds had been led away for currying. She was alone with her father.

"Wayland will disappoint them," Ferris said. "He will not live through the night. Wayland's injuries were earned in fair battle, despite what Bart would imply with his cocky behavior. He was unable to even that score, though he would let everyone think he had."

"All the same," Anne said, "Wayland's head will ride a pike somewhere. Here?"

"Not if Lord Forbes arrives. It was a grave and pitiful moment — Lord Forbes's passion was needed elsewhere and he had not the time to take these Gifford brats to task for this. He was consumed wth Edward and his needs. He did, however, tell them sternly that he considered this act to be foolhardy and wasteful."

"It has long been said that the deFraynes would do this to us. Papa, I must know if it is so, truly so. Would the deFrayne men take our young Trenton, bind him, execute him . . ." She couldn't finish. She couldn't even bear the thought of what they planned for Dylan.

"Aye, they would have, under the command of their father, Lord deFrayne," Ferris replied, his eyes focused on some distant point straight ahead, not looking at his daughter. "No more. Lord deFrayne fell in battle, and Lady Daphne has the respect of all her sons. 'Tis not in her nature to commit such atrocities."

"Do you *know* her?"

"I did once, before she wed Lord deFrayne. Although she was bidden to support her husband's decisions, whether or not she approved, unless she has greatly changed, she would not sanction an act such as this." He turned and looked at Anne. "Your courage and wisdom will be tested as never before. Do not doubt me when I tell you that no other member of this family will take pity on you as I do. Do not let them know your heart. It will go worse for Dylan . . . and you."

"Papa . . . Papa, I almost told you. When you sent me to mass after my introduction to Lord Forbes . . . and again, when Minerva died. Would you . . . would you have . . ."

"Ah, Anne," he sighed. "Even knowing something of what you felt, I am not sure I would have tried to help you."

"Will you try to help me now?"

"You have but one road to travel, lass. But I will do what I can to save Dylan's life."

"But Papa — "

"Someday you will understand. Someday."

It was an odd twist of events that Anne stood in the tower on blistering afternoons to watch, this time, for Brennan. Sir Wayland had not lived long enough to be a good waste for rope in the cask room. Somehow Lord Gifford had managed to convince his sons to do nothing dishonorable to his body. Anne thought she saw disappointment glittering in her mother's eyes.

For two days Dylan had been tied below them. She could feel his presence flowing upward. She knew his health to be good, for Ferris had tricked them into washing and feeding him. "Had I known you were simply going to starve him to death, as he lay in his own filth, we could have as easily tied him to a tree and let him rot," he had said.

"Your father is right," Marcella said. "Keep him well. Perhaps we will do better by having him."

And so her plan began. There was only one other deFrayne son yet alive. Sir Cameron had managed to ride away from the battle. Marcella resumed her letter writing. She carefully considered every detail, from time for travel to the effects of battle on Sir Cameron, the only deFrayne to escape. She discussed the details with her sons. Anne wished she could hide in her room and remain invisible, yet she feared to miss any mention of Dylan and his proposed fate. She lingered on the fringes of her family's conversations while they plotted; she watched longingly as the door to the cask room was opened and food was taken past the lounging guard to feed Dylan.

"The letter will be addressed to Madam deFrayne," Marcella said, refusing to title Dylan's mother. "We will call for a ransom to be paid for Dylan's safe return, accepted only from Sir Cameron. That should do."

"I doubt you will receive much. Lord deFrayne is dead and all their money gone to battle. If attainder is not placed on them now, it will be soon — the moment Edward is crowned."

"All the better," Marcella said. "Let her trade family lands for her son. We will have to hurry, for Edward will shortly take his crown and the attainder will be his. If we take possession first, there will be no attainder on their possessions, for they will aleady belong to us."

"And you will then let him go?" Ferris asked.

Marcella laughed. "Let him go? Nay, my lord husband, but we will have them both. The only living deFraynes other than

Daphne. Neither son has sired an heir and I think perhaps Daphne is finally too old." She lifted a thin blond eyebrow as she regarded her husband. When she smiled her cheeks puffed out. "What do you think, my lord?"

"I do not understand why you wish to slay these youths. They could be our own sons, and I doubt Lady Daphne would do the same."

"Do not defend her to me," Marcella snapped. "When the deFraynes are all dead, our family can live in peace." She calmed her voice, but it seemed to take effort. Anne suspected that peace was the least of what Marcella wanted. And since Giffords had not been assaulted by deFraynes for so many years, she could not understand this lust for deFrayne blood. She knew the old tale that deFraynes had killed Marcella's father, but that had been so many years ago. "And do not delude yourself, my lord. The deFraynes would have sent our sons' heads by now."

"I would not rest easy in their chains," Quentin said.

"Nor I," said Bart. "Madam is correct. They should be executed. But I am for trying to get Heathwick in the bargain. Let us offer to ransom them before we kill them."

Marcella smiled at her second son. He had no estate; she could count on his support.

"I am for sparing their bodies, whole," Trenton said, looking shyly between his older brothers. He gulped as if the sight of the battlefield was still fresh in his mind. "Too much is too much."

"What matter? So long as they are finished. Edward will thank us."

"I doubt that, madam," Ferris said. "As a matter of fact, Edward forbade such as criminal action. He instructed that only the lords be executed. And I remind you all — Lord Forbes did not approve of this, and may yet put a stop to it."

"Do you think we have common soldiers?" she chided him.

Anne glanced toward the cookrooms. The cask room was just around the corner. The maid returned from the cell with an empty tray. The guard did not look up. The maid walked into the common hall and handed the key to Marcella. She attached it to her belt as she continued. "If Lord deFrayne fell in battle, it is first to Cameron, then to this lastborn son that the demesne will pass. These are noble heirs — for Lancaster."

"Sir Cameron will not be tricked."

"Oh? I think you are wrong."

Anne glanced at her mother's belt of keys, shears, prayer beads, pouch of medicines and herbs. She wondered how she might get that key. But even so, there were now guards posted though the night at every entrance to the keep, as if the one by the cask room door was not enough.

"We will give Sir Cameron plenty of time. Almost a fortnight should do nicely. If he does not come with the ransom for his brother by the twentieth day of February, the youngest deFrayne will die. By hanging. And then dispatched . . . slowly . . . to his mother."

Anne gulped. To be hanged and then cut into pieces.

"Who is it you wish to hurt by this action, madam?" Ferris asked. Anne had heard her mother and father argue before, but the tone of Lord Gifford's voice was never more fierce. "Surely it is not the deFrayne men. If they are already dead, your gruesome acts will cause them no pain. Do you feel that Lady deFrayne has not yet suffered enough? Her husband and eldest son are both dead. One would think you desired to meet Lady deFrayne in battle. Perhaps this has nothing to do with the rest of us. Perhaps this is a personal battle."

Marcella glared at her husband. "Do you beg me to spare the deFrayne men, milord, or do you plead for their mother?"

"Madam, does your cruelty know no bounds?" Ferris asked, shocked. "I have seen heads roll on the turf of a battlefield, a sight that I am somewhat accustomed to, and still it sickens me. Young heads," he said, rising to his feet and grasping a handful of Trenton's hair, jerking his head straight. "Boys, about to become men, die. Is there not enough blood to satisfy you? Is it not enough just to kill them?" He released his son's hair. "And though I doubt Lord Forbes has any love for deFraynes, you risk his anger by this thing you want to do. You had better think again."

Marcella seemed unimpressed. " 'Tis often done, as Lord Forbes knows. Execution is not a pretty sight; I could not see my children thus, but the enemy? His blood is foul. Therefore, it spills."

Ferris looked at her long and hard. "Send your letters, then, but without me. I will have none of this. I will go where all the men of this house should be, all the men who are so eager to be jewels in Edward's crown. I will find Edward's army and you can be sure that I will not return in time to see you perform this terrible, terrible deed. If I return at all."

"Do you abandon your sons, my lord, in their moment of triumph?" she asked.

"Humph, what need have they for a father? They have you — clearly *you* are their lord and master!"

That said, Ferris turned on his heel and stormed out of the hall, out into the cold air. Anne longed to go with him, to talk to him and seek his advice.

"Madam, my lord makes sense," Trenton said. He seemed to shiver slightly, as if he imagined himself held in the deFrayne cask room. "There need be no unnecessary brutality. It should be enough to return their bodies. I would expect as much."

"Then if it suits you all, we shall only hang them."

Trenton shifted uncomfortably. "I have no objection to the ransom you plan; Bart has need of an estate. But my father speaks true; killing both deFraynes could anger Lord Forbes. He was opposed to our taking prisoners out of Edward's camp. And if I do not hie myself back to Edward's army, my fortune is dust. My inheritance does not compare to Quentin's or even Bart's. I should go with Father."

"You worry needlessly. Lord Forbes will see you fixed," she said, glancing at Anne. Anne hung her head quickly. She could not meet her mothers eyes.

"Not if he is angry," Trenton said. "Not even for Anne."

She looked at her brother. She would have smiled at him, but did not dare.

"Trenton met his match on the field, madam. We went searching for him and found him leaning his head over the stream."

Bart chuckled. "He will overcome it, given time. Watching the deFraynes die will hearten his appetite for blood. If . . . he is to do a man's work. But if he wishes to make his fortune singing poems . . ."

Trenton's jaw muscle worked tensely, and he frowned at his brother. "If you would like to hear me admit that what I saw disgusted me, Sir Bart, I have no objection. You may even ridicule me if it makes you feel stronger and braver. Aye, most of your courage comes from taking advantage of those weaker than you. Surely you will stand bravely while a tied man is hanged, but would you meet him on the field? I did not see *you* in the fighting —"

Bart bolted to his feet as if he would take on his younger brother, but Quentin was quicker. His thick arm crossed in front of Bart's chest. "This is useless," he grumbled. "Sit down. No more of this, or I'll take care of you both." He waited patiently while Bart returned to his seat. "Madam, I know you have waited long to see captured deFraynes at your disposal. Were my father killed by them, I would feel likewise. But we must consider Father's concerns. We dare not upset our new alliance with the earl."

"If you are my sons," Marcella said sternly, "you will stay until this is done. Then you may join Edward."

Quentin, Bart, and Trenton looked between each other, checking eyes. Anne edged toward the stair. She saw her brothers' passion for deFrayne blood waning; she hoped they would go with her father. But finally Quentin spoke up. "We will stay with you, madam, and see it through. I am for the capture of Sir Cameron, if possible, but I will not support theft or indecent execution. If it must be done, it will be done civilly. A quick death and proper burial."

"I thought I raised men."

"You did, madam. Men. Not dogs."

Anne slipped away. Small mercies had come to mean a lot. That they would not cut him to pieces almost caused her to drop to her knees and give thanks. She fetched her cloak and went out of the keep by the back stairs and wandered about

Raedelle in search of her father. She did not find him the whole of the day, nor did she see him in the hall for the evening meal. She tossed and turned through the night, wondering how to have a word with him before he left.

Then came a light tapping at her door. She had no idea the hour; the sky was black and the castle was not astir. She ran to her chamber door and quickly threw it open, as if Dylan might be standing there. Ferris wore his chain mail and carried his shield. He held a finger to his lips, warning her to be quiet.

"I will go for Lord Forbes. Perhaps he will come, if I explain what my wife would do."

"Be careful, Papa. I will pray."

"Two things, Anne. First, wisdom and caution while young Dylan is prisoner here." She nodded, eyes wide. "Do not attempt to free him. You will be caught — both of you. His death will only come faster. You will not be spared much misery. I fear death would seem welcome." She nodded in agreement. She knew better than that. Even if there was a way to get him out of the hall, she could not fathom a method of passing through the gate. "Second," Ferris went on, "no matter what, no matter if Dylan is freed or killed, Brennan Forbes is your hope. Your only hope. Do you know it?" Again she nodded. "The earl loves you deeply, praise God. Do not in a foolish moment forget what that means." She shook her head. He reached out a hand and touched her dark hair.

"I love you, Papa. God's speed. Be safe."

She listened to the shuffling and clinking sound as Ferris descended the stair and left the hall. She lay still in her bed for another hour as the sun began to rise, and then she rose to dress, wondering how to face the day. There was more hope now than there had been. Brennan might come and stop their execution, even if he was likely only to transfer Dylan's captivity to Edward's camp. Still, Dylan was safer with Satan than in this keep.

She began to dress, pulling on a new working apron over a dark blue kirtle. She went to the small coffer on her table and opened it to retrieve the ring Brennan had given her. She stared in some confusion at what she saw. A long, heavy iron key rested atop a pouch. She lifted the key and the pouch gingerly, as if they would bite her. Her first thought as she touched these articles was that someone had stolen them from Marcella and placed them in her coffer while she slept, or earlier, when she roamed Raedelle in search of her father. But on closer inspection she could see the pouch was sewn of a different fabric from the one her mother carried. She moved backward, dropping down onto the bed, looking at the pouch in one hand and the key in the other. She faintly remembered. It was Minerva's. And then she knew.

The castle was asleep, the hour still before midnight. With a long nightdress covered by a smock, a thick shawl that almost reached the floor, and a small bed cap on her head, Anne ventured into the common room carrying a candle. She could see the guard before the cask room door, sitting on the rushes, leaning against the door. She nodded toward him. She ventured on into the common room and filled a chalice to the rim with dark red wine. She walked back toward the stair, carrying the brew. She paused at the foot of the stair, pensively, as if a thought had interrupted her progress. She turned and looked at the guard. Their eyes met briefly. She knew this one, and she smiled as she walked toward him.

"Good eventide, Delbert. I've come for a cup of cool wine. I know you cannot leave your post for any reason. May I get you one?"

He sat up straighter. "I . . . ah, thank you, my lady. That is very kind."

"Here then," she said, handing him the chalice. "I'll simply get another." He started to take the cup to his lips. "Are you not allowed a stool or chair?" she asked.

He shrugged. "I thought it best to place my back against the door, lest it move while I'm looking the other way."

She laughed lightly, teasingly, and the guard blushed. He was quite young and still a little shy with women, at least noblewomen. "I thought he was tied?" she asked.

He grunted and stood to a towering height, thin and long-limbed. "He is tied, my lady, but I have been warned. . . ."

"Oh, I know," she said. "He is said to be very dangerous." She turned, placed her candle on the rushes, and went into the common room in search of a chair with arms. She dragged the heavy oaken chair toward him, cutting a path through the rushes. "You might as well be comfortable. I've seen him, this prisoner. There is no possible way that he can overpower you; he is not nearly as large and strong as you are."

The guard looked at the chair and frowned. "Sir Quentin might find my comfort amiss."

"Then I suggest you return the chair to the common hall before Sir Quentin rises." She lifted a brow. "You do plan to stay awake through the night, do you not?"

"Of course, my lady."

"Then be comfortable. You can place the chair here, prop your feet on that keg, and never take your eyes from the cask room door." The instructions she fed him with her guileless gaze and sweet smile had the heavy oaken chair away from the door and the sentry's back to the common room. She hoped for the best. If it did not work tonight, perhaps tomorrow night. There was always a different guard. "Good eventide, Delbert."

She went back to the common room, drew herself a new chalice of wine — this one void of Minerva's herbs — and went up the stairs. She stood at the top, breathing deeply to calm her frayed nerves. She waited a long moment, put a foot on the stair, and then retreated to wait still longer. She couldn't be certain how much time should be allowed for the herbs to take effect. If he did not drink the wine, there would be no deep sleep for the guard. She tried to think of an excuse she could give if she was seen in the common room a second time.

Finally, she bolstered herself, descended, and sighed audibly when she saw his limp form in the chair, his sleeping head tilted to one side. He still held the empty chalice in both hands, clasped over his stomach. Carefully placing her hand on his shoulder, she gently shook him. He slept. She took what might be her only chance.

Six steps led down into the damp, windowless cask room. Here they stored kegs of winter ale, wine, and a few bags of grain. This area had been dug under the stairwell many years before and was not intended as a hold for captives, but it served well. There were very few places in the small hold where one could stand to one's full height.

Dylan's head was upright, his eyes slightly glazed. His hands were bound at the wrists and held over his head by a rope attached to a beam above him. Very little protection from the cold had been accorded him; there was a pelt of furs beneath him, but no jacket or cloak. Tears stung her eyes. She placed the candle and the chalice of wine on the ground, not even covered by rushes here, and gently knelt beside him. Her cool hand trembled slightly as she caressed his cheek and his vision seemed to clear.

"Another dream," he mused. "They become ever more real."

She raised up on her knees and loosened the ropes at his wrists, freeing his hands. "Not this time, my darling. This is not a dream."

He rubbed his chafed wrists and stared at her in wonder. "How have you come here?"

She shrugged her shoulders, modest in her victory. "I put sleeping herbs in wine for the guard and used my own key on the door."

He put his hands under her thick shawl at her waist and brushed her lips with his. Her hands caressed his chest. "Anne, they will kill you if you're found here."

"They will not find me. I have studied their habits. My family sleeps soundly, their good fortune brings them sweet dreams. But they are not careless; all doors to the keep are bolted from within to keep us safe from attack, and to keep the guards posted outside from coming within the hall to swill ale in the dark, boring hours."

He thought for a moment and then he smiled at her. He touched her face. "My clever vixen. I would not have expected so much."

Anne retrieved the chalice, now only half full, for she had

extracted a few swallows of courage for herself. She passed it to him and watched as he greedily swallowed the wine. The empty chalice dropped to his side and he closed his eyes in new-found comfort.

"Would that I could put a legion of guards to sleep, Dylan, and give you freedom."

"Nay, you have dared too much already. I am a madman for want of you, Anne, but I want you to *live!* It is the only comfort I have in these last days."

"You may yet have freedom, Dylan," she said, her eyes cast down so that he would not see the pain there. "My father has somehow taken pity on me and has gone to appeal to Brennan, Lord Forbes. Brennan does not approve of your captivity or ill treatment. He would have had you kept with Edward's other prisoners. Perhaps he will come." She shrugged lamely. "Edward has not called for many executions. Just attainder when he is king, and exile. Only the highest nobles . . ."

"I saw my father fall, *ma chère*. And I know why Wayland did not join me here."

"At least my family did not deal those blows. Brennan will free you, if he comes. He, of all, gives credence to Edward's desires."

Dylan laughed at the irony. "He will not help me if he knows what I am to you." He lifted Anne's chin with a finger and looked at her seriously. "You must never tell him. He will care for you and keep you safe."

Tears threatened again and she nodded as bravely as she could. She knew their love was doomed and she would go to Brennan. There was no other way. But, determined not to discuss their torment in these few precious moments, she leaned toward him and took comfort in his embrace. "Hold me, Dylan. For just a little while."

"Like so many other times," he sighed, kissing her brow and stroking her back. "Do you know the number of times you have crept through the night for a few stolen kisses?"

"I know each moment, each touch, each time I had to leave you."

"There has been so little, yet so much. Oh my Anne, I failed you. I should have come for you sooner, then I would not have been with the others at Mortimer's Cross."

"Nay, I failed *you!* If only I could run with you now — I would make no excuses, I would not delay. Oh Dylan, I'm so sorry."

He was quiet for a long moment and when she lifted her head from his chest she found his eyes on her face. "We'll take whatever comes," he whispered. "And we will not live only to lament what we can not have, but let what we have had give us joy. Private, secret joy . . . perhaps . . . you promised me, Anne. Promise again that you will never let this love we feel . . ."

"Dylan," she whispered, her fingers on his lips. "No more promises need be spoken, Dylan. I love you now, and I will love you until I die." She replaced her fingers with her lips. His wine sweetened breath was warm and moist on her face, his lips opened hungrily over hers. She met his tongue as she caressed his chest with her cool hands. Her small tongue darted between his lips as her fingers opened the worn linen shirt that he wore.

His kiss drew the life from her, yet filled her with life. While his hands moved over her back, over her hips and thighs, his mouth captured hers with a desperate hunger, yet commanding power. She leaned toward him, closer and closer, until her chest lay against his, the sheer cloth of her nightdress barely concealing her flesh. She heard him moan, felt his quickened heartbeat, tasted his wine and lust. She knew this time she would belong to him and her body ached to be full. Her arms tightened around him, drawing him closer.

Dylan's breath caught and sudden passion engulfed him. He pulled her against him, feeling her fingers knead his well-muscled back. Her shawl slipped and the press of her full breasts against his chest stirred him wildly. He was filled with her: her smooth skin, her sweet scent. He had wanted her desperately for so long, and now, when he faced death, never to taste the sweet joys of her body, he knew his control to be lacking. His lips moved from her mouth to her neck, then her shoulder; he bit her loose, silky hair. She tasted of honey and wildflowers. He slipped her bedgown down to expose a firm breast, greedily filling his hand, then his mouth. He heard her gasp as his tongue brought the small bud of her nipple to erect hardness. She pressed his head harder against her bosom as if to hold him there forever.

He raised his head to look at her. "It is dangerous for you to be here," he whispered.

"They will not find me, Dylan, I —"

"The danger is in my arms, my Anne. Before, when we talked about our someday, I had more to live for, a reason to protect you from even my desire. Now —"

"Dylan," she whispered, her hand on his cheek as she looked deeply into his eyes, "now is all we have. Perhaps all we will ever have."

His lips covered hers again. Anne's mind reeled with desire and she welcomed the feeling of the cold, clay floor against her back. Only her woolen shawl came between their bodies and the ground. As he lay gently atop her, she could feel his maleness rock against her sex and she strained against him. She felt as if her body was flooding downward toward him, welcoming and inviting. Her skin was never more alive than under his fingers and lips. She craved a deeper taste, a deeper drink.

The candle flickered from a draft and the scent of bodies and lust mingled with the odor of ale and wine. He pulled away to draw her bedgown lower, to raise it higher, to look at the beauty of her young body. He spread her long hair out to her side, lifting a handful of the thick, straight mane to his lips. She closed her eyes as his lips and tongue titillated her breasts, her waist, the inside of her arm.

She opened her eyes to the sound of his voice. "You are so beautiful," he whispered. With eager hands she reached for the drawstring at his waist and loosened his chausses. He had been reduced to very little clothing, and only his worn hose and a loincloth covered his straining member. Instinctively, without a single thought of modesty or reservation, her small hand closed around his throbbing erection. He moaned low in his throat, his eyes closing briefly. She trembled from the sheer power she felt.

Dylan rose above her. His eyes were a hardened blue, much like what she had seen as they led him into Raedelle as a prisoner, but this time the stony quality came from passion. Again, his jaw pulsed with tension. She deftly pulled the chausses down to his thighs as he knelt above her. His hands touched the outside of her thighs and she opened her legs to him, inviting him into the secret softness within. Her eyes were locked into his as her hands gently caressed him, enjoying the sensation of having so much of him in her small hands. He moved slowly, carefully, until he knelt between her legs.

"Anne," he whispered, his eyes earnest, almost stern. "Anne, my beloved, are you sure?"

She rose slightly, locking her hands behind his neck to draw him down to her. "Never more sure, Dylan, my love. Never more sure."

He slowly lowered his mouth to hers and planted small kisses on her lips. "You must not cry out, love."

She clung to him, answering by holding him hard against her mouth, opening her lips beneath his. She felt him as he gently probed and then moved into her. Dylan hesitated, holding still for a moment, her lips captive in his, and then with a single, abrupt thrust, he ended her virginity. She jumped in surprise, in pain that was as sudden as it was glorious. Her eyes opened wide; she saw his blue gaze, serene and controlled. One of his hands rested under her neck, the other under the small of her back. Her body slowly relaxed, her eyes closed. And he moved in a rhythm — a slow, even thrusting that grew to a rapid frenzied pace that engulfed her, possessed her, until she moved with him. They rocked together, every motion in unison; one mouth, one body. And very soon there was a rising tide that swept Anne away to another place and time. Her body shook with a fiery spasm of rapture; a fine mist of perspiration gathered on her upper lip, at her temples. Tears swelled again. Such beauty; such ecstasy. She had never doubted that it would feel so. She always knew this coupling, with Dylan, would hold incomparable joy.

*   *   *

Their minds returned to the cold, dirt floor of the cask room. Anne rested in Dylan's arms. It was odd that it should feel so natural when they risked certain death for this. Anne would not move. She wished to keep this moment, this union forever.

"It is a rare thing for a virgin to have that joy . . . the first time," he whispered.

"Is it? I had never doubted it would be joyous."

"What are we to do? I love you so."

"Hold me," she murmured. "Maybe dawn will have the decency to stay away."

"Nay, my Anne. We will surely face the dawn."

When Dylan withdrew she closed her legs, holding his seed within her protectively, praying a life would be conceived. She did not tell him so. She had already said everything with her body.

"If he has ever had a virgin, he will know," Dylan said. She silenced him with a whisper. "You make love to a dead man, Anne."

"Dylan, do not despoil me with sadness. It is pointless."

"Aye. Should I regret? Twas a selfish act."

She felt a laugh rising in her throat, choking her. And then she felt ridiculous. There was no humor in this, yet she wanted to laugh. "Selfish?" she said, looking at him, her eyes shining. "Oh yea, Dylan, we two are so selfish. We have asked God for so much." The feeling of laughter failed her completely to tears, but she would not indulge. Not now.

"I am afraid for you to be here. Please go."

"There is yet time, Dylan. I will go long before sunrise. And if it is possible, I will come again." Every night, she thought, until the twentieth day . . . unless Brennan came back to her and could amend this atrocity. "Dylan . . . my love . . . I know that everything has changed; I know there is no possible way for us to plan . . . but Dylan, believe me when I tell you my love for you is eternal, even when I wish it otherwise for both our sakes. I still believe we will be together one day. I will never lose faith."

He kissed her lightly. "Someday, then, my only love."

Chapter Six

AS SHE RETURNED to her chamber, Anne passed the guard. He still slept soundly in the predawn hours. She hurried to wash and change her clothing and sat on the edge of her bed until the first faint rays of sun began to lighten the horizon. Then she returned to the common hall and gently shook the guard.

"Delbert. Sir Delbert."

He roused slowly, sighing in his sleep, a smile on his lips as if some maiden of his dreams tickled him.

"Delbert," she insisted, shaking him more roughly. "Wake up!"

He opened his eyes, blinked as if to place himself, and then the chalice fell to the floor as he shot to his feet in embarrassment. "I . . . ah, only nodded off for a moment."

"A poor moment," she said, shaking her head. "Lucky for you I was the first to come downstairs. Return the chair to the common room, Sir Delbert, and mind your post before Quentin finds you thus."

"Aye," he said absentmindedly, still groggy and a bit wobbly on his feet. "Worse . . . Sir Bart . . ." She made a mental note to check the guard's size before again administering the herb to the wine. "I . . . I just nodded off for a moment . . . just a moment. . . . Quentin will . . ."

"He won't know, Sir Delbert. I certainly won't tell him; it would do neither of you any good. Just be careful from now on."

"Thank you," he said, dragging the chair back to the common room. Anne stooped to pick up the chalice and kicked a few reeds and rushes back over the path the chair had made. "Thank you, my lady. I am in your debt for your silence."

"I'm pleased to help you, Sir Delbert," she smiled. "You're one of my favorites. Just don't tell anyone that I cover your tracks — word would reach my brothers in no time at all. Silence on the matter, then?"

The next night did not go so well. The guard, an older man, had sleep on his mind from the start, and had not neglected his comfort either. He had already pulled a chair, stool, and a heavy fur to cover himself from the common hall. He accepted the offered wine and leaned his chair against the cask room door. Anne frowned her displeasure, checked him several times before finally giving up, and then listened to Quentin's rage in the early hours when the guard was found drunk and sound asleep. He denied having had a great deal to drink, and, thankfully, for some reason he did not mention having seen Anne or accepting wine from her. Perhaps he did not remember. Anne was fairly certain he would not be guarding Dylan again.

On the third night she found another new guard had been posted, and the trick she used on Delbert worked equally well on young Stephen. She was in Dylan's arms once more. On the fourth night it was Delbert again, for he had been successful in guarding the prisoner. It helped immensely that the guards were becoming more relaxed. It was a pleasurable duty to drink wine and sleep the night away without incident.

"Every night I hold my breath, waiting for the sound of that door opening," Dylan said. "And then when I hear you come,

I tremble with fear that you will be discovered. It is not fear for myself, love, for my death will come or not, as God wills it. But for you. I could not bear it if any of them hurt you."

She smiled, dropped the heavy fur and her gown to the floor, and lay in his arms. "Something has changed, Dylan Trenton has left Raedelle; he opposes your execution, and when he saw that he could not convince my mother or brothers, he left to find our father. Perhaps . . ."

"You must not betray your heart, Anne," he said passionately. "Promise me you will not try to argue for my life."

"Dylan, I —"

"*Promise!*"

"I will not. But I will hope. You cannot ask me to stop hoping."

"Until Lady Gifford leaves Raedelle in protest, your hopes are useless." He sighed and nuzzled her neck. "The price you pay for this may be too high."

"I'll accept whatever fate brings; I have seen how powerless I am to direct it. Once I thought it was all a matter of how cleverly we could plan, but now I see that we are puppets. If death is the worst that can befall us, perhaps we'll have each other in the afterlife." She snuggled close to him. "The only thing in my life that I lament is that I cannot recall the day you said, 'flee with me now.' " She sighed. "If I ever hear those words again, I will not hesitate."

"Love me now, Anne."

Every time could be the last time; the impending danger only made their loving richer, deeper. Once it was every kiss that could be their last. Now, as lovers, they met each union of the flesh both famished and fearful. Every touch tingled until it glowed and became hot and savage, covering them in a shower of spiraling embers that led them to blissful ecstasy.

They made love out of hunger and fear, but also to empty their heads, to escape their doomed destiny. Both would have luxuriated in their being together, talking, sharing their dreams and then making them come true, had things been different. But when they spoke, if apprehension and torment began to color their words, they tempered each other. If Dylan spoke with worry about Anne's marriage to Lord Forbes, her hand slowly moved to touch him in a way that drove all worry from his mind. When Anne trembled in fear over his imprisonment and impending execution, he knew the way to touch, to kiss, so that her trembling was of another source. Every night they forgot their troubles thus, each becoming half of a single body that swayed in passion.

They thought they had found a rare and enduring love when their lips had first touched two years before. Now they knew.

Lord Gifford stripped off his armor and approached the gates of Heathwick on foot, leading his destrier. His shield was attached to his saddle, his spurs were removed, and no weapon hung from his belt. The castle was dark in the setting sun; they should have been lighting torches or cressets around the wall.

A single guard looked down from the parapet above the gate. Heathwick had no moat, but only the heavy double doors. Their protection appeared minimal. Had they lost so many? "Who goes there?" the guard shouted down.

"Ferris Gifford, Lord of Raedelle. I come alone and on peaceful terms. I must confer with Lady deFrayne."

The guard paused. "And if I open the gate and there is an army in the brush? Why does a Gifford approach a deFrayne unarmed?"

"I have news of the capture of Sir Dylan. If you doubt my word, lower a single rope and I will scale the wall. Alone."

"Wait," he instructed. And the wait was a long one. Finally there were some torches lit around the gate, but not in the parapets surrounding the outer wall. Ferris had seen the old deFrayne keep before, but he had never been within. He shuddered with apprehension. If Daphne had already fled to safety, whoever was within might slay him instantly. Or perhaps take him prisoner and offer a trade with Marcella. Then he sucked in his breath as the great gate began to squeak and move.

Daphne stood with only one man at her side. She was dressed in black, in mourning, and her head was covered with a shawl.

As he approached her he could see a faint smile on her lips, a sad smile, and from under the shawl he could make out wisps of her light auburn hair, just beginning to gray at the temples. Her eyes were the same, still the deep sparkling blue of her youth, unchanged, perhaps even enhanced by the hardship of her life. She was not so very different from the way he remembered first seeing her, thirty years ago. Oh, he had seen her since, but they kept their eyes averted. They had not spoken. He fell to one knee before her. "Madam, I am sorry for your grievous losses."

"Stand up, Ferris," she said quietly. "I don't know why you've come. There are not many soldiers here; let us be honest with each other for once."

He stood shakily and then met eyes with Cameron, whose eyes were cold, filled with a growing rage. Ferris looked away before he saw too much of Cameron's hatred. He knew the young man must wish fervently to spill his blood. He hoped he could at least speak before that happened.

"Come into the hall for — "

"Nay, my lady, I come only this far. I need not tell you that if my family ever learns of this sojourn, they will be hard pressed to forgive me. I come here as a traitor and I will speak quickly and go into the night again."

"Why have you come at all, Ferris?"

"Madam, my lady, I could not have come if Lord deFrayne had lived. I know your lord husband would not have stayed his blade long enough to hear me. But your losses have been many, and I believe you dislike unnecessary bloodshed." He glanced at Cameron quickly, furtively. "There is only himself, and Dylan now. And if Cameron answers the call from Raedelle with a ransom, he will be captured and killed."

He noticed the young knight stiffen. He was not yet thirty, but had the face of a hardened youth. He had the same sandy-colored hair of Dylan and their mother, the same deep turquoise eyes.

"We suspected as much," Daphne said.

"Then I will be brief. They plan an elaborate execution for

the twentieth day of the month. I suspect you can manage a rescue by then, if not before. I have brought you a tunic upon which the arms of Ayliffe are sewn. If your fingers are nimble and skilled, my lady, you can fashion a banner. Raedelle would be opened to a troop of Ayliffe. But I warn you, there is one chance only. And do not let this son enter; let him send others in his stead. Should anything go awry, you would lose them both."

"There are not many left, Ferris," she said. He was amazed by the strength in her voice. But then, she had always been strong. She was so small beside her grown son, yet Daphne had always had great courage. She had somehow managed to rise above hate, jealousy, and vengeance, though her life with Lord deFrayne must have been hard. Why had Marcella, so sturdy and determined, embraced the weakest of traits?

"I pray God you have a few." He looked at Cameron. "Cast about for some worthy marauders, thieves, anyone you can find. With luck you will not have to stand and fight, but ride in and ride out."

"How is it your family knows the arms of Ayliffe so well? I know he is for York — word travels fast among the vanquished, but that alone would not open a heavily guarded gate."

"The earl is betrothed to my daughter." He paused. "My youngest. Anne." He watched Daphne's eyes close and a pained expression swiftly crossed her features. Cameron could not see his mother's reaction to the news, for he stood at her side and his eyes were focused suspiciously on Ferris. So, she knew. Both her memory and her shrewd instincts would have brought the truth to her . . . as it had to Ferris. He tried to explain. "The earl values her highly and would do anything in his power to make her happy. Further, he opposed the devilry of my sons taking captured deFraynes out of Edward's camp to Raedelle. But Lord Forbes was unable to intercede further. He was needed elsewhere."

A vague smile replaced Daphne's pained expression. "This betrothal to one so mighty must please your lady wife a great deal."

"Marcella is enjoying it heartily, I assure you. Retrieve your son, madam, and then get thee out of England."

"I will stay," she said softly, almost in invitation. "Women do not suffer under attainder. My sons will go away. Both of them."

Was it so well understood already? That Edward would be king? And did he perceive her correctly — that she would remain here, a place where he might easily find her?

"There is this place," she said, barely glancing around, "that I will try to preserve until a more peaceful time. Lord deFrayne is dead; our cause has been hard for the king. If Edward is crowned, perhaps something can be done for my sons one day. I will stay; I will keep the wall for some warlord until I am banished, or peace comes again. This is Cameron's. If not now, someday in the future then."

"Madam, you should flee England with your sons. No one can be certain of the safety of these walls with Henry's enemies everywhere."

She smiled patiently. "Ferris, there have always been enemies all around me. The enemies grapple for a crown now, but it is not very different than when they simply fought for the sake of fighting, for the sake of perpetuating an old, very tired argument."

Their family differences again. Of all those involved it was first only Ferris and Daphne who wished it could be forgotten. If not forgotten, negotiated, laid away, if only in an uneasy grave. They had tried reason, but reason failed in the face of hostile hearts. There were always many who did not want to forget. "Madam, my lady wife . . ."

Daphne closed her eyes and her mouth took on a rigid, irritated grimace. She slowly opened her eyes again. "Ferris, it is too late for all that now. I know it is Marcella who holds my son. I know her hatred for me is fierce. Say no more."

Ah, but that was the reason for Marcella's scorn and treachery. Because Ferris loved Daphne. He had loved her when she was a girl, just as Dylan loved Anne. He courted her secretly and when her father learned of it, they tried to convince the families that much could be gained by a marriage. But Daphne's father saw a better end in quickly giving her to the heir of Heathwick, who was more powerful and richer than any Gifford. Ferris lost her. He waited years to wed, and finally took the hand of the daughter of a knight bidden to the Gifford house.

Marcella's father had nudged her toward Ferris for at least four years, but it was not until after Daphne had borne a son and Ferris's own brother and father were dead that he took Marcella to wife. By that time the rumors of his love for Daphne had circulated well. Marcella married Ferris knowing that he had loved another, and, he suspected, expecting to change that. But one cannot change one's own history. His wife had never forgotten nor forgiven him. Not for one moment. Every child she bore him she brought forth with a vengeance, reminding him of all she did for him. She taunted him that Daphne could never do so much. She bitterly reminded him that Daphne had not defied her father for his sake. She asked him, too frequently, what he had found to love. Ferris could never answer her taunts, reminders, or questions. When he married Marcella he had resigned himself to life without Daphne. But he could not despoil the memory of her, or their love, by responding to Marcella's jealousy.

He let his eyes focus on Daphne's for a long moment. He would say nothing in front of her son, but in his eyes, in hers, there was a promise. He would breach his marriage contract now, and Marcella be damned. Anne would be cared for, and he could not indulge his wife's cruelty another day. He had tried to love Marcella, just as he had tried to temper her harshness, her hatred. Ferris had been true to his marriage oath, but it had gained him nothing but loneliness. Even though he had taken Marcella from the humble home of a knight into a baron's castle, she was never satisfied. Perhaps he did not love her passionately; he had never loved nor wanted her as he had Daphne. But he had been true, he had been loyal. What more she wanted, had not been his to give.

It was first his word, his honest attempt to be a decent husband that kept Ferris from Daphne. Later, it was the fear that he would endanger the woman he truly loved. Now Ferris deeply regretted his reticence, for his life was nearly over, and he had not yet lived. He no longer had to lie awake nights wondering if there was any way to creep past the powerful Earl of Heathwick; he was no more. Neither was the keep stout or well protected. Maybe, after all these many years . . . even the moment tempted him. She had invited him into the hall. But, there were battles to fight and her son stood at her side. Soon, he told himself. Soon.

"Will you accept one cup of wine, Ferris?" she softly asked.

"Nay, madam, not this time." He turned and went to his horse. Behind him he could feel Cameron shift, ready should Ferris draw a sword. When he turned back with the white tunic bearing the Ayliffe badge, he found that Cameron's hand was on the hilt of his sword. He passed the tunic to Daphne. "Work quickly and well. And . . ." He faltered and looked at the ground. "If you fight, spare any of mine you can. I love my sons, too. This is not really any fault of theirs."

"I know." Her voice was breathless; a soft, quiet gust of air. No more.

Ferris turned to go back to the gate. He had thought himself old, until he'd looked into her eyes. She gave him back his youth. She was strong, invincible, wise. She was still the most beautiful woman he had ever seen. The gate creaked to let him depart.

"My lord," a man's voice called to his back. He slowly turned to regard Cameron. "My thanks."

Ferris nodded. For what? He might have endangered his own family to show one small, parting loyalty to the woman he had always loved and admired. He hoped he would not regret his decision. He hoped Cameron would not retaliate. The plan was simple and clever, but the cost could be extravagant.

"What ails you now?" Marcella demanded of her daughter.

"Naught, madam," she replied.

"You keep so much to your rooms, it slights us. I will not have you carry tales of abuse to the earl."

"Nay, madam, I only suspected my company was unwelcome, but if it pleases you, I will join the family more."

"It pleases me," she said shortly.

But it was difficult for Anne, for she was tired. Night after night she went to Dylan in his dank, cold cell. On only three nights in twelve was she unable to reach him. With the day of his execution fast approaching, exhausted and nervous and with no sign of Brennan, Anne feared her feelings were transparent. She worried that if she were seated with the others in the common hall, listening to her mother carry on about the plans for Dylan's death, she might burst into tears. Anne had watched the slow construction of an elaborate scaffold for hanging in the outer bailey. It was finally completed.

A missive had arrived from Lord Gifford, filled with exciting battle news. Margaret of Anjou, Henry's wife, had collected large armies of raiding Northmen, and her troops were laying waste to the entire countryside in their advance toward London. Ferris, himself, was with Warwick, Edward's rich and powerful advisor, and the captured king, but his location was undisclosed. Lord Forbes was still with Edward and moving toward London to join Warwick, and then they would face Margaret's army for a final decision that would be quick and bloody. He suggested they wait to celebrate, for Margaret's Northmen had a reputation not only for strength, but for unbelievable brutality. They had unleashed whole cities full of homeless beggars to roam the countryside; innocents were burned out of their homes, robbed, raped, slain. Margaret's only way to pay these vicious mercenaries was with booty. He warned his family to take special care to keep the doors closed tightly to any approaching army that did not bear a banner of either Raedelle or Ayliffe. Margaret's men had left only waste and carnage in their path.

He made no mention of Trenton, but Marcella did not seem concerned. "No word comes from Cameron deFrayne," she said. "Tomorrow, then."

Tomorrow.

"Madam," Bart said, "I think we test the wrath of both Warwick and Edward in our delay — one the richest man in England, the other the would-be king. We should ride toward London at once and hope to find the right army."

"Soon, Bart."

"Madam," Bart pressed, "like you, I would welcome a chance to capture Heathwick and kill the deFraynes, but if there is no ransom paid, no title for lands brought to us by Cameron deFrayne, what is to be gained by killing Dylan? What will you do if Lord Forbes is angry?"

"You?" she asked Bart. "You hate them. I thought you would relish —"

"I would relish an estate, be it Heathwick or another. But if there is no Heathwick for me, and if Lord Forbes is angered by this execution, perhaps he will not —"

"Anne," Marcella snapped. "Tell your brother you will petition the earl."

Anne looked up. She stared at Bart levelly, knowing she must use this moment well. She took a deep breath. "Lord Forbes promised to succor this family. Of course, he approved of us all then. . . ."

"Do you see?" Bart said. "Will you risk all?"

"There is no risk. How have you become so skittish?"

"Delay the hanging. Await the earl's approval."

"Nay!"

"Good sense is not skittish," Quentin said, his voice low and calm. Quentin never had time for nonsense; he was direct and confident. "Bart has a point that must be considered," Quentin went on. "Father has warned us of the strength of Margaret's army; if something goes awry and Edward does not win his crown, we could bargain with the life of this —"

"Nay! DeFraynes killed my father. Tomorrow he dies. If Henry continues to rule after this, we may deny knowledge of the execution."

Anne's heart beat wildly. Would her brothers stop the execution? She tried to appear calm, but prayers ran wild through her head.

"I am in agreement with my brother, madam. You rish Bart's opportunity to please the earl. With all due respect, this vengeance will not bring your father back to you, and could ill serve us. In Father's absence, I should make the decision. And I think we have dallied here long enough."

Marcella's eyes sparkled with anger. "In your father's absence, while he lives, I make such decisions. And I say he is to be killed."

Quentin stood. "Then I shall displease you, madam. I will leave to follow Trenton, who has proven to have more sense, if not more courage, than the rest of us. Too much is at stake to dawdle here for an unnecessary event that only feeds some age-old vengeance of yours. What you do in my absence, I cannot prevent. But I order you in this: you will hold your ritual after my departure."

"You abandon me now?" she asked, furious.

"Yea, madam. I think this has gone far enough."

Tears gathered in Marcella's stormy eyes. "You are too young to understand. You were not yet born when a raid on my father's troop cost his life. DeFraynes murdered him, and sent a messenger to my mother with his hand, the ring of his family crest still worn on his finger. And why was this done? Because my father approved my marriage to the Gifford heir. Do you not see?"

Quentin looked down. He had never before defied his mother. But there had never been so much at stake. "I concede your hatred was hard earned. But I would think you would have enough revenge through our victorious army; the deFraynes will fall — they need not also be murdered."

She stared at Quentin for a long moment. Bart looked away from his mother's eyes and Anne held her breath. Marcella stood. "Sniveling cowards. I will avenge my father alone!" And with that she rushed out of the hall, up the stairs and to her chamber.

Quentin turned to his brother. "I am leaving Raedelle to find our father. I think if you are wise, you will come with me."

Bart thought for a moment, then nodded. "I am not bound to risk my fortune for any of them. I have seen one of them die; that will have to sustain me."

For many nights Anne had been able to pretend that morning would not come. She had been concentrating on the moment, refusing to mar the magic by looking toward the end of it all. The pretending was over. She had never mentioned the talk about Dylan's hanging that she overheard in the hall, nor even that there was a day established for the event. But on this night she was silent with Dylan. When he touched her, she did not quickly yield to passion. She found it hard to look into his eyes, even though she wanted to memorize each small detail of his face, lest she ever forget.

"Tell me, then," he said, finally.

"There is nothing."

"Oh," he sighed, "I suspect there is much. Perhaps they have chosen tomorrow as the day. Perhaps you know, certainly, this is our last night."

She met his eyes. "Oh Dylan, it is my mother," she said, yielding finally to the tears that she had previously held back. "My father has already gone from here in defiance of her plans, refusing to be a part of this. Trenton has gone, and even my brothers have argued for your life, if only to protect themselves. Now Quentin and Bart will depart to chase Edward's army into battle, but my mother will not be stopped. She will see you killed, or will die trying." And she lay in his arms and sobbed, heart-wrenching, painful tears too long unshed.

"You will need strength, my love. Come closer, here." He pulled the fur around her and held her. "We have come to a time, now, when there is little left for us to do but hold each other fast until the dawn." He chuckled low in his throat, a brave sound. "I reckon many a dying man should like to spend his last night thus. Here now, my sweet love, we have given and taken all there is between us. Perhaps we will be joined in eternity after all. There is always hope."

"How can you speak of hope now," she cried. "All is lost. It is nearly over."

"Anne, my Anne . . . even while I argued against your hope, calling it useless, it urged me on through these dark days. If you do not hope, how can I be strong? Nay, until the rope snaps my neck, I will hope. Cry if you must, but when you've shed your tears, you must still *hope.*"

"Oh Dylan, what am I to do?"

"Whatever you must, my love. Whatever you must."

He held her closely for several hours. There were very few words between them, and when his lips touched hers to say good-bye, he cupped her chin in his hand. "Do not give in, my sweet love. We have always thought each kiss might be our last, and yet there has always been another. There will be again. Believe."

Anne would have stayed and let them find her in his arms. She would have braved the rope with him, but for one thing. They had been as one, night after beautiful night. She had never mentioned a child to Dylan. She hoped one had been conceived. If Dylan must die, she would bring his child to life. For that reason only, she left him.

When she pushed open the cask room door, the guard was still slumped in sleep outside. Dawn would break soon. She would have to hurry to her room, lest she be found. She did not worry about the sleeping guard; let her mother or brothers find him and punish him. There would be no more nights in the cask room. Marcella would have her way.

"So this is what you have been about."

Anne gasped and turned toward her sister's voice. Divina stood between the common hall and cookrooms, her arms crossed over her ample chest, one shoulder leaning against the wall. She smiled with superiority. Anne could not prevent the hot flush as it rose over her face. Her lips were white with fear, her cheeks blazed with shame.

"Divina . . ."

"Night after night, little sister? I wonder what will happen to all your pretty gowns now?"

"Divina, do not be foolish! We need this alliance with Lord Forbes . . . all of us . . . you . . ."

"Me?" she asked, laughing. "Through you, you must mean. But I perceive a better way."

"Nay, Divina, it cannot be! He does not . . ." Her voice

[107]

trailed off as she regarded her sister's cold eyes, taunting smile. They both stared at each other while the guard slept on, peacefully dreaming dreams spun by old Minerva's herbs.

"Anything is possible," Divina said coyly.

"Do not lie to yourself, Divina. Not now! Mother wished for the earl to consider you, but he would not. He is not eager for just any bride: he is rich and has an heir . . . and mistresses," she lied. But the lie brought some reaction to Divina's narrowing eyes. "Divina, I will speak to the earl about a betrothal for you —"

"You let him spoil you then," Divina said. "Why else would you creep into his cell? You surprise me, Anne. I thought you were more clever. I thought you —"

Anne's face lost color. She tried to meet Divina's eyes, but she was caught in a snare and could not lie well.

Divina chuckled. "How foolish we all have been. We thought you had begun to love Lord Forbes. He will not take you now."

"He *loves* me, Divina; he told me so. Lord Forbes will not take you, no matter what you tell him. He may cast me aside, true, but you will not stand in my stead. Divina, use caution. If I am wed to the earl I can help you. If he rides away from Raedelle in anger . . ."

"You have become vain," Divina said. "He pampers you and buys you trinkets and you think any sin will be pardonable in his eyes. Poor Anne. It will be the convent for you after all."

"Why do you hate me so?" Anne asked, shaking her head forlornly, tears coming to her eyes. "Why could we never care for each other?"

Divina's lip curled and her eyes glittered in much the same way Marcella's would. "Because you have always taken what was to be mine. You were Minerva's pride, Father's joy, and now you aspire to be a countess. But it will not be, little Anne. Minerva is dead, the earl will change his mind, and even Father will not forgive you this."

Anne's eyes grew round at this revelation. She was stunned to think Divina had ever been jealous of her. "Minerva took me because Mother would have none of me," she said. "Mother favored you, clothed you well so that you could catch a rich husband. And Father —"

"*Father*," Divina said in a huff. "Father, who always said 'Why do you ignore this pretty child?' and 'Anne is too good for the convent.' Father held you on his knee while I was left to follow Mother and beg for a scrap of attention. And did I betray them? Never once; I am pure. You have lain with our enemy . . . and this time you will not take what should be mine."

Divina turned away, her skirts swirling, and made for the stairs. "Divina," Anne called, but her sister did not turn.

Anne stood for several minutes, the guard's snoring distant in her ears. Her trembling slowly abated, but she could barely move. I have failed again, she thought. Should I have denied it? she asked herself. But the truth would come soon enough. She had meant to live on for Dylan's sake; she had hoped to bear him a child. Now she did not dare predict the outcome of the day.

"Madam, I have something to tell you," Divina said. A maid was pouring water into the washbowl and her mother was sitting up in bed. "It is important, private." The maid glanced at Marcella and, at her nod, left the room.

Marcella swung her legs from under the quilt and reached for a wrapper. Her graying hair, mussed and hanging to her shoulders, made her long face look sallow. "Be quick, Divina. I have business this morning."

"Aye, madam. Do you know what your youngest child has been about? While our guard sleeps in the hall, Anne has been in the cask room with our prisoner." Divina smiled at her mother's shocked expression. "DeFrayne has spoiled her; guilt burns her cheeks and she begged me to be silent."

"You . . . *saw* her?" Marcella asked in a whisper, her eyes blazing and almost wild.

"I left her moments ago. She uses her own key and wore only a thin bedgown. 'Tis plain enough they —"

"Nooooo," Marcella shrieked, jumping to her feet. Her pale complexion became pasty white and her mouth twisted. "No!

Not *again!*" She rushed toward her bower door, her wrapper still below her shoulders. Anne had not protested the imprisonment, nor the execution. She had said nothing at all. How could she have gone to him . . . and why?

Marcella stopped suddenly, her hand on the latch, and leaned her forehead against the cool oak. "No," she murmured. Could she love a deFrayne? How could such escape her notice . . . there must have been signs.

"The earl will not take her now," Divina said from behind her. Marcella could not mistake the delight in her daughter's voice. She turned back to Divina, slowly trying to grasp the situation. Her heart pounded in her chest; her head felt light, and she was suddenly dizzy. *Ferris* had argued to spare him. *Ferris knew!* How had they managed to fool her?

"I'm sure when Lord Forbes learns the truth, he will find a pure bride more —"

"Hush," Marcella snapped. "Let me think."

She shook her head to try to clear the haze that had engulfed her. Her daughter had soiled herself with a deFrayne. Blood lust seeped into her heart and she clenched her fists. Damn her, she thought. If it was not enough that her husband had lusted after the bitch, Daphne, now her daughter did the same. And if that insult was not enough, she had thrown away the single chance of using the earl's influence to gain power and wealth. She snarled in rage. The girl had done only one thing right since her birth; she had captured a rich and influential earl. "I will beat her 'til she bleeds," Marcella muttered.

"The earl will not find her so pretty then," Divina said.

"Indeed not, he —" Marcella stopped abruptly. "No one else knows?" she asked Divina.

"I came here straightaway, madam. I thought you should . . ."

"Good. Good. The earl must never know." Her mind was tangled with ideas, plans. Anne had never argued for Dylan's life, nor had she tried to sneak him out of Raedelle. That could only mean one thing; Anne intended to marry the earl because Dylan was doomed to die. Then how, Marcella wondered, did Anne hope to pass off her lost virtue? Had the earl had her first?

Forbes had panted after her skirts like a dog with a scent; perhaps she had yielded to Forbes to cover her misdeed. Anne was either a very stupid wench, or she was clever enough to be certain Lord Forbes would still take her.

"She must be very confident that the earl will not begrudge her lost innocence," Marcella mumbled, merely thinking aloud.

"She will be very surprised then. The earl will find me —"

"Don't be a fool! The earl does not want you! Have you not seen enough of his besotted lust to be convinced? He wants Anne. So, he will take her as she comes."

"But Mother —"

"If you say one word about this I will have you stripped and lashed. My silly daughter has risked our alliance with Ayliffe, but it is not gone yet. Soon enough, I will understand her plan."

"But Mother, if you tell Lord Forbes the truth and offer him a pure bride, he will be grateful. I was to marry first; you cannot let her go to him now. It would be a disgrace. What man of reputation would take a whore to wife? She is a whore; I am a virgin!"

Marcella barely heard her daughter's arguments and pleas. She was thinking of Anne, whom she had always considered a bother and nuisance; Anne, whose birth had caused her not only great physical pain, but also heartache. Anne's birth had changed her, had brought the hard truth home, and she had hardly been able to look at her since.

She had ignored the child; thus Anne had never struggled to please the way the other children had. Then, with the earl's betrothal, Anne's opinion of herself had become lofty. She threatened to withhold the earl's influence from her family if they did not tread carefully on her good nature. Hah, Marcella thought. That was before. Now Anne would work hard to see her family bettered, or the earl would be told the truth.

"My daughter will use her wiles to help our cause now," she said. "Aye, my daughter will work hard to please me now."

"Mother, you cannot mean it! You must not allow —"

"Shut up, Divina! If you say one word, I will beat you until you bleed!"

"Mother . . ."

Marcella ignored the tears in her daughter's voice. The sky was growing light. "Dress yourself. Now I have even better reason to see the bastard hang."

Divina crept from her mother's room, her head down and tears wetting her cheeks. She walked listlessly toward her own chamber. She greatly regretted her misjudgment. Had she been wiser, she would have used Anne's offered influence for her own case. Now, since she had turned the information over to her mother, it was useless.

Marcella dressed hurriedly, not even taking the time to have her hair brushed. She pulled a wimple over her knotted mane and went hurriedly to Anne's bower. She opened the door and saw Anne, fully dressed, seated on her bed. Anne slowly turned her gaze from the emerging dawn, toward her mother.

"He will die in any case," Marcella said.

Anne, dry-eyed and grim, lifted her chin slightly. She would not stand.

"How do you plan to trick the earl? Did he steal your virginity first so that you could take deFrayne between your legs without reprisal from your husband?"

Anne stared at her mother levelly. She would admit to nothing. She would not cooperate.

"Whatever your intention, daughter, you will help your family now; you will urge Lord Forbes to do right by your brothers, or I will tell him what I know. Remember, Anne, that at any moment of my choosing, I can tell Ayliffe that you cuckolded him with deFrayne."

"At any moment, madam, that you feel you can afford the cost to the Gifford family," she replied calmly.

Marcella smiled. "We understand each other. I confess, I did not think the day would ever come." Marcella slowly pulled the bower door closed, leaving Anne to consider what had been said.

Chapter Seven

MARCELLA WAS SEATED in the hall when Quentin entered. He was alone and she hoped that Bart was staying to stand beside her, but he dashed her hopes instantly. "Will you come into the courtyard and bid us farewell and God's blessings, madam?" Quentin asked. As Marcella looked at her firstborn child, she thought how strongly Quentin resembled her father and brother, both dead over twenty years now. She had always favored Quentin, but she understood Bart better. Bart was the last one she expected to cross her.

"If you rescind your decision and await the deFrayne hanging before you depart, of course I will pray for you. Otherwise . . ."

"Nay, my lady mother, I cannot do that. I regret to say that had you quickly ended his life, I would have been standing beside you, but these many days of waiting have brought me a vision or two. I see that Father is completely right; you satisfy an old vengeance when these deFrayne men are actually prisoners of York, and should be given to him to settle any score. It was not a deFrayne-Gifford war in which they were captured. We should be with our father now."

"Then you will not change your mind?"

He slowly shook his head, and she could see by Quentin's eyes that he had managed to form a pact with Bart. "I would stay to change *your* mind but for one thing — our father is fighting for the duke alone. I hope he can forgive us for our delay, for this is nothing more than folly that keeps us here."

"*You* brought the deFraynes to me," she nearly shouted.

"Aye," he shouted back. "And then I buried Sir Wayland. Do you know what I felt? My fiercest rival, from an argument so old that I cannot even remember the cause, was finally dead. And I felt mourning come to me. *Mourning!* I have been meeting Wayland in contests for ten years, as my brothers have met Wayland's brothers, as men-at-arms in green have met blue for so many years. But when we passed on the road, or in the feasting celebrations at tourneys and fairs, they did not raise arms against us. Nothing more than heated words crossed, never swords or axes. Had we been captured, I doubt we would have been treated thus. I think the conflict could finally be resolved if you would release deFrayne."

"Bart would not agree with that," she said.

"Bart is a young fool, and you have done much to encourage him. But even Bart sees the folly in angering our liege lord. He will not stand by you while you whittle away his only opportunity to prosper."

Marcella frowned blackly. How dare Quentin place such an accusation on her. Anne had done more to threaten the earl's support than she ever had. But she could not say anything. The moment that information was out of her hands, Anne might be out of the earl's good graces. She was not foolish enough to think that Earl Ayliffe would continue to support the Giffords without his chosen bride.

"Let him live," Quentin entreated.

"Never! He must die!"

Quentin's shoulder's slumped in exasperation. "Then carry on your revenge alone, madam. You may, in your action, spawn another six decades of hatred and death."

Marcella's mouth was set in a vitriolic grimace, her hands so tight on the arms of her chair that her knuckles were bleached.

Quentin turned to leave. She half rose, tears of rage stinging in her eyes. "They killed my father," she shouted at his back.

Quentin faced her one last time before leaving. "Someone has to be first to stop the killing."

There was nothing more she could say. When Quentin was a boy she could incense him with tales of her father's wrongful death because Quentin could not bear the thought of losing a treasured father. But too soon it became only the death of a grandfather her sons had never known.

Marcella told her children, when she deemed them old enough to really appreciate her tale, that she had been sought after for marriage by a member of the deFrayne household, but her father, a Gifford knight, refused to be allied with those treacherous heathens. Her father's murder, then, was in retaliation, since he gave his daughter to the Gifford heir. It was a lie. Marcella had not been desired by any man. Not even her own husband.

Marcella *had* suffered unbearable pain at the hands of the deFraynes, though her father's death was incidental to her suffering. Her children would not understand the truth, and she was too ashamed to tell it. Marcella had been fourteen when her older brother was knighted and, like their father, pledged allegiance to Lord Gifford, Ferris's father. Ferris was the second Gifford son, but the eldest was weak and frivolous and the old lord was tottering with age. Marcella fell in love with Ferris the first moment she saw him.

But Ferris, so tall, strong, darkly handsome, and distant, never looked Marcella's way. She watched him with longing every time they attended the same event. At tournaments, fairs, Saints' days, even at mass . . . but Ferris was far, far away.

Things were not so very different then, although the hatred the Giffords felt for the deFraynes was somewhat fresh still, only thirty years old. But the king had ordered a stop to the fighting between the families and issued a decree that they could meet only in fair competition on tourney fields to bleed out their anger. And so it had been Gifford sons pitted against deFrayne sons then, as it was now. And whenever those two houses met, the crowds were wild with excitement, knowing the rivalry was so deep that each side wished to kill the other. It never failed to be an exciting match.

Sir Ferris, as a young and handsome knight, met deFrayne heirs just as Quentin met Wayland, and he passively accepted Marcella's tokens and good wishes. Marcella did not understand his reluctance to consider her; she was a young woman of many assets. She was fair-colored and pale, which she thought all men preferred. She was large-boned, tall, not pretty, perhaps, but she would birth many children with ease. And Marcella was very clever for a young daughter of a knight; she could read and cipher, rare talents among girls. She had been reared at Raedelle, although in the home of a knight and not a baron, and she did not set her sights on the eldest, the heir, but on the second-born son. Ferris need not marry nobility, but only marry with wisdom and give the Gifford house many children. Marcella was eager to do this for him. She was as strong and smart as any man and could easily look him square in the eye; she could be his equal if any woman could.

But the young knight had eyes often glittering in the direction of a young, slight woman. Her hair was not golden, but an odd, light brown that was streaked with gold and red. She was tiny and dainty and no doubt would have trouble with childbearing. She appeared frail and was so pampered by her parents, it was doubtful that she had the mettle required to manage a man's home. Marcella had hated her on sight.

Many saw the way Ferris looked at this dainty one, and rumors started. They were lovers, it was said. The girl, Daphne, was also the daughter of a knight, but a knight of more impressive means than Marcella's father.

Marcella heard that the two young people desperately sought alliances from nobles and priests to help convince their respective families to allow them to marry. She ached for attention from Ferris; she was afraid she would lose him. But Daphne's father went straightway to the young deFrayne heir, Lord deFrayne, the richer noble, pledged his fealty there and had his daughter wed before her purity could be tainted by a less wealthy

Gifford. Daphne was spirited away to Heathwick and became a countess overnight.

At first Marcella was relieved that Daphne was so quickly whisked out of the way. Slowly, relief faded into resentment, for Ferris was hostile, brokenhearted, and even more distant. He refused to marry at all. He stayed away on campaigns as often as possible, as if in wait for Daphne. He paid no other woman the slightest attention, though Marcella's father and brother tried to interest him in her.

In the next three years both Ferris's father and older brother died of a winter illness that took many lives in Raedelle. Ferris, now Lord Gifford, was forced to come home. He held full title. He was not the strong man he had been. Oh, his arm was as strong, his lance as skilled as ever, but he seemed dispirited. His eyes, deep brown and fluid, always seemed far away and dulled by pain. He was sullen and quiet. But he was a baron with a large, though only modestly rich, keep. There was pressure from the crown to marry or see his family estate dispensed to strangers when he died. Almost in resignation Ferris took Marcella as his wife.

In the beginning Marcella intended to change Ferris back into the young gallant she had fallen in love with. She tried to show him passion, courage, strength, and wisdom. Then, in her first year of marriage, when Marcella was swollen with her first child, her father was killed in the uprising in the north. It was rumored, though never proven, that the deFraynes had attacked the Gifford troop from within the battle. The rumor incensed her, for it fed her jealousy toward Daphne. She had Ferris, but she did not feel with certainty that she had taken him away from Daphne. Marcella swore vengeance on the deFrayne family. Ferris tried to quiet her rage, which caused her even greater anger. Ferris said he thought it was feasible that returning soldiers, embarrassed by their numbers lost in the fray, had to invent some excuse for failure. He was all for ending the hostility; it had caused enough pain and heartache.

She tried for ten years to change his mood of indifference. If he would say he hated all deFraynes, she would have considered it a small victory, but instead he would only admit to hating Lord deFrayne, and she knew well enough what that meant. Ferris eventually took pride in his sons, but he never met Marcella in passion. He never said he loved her. He ignored her great skills in managing his home, her ability to give him children so efficiently. He even chastised her for assuming too many duties, for making decisions that were his to make, for being obstinate and presumptuous.

His faraway eyes never met hers. She had thought that her devotion and her hard work would draw him closer to her, if not to love. But he had not loved her. He never prized her. Marcella's disappointment gradually turned into bitterness and hate.

Then there was Anne. Marcella had given birth eight times, and only three times had she failed to produce a living child. Anne came last, and the birth was difficult and dangerous. Marcella was abed for months following Anne's birth, and the child was troublesome to manage; she cried often and loudly. Marcella thought she was dying, but Ferris still did not kneel at her bedside and speak endearing terms of love, of caring. Finally, she told him that she thought it would be dangerous for her to attempt to have another child. She had talked to the midwives and learned some methods known to work toward keeping a woman from coming with child, and she was willing to explain them. But she did not have the chance. When she told her husband that she dare not have another child, he told her that he did not expect it of her. He slept in a different room and did not return to her bed.

Anne's birth had brought the final, blinding truth. Ferris did not love her and never would. Her pain was so intense that she refused to hold the child even when she was well enough. Her indifference to the new baby only caused Ferris to dote on Anne. Marcella turned her attention toward her sons, determined to build them into important men who would not only appreciate her, but go to great lengths to please her. Divina had some of what energy there was left, but Marcella could hardly bear to look at Anne.

The insult grew and grew, for Ferris cossetted the lass and

his old nurse pampered her. It was enough if they kept the bothersome child out of Marcella's sight, but as Anne grew older she became more difficult to avoid. And as Anne passed the age of twelve, Marcella was alarmed to see that she had some of those same qualities that had aroused her jealousy toward Daphne: she was small, pretty, docile-natured, and Ferris loved her deeply. Marcella had intended to get her into a convent as soon as Ferris would allow, but the maid had haplessly snared a rich earl . . . one she didn't even want . . . just like Daphne deFrayne. Sometimes, when she lashed out at Anne and hurt her, it was almost like hurting Daphne; she was hurting the one Ferris loved most.

Learning that Anne had betrayed their cause by an alliance with Daphne's son had nearly killed Marcella. The pain was as real as it had been when she was a girl and tossed on her pallet, weeping, because Ferris longed for Daphne. But the pain had given way to common sense when the sun rose and her head cleared. Anne would watch the hanging. Marcella would end with the rope any notion of Gifford loving deFrayne.

She told herself that it was her husband's fault that all of this was taking place, that all she had ever wanted was Ferris's love. But it was not true. She might have found his loyalty and devotion, if not his passion, in many actions toward herself and their children. It was because she wanted something greater than his love that she suffered. She wanted him to hate Daphne deFrayne. And he would not. Any way she could hurt the woman would satisfy her — by a sharp blade, by a broken heart, through envy, anything.

Marcella signaled a castlemaid. "Tell my daughters to attend me," she instructed. "Both of them."

Marcella called for the master of the guard. She quietly asked him if an executioner had been selected and told him to proceed. She walked into the courtyard alone, waiting for her daughters to join her. She faced the gibbet, her heart pounding. Damn them all, they would allow her this much. She could never have what she really wanted to have, but she would have a little deFrayne blood. And then she would deal with Anne. She would have what she wanted, and that clever little lass would help.

Dylan was dragged from his cell and into the cold February air. His hands were bound behind his back and he was given no woolen shirt or cape. He squinted painfully from the light. Two liveried guards held him by the upper arms, pulling him roughly along, and he stumbled several times.

He had expected to see one hundred or more uniformed men-at-arms lined up to inspect the execution, but there were only about thirty men. He had envisioned a more glorious departure than this, perhaps passing through a tunnel of crossed halberds en route to the platform, but it was a solemn and ill-attended event. Even the Gifford knights were absent; the hanging was to be viewed only by three women dressed in dark clothing. He knew which was Anne, but he did not look at her as the guards dragged him toward the platform.

"Madam, where are the Gifford men? Are they too squeamish to watch their captive die?"

"If he says another word, stuff his mouth," Marcella instructed.

Dylan noticed the other three surviving captives had been brought out and were standing in front of the platform, their hands likewise bound. But there was only the one rope. He looked at Marcella and laughed at her. "You will have a busy day a-hanging, mistress," he taunted. "I hope you had a stout morning meal."

He braved a chance look at the sisters, at Anne. He saw pain and fear in her eyes, but the slightest almost secret smile on her lips. For what reason could she smile? To give him courage? Assurance? He hoped she had not plotted something. But as he wondered about her expression, a guard did his mistress's bidding and stuffed a dirty linen cloth in his mouth to still his tongue.

He was to be first, it appeared, for they dragged him up the steps and stood him under the rope. The guards feared to release him, and the noose was in the hand of the executioner when the tower horn sounded three blasts. Dylan did not know the code of this castle. He had no idea what the three clarion blasts signified; it could be an attack, returning knights, or even a pilgrimage of monks.

Marcella looked toward the gate. "Ayliffe, my lady," the guard shouted.

She looked back toward the platform. "Proceed," she called.

Anne pushed Divina out of the way and touched her mother's arm. "Madam, it is the earl! Wait!"

Marcella regarded her daughter coolly for a moment, then a slow, evil smile appeared on her lips. Dylan watched from the platform. Marcella looked back toward the executioner. "Proceed," she called.

The executioner paused. There must be grave indecision here. Dylan had heard from Anne that everyone but Marcella had opposed this hanging, and knowing a castle as well as he did, he knew that any kind of disturbance in the noble family was heavily gossiped about among the men and the residents. No doubt lounging or dining soldiers and knights had overheard this conflict.

The gate began to creak as it was opened. "*Proceed!*"

Anne ran toward the gibbet, and Dylan was thankful for the gag that prevented him from crying out to her in warning. He silently prayed, *Do not betray yourself, do not.*

"The Earl of Ayliffe approaches," she shouted. "He does not approve this execution."

The executioner's arms dropped to his sides and he backed away, but the guards maintained their hold on Dylan's upper arms. Anne turned her back on Dylan. She could not trust herself to look at him.

A small troop wearing the Ayliffe tabards and carrying the earl's banner rode slowly into Raedelle, and Anne scanned each face for that of her betrothed, but it was soon clear he was not among them. Their leader was a herald who wore the badges of Ayliffe and York and rode ahead of the group with a scroll. They did not appear to be outfitted for fighting. She could only think that Ferris had reached Brennan and the earl had sent this entourage on his behalf. "Who will receive letters from the earl of Ayliffe?"

There was a stillness as Anne and her mother met eyes. Gifford was Ayliffe's vassal. Ayliffe could not be ignored. It would be considered treason. Finally Marcella stepped forward. "I am Lady Gifford."

The herald unrolled his parchment. "This is to inform the keep of Raedelle that all prisoners taken in battle by forces of Edward, Duke of York, are to be released into the custody of the Lord Brennan Forbes, fourth Earl of Ayliffe, for transport to the army of York. These prisoners will be ransomed or executed, as deemed by his lordship, York, in London. Madam, by his orders. Do you comply?"

Marcella stood rooted to her spot, speechless. She wished her men would refuse. She would order them to slay the messenger if she thought there was any chance they would obey her. But no one in all of Raedelle would chance defying the mighty earl. Finally, after many long minutes, she turned in a swirl of black skirts and fled into the hall. The herald raised a hand toward the Raedelle guards, and the prisoners were dragged forward. There was a good deal of shuffling about as the four men were hoisted, still bound, onto the saddles of palfreys. The herald and a few of his men shared a drink when a bucket and ladle was brought and exchanged brief gossip with the Raedelle guards. And then the troop turned to ride slowly out of Raedelle's gates.

Dylan looked over his shoulder at Anne. His eyes twinkled; he had escaped death, but briefly. Now he would be transferred to Edward's army, but with luck and time, perhaps he would defy death again.

Divina followed their mother, but not with the same angry strides. Anne knew from whence her sister's disappointment came; she had failed in her mission to rob Anne of marriage with Ayliffe. Divina's eyes were red-rimmed, and she hung her head in despondency. She must surely know the truth; Divina did not have favor enough to come between her mother and a plan for plenty.

As the Raedelle gates closed Anne crossed herself. She gave thanks to Brennan and God for Dylan's life.

*   *   *

Lady Gifford was strangely subdued in her defeat, while Anne had expected a great deal of ranting and raving. The keep at large seemed as if in mourning as each resident crept quietly around. In late afternoon the horn sounded once more and again announced an Ayliffe troop. Anne had to fight panic. Had something happened? Did the troop return the prisoners to Raedelle?

She pulled on a cloak and went to the courtyard, where almost one hundred men wearing the Ayliffe tunics were dismounting and calling to servants and pages to bring drink and take their horses. They were a somber, serious group and Anne wondered if they had experienced some terrible defeat. In the midst of the group she spied Brennan. A page was helping him to remove his armor and mail. Conflicting emotions hit her like a thunderstorm, and she felt her hands tremble and tears smart in her eyes. She was afraid yet relieved to see Brennan. She knew only one way to conceal her confusion of feeling.

"Brennan!"

He turned toward her and she ran to him. He welcomed her with open arms, both surprised and delighted by her reaction, and she embraced him fiercely. He was overwhelmed by this display, but invigorated and thought, briefly, how there was nothing like a battle to endear a man to a woman.

"There now, little one, you'll choke me."

"I was so worried. Is everything all right? You're not hurt?" She began looking him over, turning him around in a very wifely fashion, her eyes scanning the length of his body with possessive concern gleaming in her eyes. Brennan smiled in spite of the bad news he brought, enjoying her behavior more than he could admit under the circumstances.

He stopped her abruptly by grasping her arms. "I am fit. Another battle is done, but we were not victorious. Still, Edward hurries on to take London now. Anne, cease, we have trouble. Be still."

She stopped her examination and stared into his eyes, having no idea what to expect.

"Your father fell at Saint Albans. He is dead, Anne."

First surprise, then a fierce denial, and then finally a cry of pain came. She collapsed against Brennan's chest. How could it be so? How? Why?

"Anne, be quiet now. You will have to be strong. We must go to Lady Gifford. I know your father is beloved to you, but your mother has lost her husband. Now, can you come with me?"

She separated herself from him a little, looking into his eyes. "My father loved me," she whispered.

"I know, my sweet," he said, smiling. "But his lady needs to be informed without delay. Come."

He put an arm around her shoulders and she struggled to control her weeping as they walked into the hall. Marcella, slow to respond to yet another announcement for Ayliffe, was just descending from her chamber. When he faced her, he bowed. "Madam, I bring grievous news. Lord Gifford was killed at Saint Albans three days ago. I have brought him home."

Marcella stiffened as if slapped. Her eyes glazed, then teared. "He died a noble death?" she asked weakly.

"He fought valiantly. There were many to fight, but they were surprised at night. Warwick lost King Henry to his consort, Margaret of Anjou, and her Northmen."

She nodded slightly.

"I believe he did not suffer, my lady. I think it was swift, though I did not see it happen."

Her glazed eyes and stern expression were focused on Brennan. She said nothing.

"Madam," Anne attempted. "Would you have me fetch the priest?"

Still Marcella stared at Brennan. "You might have sent your herald with news of my lord's death before you sent them to free our captives."

"Madam?" he questioned.

"Your herald arrived this morning with your letters demanding the release of the deFrayne prisoners."

Brennan shook his head. "I sent no herald, madam. I came here myself as quickly as possible."

Marcella's eyes widened, and she looked at Lord Forbes with horror. Anne could almost see the storm building in her mother. "*Tricked*," Marcella screamed. "My God, they tricked us! We'll send out riders! Damn them! Damn them all!" And then she turned and fled up the stairs, lifting her skirts for speed, yelling all the way.

Brennan grabbed Anne by the arms and turned her toward him. "What is this? What herald?"

"It has been horrible, Brennan," she said, still somewhat confused herself. "Madam has been so determined to slay deFraynes that she has fought every member of this household in that concern. First, Father, and then even my brothers rode away from here to protest what she would do. All said that Edward would be angered by the event and that you told them not to bring prisoners here. A herald and troop wearing your colors did arrive, Brennan," she said, nodding to him. "They wore tabards of your house and carried your banner."

"I did not send them," he said. "Nor could I have spared any man for such an errand. When did your brothers depart?"

"Trenton over ten days ago and the others just this morning. Brennan, what has happened?"

He was quiet for a moment, shaking his head. "Lady Gifford is correct; she was tricked. Her prisoners have escaped, but I did not help them. Your father is dead and there was no son with him to guard his back or carry him home. Yet, the worst insult your mother feels is her lost vengeance." He looked into Anne's eyes. "I must attend Edward to London. If he has not finally won, he will soon. He will be king. I have waited for you for almost a year, Anne, and I cannot leave you here again. More than my greed for you, I distrust Lady Gifford with your welfare. If my next battle is my last, at least let me protect you with the order of widowhood. Will you marry me now? Quietly and quickly?"

Anne's eyes were wide as she listened to Brennan. Dylan had escaped. He was not a prisoner of the duke's, but *free*. The convent, she thought frantically, from whence Dylan could liberate her.

"Marry now?" she asked weakly. "Quickly?"

"Anne, I must attend Edward, it is not a matter of choice. He will be king; I will protect you better than Lady Gifford . . . and your father is dead."

If Edward did achieve his crown, Dylan would be far, far away. And if there was a child a-borning . . .

"I must bury my father," she said softly, searching Brennan's eyes. Dylan was free, but not free to come to her aid. She must give thanks for his life, but protect the life he may have given her.

"Let us bury Lord Gifford and marry. I can think of no other way, and your father would want this for you."

Whether Dylan lives or dies, Lord Forbes is your single hope, Anne. Do you know it?

If she wed Lord Forbes, her mother would be quiet for a time. Marcella would hold her tongue in hopes of Anne's cooperation in helping the Giffords achieve greatness.

"I know you must have had your hopes cast to a more splendid wedding than can be allowed. . . ."

"Nay," she said quietly. All she needed was a few days. If she did not carry Dylan's child, then perhaps the appearance of her monthly blood would fool Brennan into thinking her a virgin. Lord Forbes, though in the best of health, was not a young man, and though she could wish him no harm, there was hope in what must naturally occur. Perhaps Dylan would not be lost to her forever. She must protect herself, and if need be, a child. "I do not care for a fancy wedding. Yes, Brennan, if you wish it, we shall marry."

"Anne," he said in a breath. He embraced her suddenly, kissing her lips and her neck, crushing her with his passion and love. "Oh Anne, I thought the day would never come. At long last, my love, at long last."

"Brennan," she sighed, returning his embrace, tears stinging her eyes. "I hope I can make you happy."

Chapter Eight

IT WAS DIFFICULT for Brennan Forbes to be overly sympathetic with Lady Gifford's loss, given her reaction to the news. Out of both impatience and distress, he demanded of her a wedding to follow the burial of her husband. Marcella grudgingly agreed, and Brennan remained perplexed. As he observed her grim behavior, her dry, downcast eyes, he continued to wonder if it was the loss of her husband that she mourned, or the failure to execute a deFrayne that she grieved. Either way, he was very eager for Anne.

Nothing extraordinary was to be done, but the wedding would take place immediately. Anne assured him she would harbor no resentment for the lack of a formal wedding, and Brennan's reasons for expediency were more than sound. Edward was marching on London and needed the earl to command the gathered Ayliffe army should they meet with the forces of Margaret of Anjou en route. He had only two choices; to leave Anne in the care of Lady Gifford and go to Edward alone, or marry her and take her with him.

So the burial of the Lord of Raedelle on his own lands was quickly followed by a quiet wedding. The Gifford sons had not yet returned, and the uncertain state of the country beyond Raedelle caused disquiet during the exchange of marriage vows. But even this simple nuptial ceremony was lovely. Brennan wore his white tunic and hose, topsewn with gold thread, and badges of gold for Ayliffe sharing space with the white rose of York on his chest. Anne had donned her best sarcenet gown of a blue so weak it appeared almost whiter than Brennan's suit. A heart-shaped wimple with a long, sheer veil framed her face. February prevented them from having garlands of fresh flowers, and also absent was a prestigious gallery of guests to view the exquisitely beautiful couple.

Though battles yet to fight might lie in the back of his mind, Lord Forbes seemed to shine with happiness and youthful vigor as he took to wife the slim, dark beauty he had wanted so desperately. And Anne seemed to glow with bridelike shyness and bliss, despite the sadness she felt due to her father's recent death.

The humble bower that Anne had slept in almost all her life was their wedding chamber. A few castlemaids took pity on the lack of preparation given to the wedding and decorated the room with remnants of white silk and fir boughs. A plentiful fire was laid in the hearth and a generous night livery of sweet-meats, comfits, sugared violets and roses, marchpane, and ornate goblets beside a large flagon of spiced wine was provided for them by some kindhearted cookery maid.

"It lacks the grandness I would have had for your sake," Brennan told her.

"Pomp does not suit me so well as this, Brennan," she replied from behind her screen. There was no ritual preparation of the bride by a host of giggling maids. Nor were there dozens of drunken knights and nobles to bear the groom, amidst rounds of coarse jests, to their chamber. Anne dressed herself in a sheer nightdress that had been purchased for her by her husband. "Take food, my husband," she said quietly. "And wine. A hearty hanap for us both."

"Are you afraid?" he asked as he poured for them. He felt

more confident because of this intimacy. Brennan, having been twice married, preferred these circumstances, the absence of people attending them, the quiet of being completely alone with Anne. She was so young; he hoped to ease her into her new role.

"Oh nay, Brennan," she said. "I know you would never hurt me." Her mother had not uttered one word about her predicament since the morning Dylan escaped. She came around from behind the screen and stood before him.

The sheer cloth clung deliciously to her curves and alluded to the naked loveliness beneath. Brennan's blue-gray eyes came alive like steely fire as he looked at her. Her black hair hung straight and thick down to her thighs, and it took all of his control to pass her the cup before he ravaged her. Never in his life had he known such lust, such wanting. He thought he had overcome that selfish impatience to be satisfied that plagued young men. But since first meeting Anne, he had been beset by a sizzling, intense desire that at once alarmed and delighted him. He checked his eagerness when he noticed that her hand trembled as she accepted the ornate goblet. She caught his notice and laughed nervously. "Uncertain, perhaps, but not afraid. Brennan . . . ," she began, and quickly lost her nerve.

He touched his goblet to hers and they drank. He kissed her lips lightly, overwhelmed by his desire to crush her to him.

"Brennan, there is something —"

"Nay," he said in a breath. "If you come to me willingly, there is nothing." He took her goblet from her, placed both of them aside, and took her into his arms, this time to claim her lips with all the desire he felt.

Anne gave herself freely and returned his ardor to the best of her ability. When she felt the pressure of his tongue, she relaxed and opened her lips under his. She felt his fire; she knew how badly he wished to possess her. She embraced him and caressed his back. And when she was lifted into his arms and taken to her childhood bed, she attempted once again to excuse the matter of her chastity. "Brennan, there is something —"

"Anne," he said, laying her down and placing soft kisses about her cheeks, eyes, and neck. "Will you accept a husband's touch? By your own choice as well as your father's?" he asked.

"Oh yes, Brennan. I assure you."

"Then that is all I wish to know." And he proceeded to slowly strip away the nightdress and his own clothing. His hand, trembling, slowly moved over her breast, down to her waist. "I want you to learn to trust my touch, Anne. This need not be a chore, a ritual, but a pleasure. Yours . . . mine . . . ours. Close your eyes; love takes time. You must never think love painful in any way."

"Brennan . . ."

"Close your eyes, my love, and let me show you. . . ."

He did not wish to hear her words, and so she did not labor to form them. She allowed his every touch and tried to anticipate his desires, though shyly. It was not as with Dylan, when passion thrust them together with all the power and desperation of two merging thunderheads. Brennan took his leisure of her body, gently, slowly, deliberately; touching each place with fingers and lips. She knew Brennan's trembling was from restraint, which he employed for her sake. She almost gasped when she felt the warmth of his tongue on the inside of her thigh, but he hushed her again, and slowly caressed her, urging her to trust.

Although he was well past his fourth decade, Anne found in him all the physical attributes of a much younger man. His body was well tended, muscled, and firm. His touch was delicate and thoughtful. He was clean and handsome, down to the last detail. There was no fault with Brennan, and he aroused many pleasant sensations in her, sensations she had not expected to come. It was not the same passion, but she soon did more than simply yield. She could not have asked for a more tender, patient, and caring lover. It pained her to know that what he would find would hurt him.

When the truth became known to him, he hesitated in only a moment of surprise, but did not utter a sound. After that brief pause it seemed to increase his longing as he realized she was not intact. He began to move more desperately, rapidly. His caution ceased and his hunger consumed him. He took all of her, and she met him and moved with him as much as she could, until breathless and satisfied, he collapsed.

She could not be the first to speak, for it was obvious that he knew. She could parley the questions only so well, and it was better that he question her than to offer an inadequate explanation. She did not wish to lie to him. It seemed a very long time before he released her body, and when he did so, he left their bed. He refilled the goblets and carried them back. He handed one to her and looked into her eyes. Brennan might have wished it otherwise, but if ever Anne had seen fatherly disapproval, it was then.

"Perhaps you should have insisted, Anne, when I would not hear you."

She looked down into the deep red wine. "I would have told you sooner," she said, "but I was sore afraid you would not take me."

"Had you told me sooner, it would have been better. Had you told me when it happened, it would have been better still."

"But Brennan, I could not," she said, looking up at him.

"It was long ago, then?"

"Oh . . . so long ago."

"You were forced?" he asked.

"Of course," she said, though in her mind the only force had been the circumstances. But indeed, for a woman in love, such circumstances.

"Lady Gifford is neglectful and deceitful. She protected you ill."

"If you take her to task for my care, Brennan, I fear she will only try to discredit me." She gulped hard and said a silent prayer. "No one knows but my mother," she lied. "And I do not know why, but my mother does not love me. She wished for this union and I think she hoped you would not guess."

"Your father was unaware that you came to me thus?"

"Only my mother . . . and . . . I am certain she blamed me.

[131]

'Twas an errant knight in our household for less than a fortnight, then gone. Brennan, I swear, my chamber door has been locked since then."

He saw a tear collect on her lower lid and, with a gentle finger, wiped it away. "Poor Anne," he said. "Even in your misery did your mother not see to you?"

"Can you possibly forgive me?" she asked. "My silence misled you."

"I am amazed that you did not shake in pure fright at the thought of this night," he said.

She reached out a slightly trembling hand and touched his cheek. "Oh Brennan, I knew you would not treat me as he did. I never feared you. I only feared to shame you."

"If you can tell me you love me, if just a little, all thought of shame flees from my mind."

"I do love you," she said with great sincerity. "I love you deeply, my lord and husband." And it was far from a lie she told. Brennan was her salvation, her hope. And if she used him, it was her most ardent purpose to serve him well and honorably. She wished nothing more than to shower him with her gratitude.

He set the goblets aside again, moved by her words. "Then perhaps it is better thus; for me at any rate. I am an old man without the time and patience for skittish virgins. I prefer a wife, in truth — a *wife*."

"Let it be me, Brennan," she said, putting her arms around his neck. "I wish only to please you."

Their baggage was loaded on a cart, almost entirely Anne's belongings since Brennan did not keep much at Raedelle. He traveled with a soldier's baggage, light in clothing and heavy in gear. Anne would ride a docile mare and there was no female servant to attend her. Brennan alone would serve her needs.

The Gifford sons, reunited, returned to Raedelle on the very morning that the earl and his bride were to depart. Brennan was in a hurry for London and could barely pause long enough to speak to the knights. Anger still shook him when he thought of Ferris and the way he died, without his sons to return his body. But they were all gathered in the bailey, the earl leaving, the Giffords returning.

Quentin saluted him and approached, the others hanging back. "Have you had word of your father's death?" Brennan asked.

"Aye, my lord, to our shame. We will do a long penance for our neglect. Though Trenton tried to locate Father before Bart and I even left Raedelle, it was not to be. We found Trenton in the aftermath of Saint Albans; you had already carried Father here by then."

"Your penance will not bring him back, nor give him the burial he deserved, with his sons crossing swords over his body. It should come as a painful lesson to you."

"A sure and painful one, my lord," Quentin said.

"I am for London. I am taking my wife," Brennan said, indicating Anne over his shoulder. She stood a short distance away, heavily cloaked in a hooded mantle that reached the ground, patiently waiting beside her mare. A look of relief crossed Quentin's features; Bart came forward with a smile on his lips. Their families had united despite the sorry behavior of the Giffords. Bart was most grateful for that.

"I would lift a cup with you, my lord, but it is clear you are bound for the road. I am well pleased my sister has wed you," Bart said, looking over Quentin's shoulder.

"No doubt you are," he said shortly. "There may be fighting along the way, but you could join Edward in London."

Bart came around his brother, standing beside him. He smiled confidently. "Perhaps less fighting than you expect, my lord. We have heard that London is barricaded against a possible attack from Margaret's heathens, but the word along the road is that her Scottish soldiers are deserting — running home with all the booty they can carry. She thought to entice them with her permission to pillage what they would, but now that their load is heavy, they do not desire more. They care not who is king here. The city should prove to be no problem. I, for one, would be honored to travel with you. Would you allow us enough time to make fresh packs for travel? We still have to find the sixty men we left with Edward's forces."

"Fewer than sixty now, but you're welcome to ride with this group. Your presence in London might help Edward forget that you left Mortimer's Cross with his hostages. And you might lend your arms to your sister's protection as we travel. That may help me forget how poorly she has been protected here."

"The deFrayne captives? Are they dead now?" Quentin asked with some hesitancy.

"To the contrary, they all escaped. Some trickery with costumes that appeared to be sewn for Ayliffe men-at-arms." Brennan's brow furrowed as he saw Quentin's lips tugging at a smile. Bart cursed under his breath, and Trenton, who had been digging in his pack, looked up expectantly. "You do not seem displeased by the fact," Brennan said to Quentin.

"My lord, I was late in coming to good sense, but we yielded in the end; Father was right and we had no excuse for what we did. I am glad there was not an execution. It is the king's business. I am for meeting them in fair contest, whether on tourney grounds or in battle."

Brennan lifted a brow and considered the others. "And you, Bart?"

Bart looked at Quentin briefly. He was not the fool to ignore the earl's reaction. "'Tis a well-known fact that we hate deFraynes," he said, shrugging. "The argument has engaged our families for a long time, and will endure a long time still — but I let it stand in the way of gaining a good reputation with Edward's army for long enough."

"Perhaps there is some hope for you after all. Let's see how fast you can ready new mounts."

Quentin gave a sharp nod, walking toward the hall, Bart close behind him. Trenton followed, pausing beside Lord Forbes. His eyes were red and his voice quaked. "I will go with you," he said grimly. "I would avenge my father."

"You may not find a chance for that if what your brother says about Margaret's forces is true. Just the same, you must pledge yourself to Edward now, or be too late. Many, I trust, will sing his praises when the fighting is done and he wears the crown. There will be little advantage in that."

"I do not care for advantage, my lord. My father died poorly; we should have been there." He glared past the earl at the backs of his brothers. Then slowly he looked back at Brennan. It was clear the boy struggled with unshed tears. "If there is no fight, then I will see my sister safely settled."

Brennan was touched and clamped a hand on Trenton's shoulder. "She will be well pleased, son. Get ready then."

Bart and Quentin already stood before their mother. Marcella was in the doorway, her hands hidden within the folds of her dark gown, her face grim. Trenton joined them and all three faced Marcella. To watch three grown men fidget in discomfort as if they wished to pass her discreetly told Brennan even more about Marcella's hard hand. He did not listen as the Gifford sons quietly offered their condolences and apologies and explained the need for their quick departure.

Brennan had said nothing at all to Marcella since his wedding. When she was free of her sons, he faced her, still angry with her, but cautious as he noticed the deep, dark circles under her reddened eyes. He neither trusted nor understood her, but he could not deny a strong curiosity. Had her outburst over the escaped prisoners been an inexplicable, irrational response to sudden shock and pain? And what about Anne?

"I am sorry to take your sons away again so soon, madam," he said, his voice quiet and controlled.

"I understand the need," she returned, dry-eyed, her mouth firm.

"You might have said something of your daughter's condition," he attempted.

He noticed a light come into Marcella's eyes, but he could not tell if it was of glee or fury that sparkled there. He knew by the curve of her lips that it was not embarrassment. "My silence at first came from the fact that I strongly desired a marriage to take place — and you were smitten with my youngest. Later, I feared to turn you against us by any confession. I was, after all, severely chastised for the condition of her clothing, a minor infraction in comparison."

"You knew?"

She gave a slight nod.

"And the knight was not captured and punished?" he asked. "Why did you not call your men to arms to avenge your daughter?"

Marcella quickly guessed the lie her daughter must have told. "Think you ill of me, my lord? 'Tis difficult for a man to understand, perhaps, but to mete out vengeance, Anne's shame would have been made public. Thank me that I did not, for she would have had to go straightway to the cloister, an unfit bride but for Jesu, had her violation been common knowledge." Brennan looked away, uncomfortable with the truth to that statement. And, in retrospect, Marcella was right. Owning Anne's virginity had never been more important to him than having her for all time, as his very own. "Sometimes, for women, silence is safer, if more complicated. But you have been liberal with your complaints; I know you think I am a poor mother."

His color deepened, almost in a blush. He bowed before Marcella, wondering if he had misjudged her. "Our families are united now, madam. I beg forgiveness and would count the matter of our differences done."

She smiled. "Succor my daughter, my lord. And my sons; they are loyal to you, York, and their father's memory."

"Aye, madam. I understand."

"My lord, I should like to assure myself that she thrives."

"I had not thought you very concerned about Anne. . . ."

"Oh? I think there is much about women, mothers, that you do not understand, my lord. I have five children and many duties to perform. I have worked very hard, and now that my work is nearly done and I can enjoy the fruits of my labors, I am alone."

He looked at her closely; there was sincerity in her voice. He had never doubted her hard work. Indeed, he had watched her perform, but while impressed by her determination and energy, he had been highly disappointed in her lack of compassion for her children. Yet, his own son, pampered since birth, was a disappointment. He briefly reconsidered Marcella's harsher methods. "Visit us," he said quietly. "And Anne may visit you at any time she desires."

"You are generous. I am pleased for my daughter."

A while later, the Gifford knights, ready for travel with new mounts and replenished supplies, bade their mother farewell. And then Anne approached Lady Gifford with a little hesitancy. Divina was conspicuously absent; the sisters had shared no parting words.

"We will depart, my lady," she said nervously. "God keep you."

"No kiss for your mother?" Marcella asked.

Anne leaned toward Marcella and brushed a kiss on each cheek. She could not remember another time in her life they had embraced. "Thank you, madam."

"I will expect the debt repaid . . . in kind."

"And . . . my sister . . . ?"

"Divina will not interfere. You must urge Lord Forbes to reward your brothers; he has much influence with Edward."

Anne swallowed hard. "Yea, madam. It is the least I can do."

"I had not given credence to your cunning," Marcella said, and Anne's eyes reflected the shock of seeing her mother smile. "I see you are very clever; clever enough to keep your mother well."

Jesu, mercy, Anne thought, noting the smile, the cold eyes, the determination. But all she said was, "Of course, madam."

Within a week Anne had buried her father, married the Earl of Ayliffe, and traveled quickly and without pampering to London. They found the city secured and quiet; shops were closed, people confined to their homes, and no merchants' carts jammed the way. Within a day of her arrival, Anne observed Edward's victorious entry into the city with his enormous army. There was no resistance from any quarter. Events happened so rapidly, with such meager preparation, that day blended into night, night into day, as she found herself suddenly changed from the childish object of her mother's scorn into a youthful, richly garbed countess.

If she had married and traveled to London with Brennan for the sake of companionship, she would have been disappointed. Queen Margaret's forces had recaptured the pitiful, insane King Henry and conflicting reports of the status of her army swirled around the city. Many said the Scots were fleeing. Others said that because of her victory at Saint Albans, she had managed to gather an impressive English force. There was little to be done but to confront her. Brennan, therefore, was constantly in counsel with various York supporters, and plans were swiftly calculated. Proclamations declaring Edward King of England were publicly read and an army was amassed. Edward the King called for every man from the age of sixteen to sixty to do battle against Margaret and secure the crown.

The earl and his countess kept lodgings close to Edward, the Earl of Warwick, and others of influence in the new court, but Anne did not perceive this as a time of glamour and excitement at court. Too much was at stake; Brennan would go again to war. Anne was left behind in apartments in the Tower of London with a group of noblewomen and servants whom she did not know. They treated her with the same cautious deference her family had shown toward her during the Christmastide days. She was beginning to learn the importance of her husband's titled position and Brennan's closeness to the king.

To her great relief, Brennan returned from battle again, victorious this time. She listened to his tales of the battle fought on the early morn of Palm Sunday in a snowstorm so blinding and furious that most of the deaths occurred from confusion and accident. Almost thirty thousand were dead but miraculously, all three of her brothers had survived. And although King Henry and Margaret had fled to safety, there was little doubt now as to who was king. Edward had proven his might, if not his right.

Brennan moved Anne into a house on Pickering Lane with a staff of servants to attend their needs. She hoped for a period of quiet to follow the battle of Towton, if not for her own sake, for Brennan's. She was concerned by the way that worry drew deeper lines in her husband's face, and she knew he needed more rest. But it was not to be. There was a heavy load of work and preparation involved in attainder for Henry's followers, making appointments for Edward's most faithful vassals, and plans for a coronation were set in motion. Brennan was kept busy and frequently away from his young bride. The weeks passed quickly. The Gifford sons, having salvaged their reputations by going to war with Edward a second time, pestered Anne with requests when they could not get Brennan's ear. Quentin and Trenton did not have outrageous requests: Quentin wished for a higher honor for Raedelle than a barony and Trenton wished for a post serving the earl. But Bart hungered after a rich estate, preferably an earldom, and was irritated by Anne's reticence. She cautioned Bart to be patient, promising that Brennan would be more generous when he had more time.

In the midst of this lonely early spring, Anne felt a new quickening within her. She knew the child was Dylan's. She held the news tightly for longer than necessary, and then asked her tired husband, late one night, if he would welcome a second son. She had not even met Brennan's first son and heir, Brainard. Though she had conceived this child in mid-February, she did not inform her husband until May. Then, she promised him a child for Christmastide, knowing it would be sooner.

Feeling the changes in her body and the life move inside her caused her to think of Dylan often, but with an odd kind of joy. She had heard that the deFrayne heirs were safely exiled for the time being, and she knew she would be bringing forth a child of the love that she and Dylan had shared. That she could bring the child into the rich, loving, protective circle that Brennan had provided only deepened her love for her husband. She grew more grateful for Brennan Forbes each day and marveled at the way she could accept the love she felt for both men. Had there been any choice, she would gladly have fled England with her beloved Dylan, but for all the painful circumstances she had endured, she was not blind to her many blessings.

Her husband was a good and strong man. She did not begrudge his basic needs, nor did she shrink from his husbandly demands. Indeed, she felt a certain contentment when his arms held her safe. In all his power, he was honest and kind, and treated her as if she were some angel of light come into his life. She stood proudly beside him during the coronation of Edward, the most handsome young king ever to live. The tiny flowering of her pregnancy was barely noticeable when, finally, business and festivities done, and filled with the need to prepare for her child, she asked him to take her home.

Anne had been easily impressed by the beauty of Westminster and Windsor during her four months while Brennan attended to the king's business. She had expected the palaces, abbeys, and churches to be exquisite, befitting a king. But, ultimately, it was Ayliffe Castle, her new home, that took her breath away and left her stunned and speechless. For all she had discerned about her husband's wealth and importance, she was still unprepared.

From the road at five leagues she could see the walled estates and towering parapets. A rich and deep river fed the moat that surrounded what could have been ten cities. She passed by seven stables, five hundred stout homes, ten thousand soldiers, one thousand of them knights. The church rivaled a London cathedral; decorated windows, ornate statues, polished oak stalls, and jeweled tapestries were more ornate than any she had ever seen.

The hall was not a hall, but a palace. The floors were laid with tile and marble and covered with rugs, not rushes. The windows were of glass, tapestries and draperies hung liberally about the walls, the hearths were full and wide, and the furniture must have been worth the wealth of ten kings. Bedchambers did not flow into one another off wide galleries as in most simple manors, but the individual rooms were connected by hallways. Even at Raedelle there had been only four bedchambers that were private and had doors instead of draperies and screens to separate them. And each bedchamber at Ayliffe Castle was hung with silk draperies. In the room she would share with Brennan there was even a separate, attached room for the bath, likewise hung with tentlike silk curtains.

Anne toured the palace in almost a daze. Hours passed and she had still seen only a portion of it. She found her husband so beloved by his subjects that each face beamed for their lord's new-found happiness when she had expected them to frown because of her youth. In droves they came to bow before her, and Brennan introduced each one by name, the terms quite familiar. She made a private oath to herself to do as well as he within a year of living here.

There were important, intimate acquaintances for her to make. There was Mistress Kirsten, who had ruled over the servants in the hall with an iron fist for twenty years. And Sir Wayne, the captain of the guard and sometimes, in Brennan's absence, the seneschal.

"This is Jane," Brennan said. "Though she is young, she has all the necessary skills required to attend a noblewoman and will serve in your bower."

Jane bobbed in a curtsey, smiling broadly with gleaming crooked teeth. Brennan had called her young when she was actually older than Anne by at least a few years. That, in addition to Jane's engaging smile, caused the new countess to laugh. "I will be grateful for your help, Jane."

"Aye, mum, I'll be doing right by you. Long's been the time I've been waiting for this, fearing his lordship would never bring me a lady to tend. Don't you worry over your hair or gowns, mum; none in Ayliffe knows better how to take care of you than Jane."

Anne nodded. No one, she thought, including the countess. She would rely on Jane for the knowledge she lacked herself. "I hope you can also help me learn Ayliffe. I never imagined anything so large as this."

"Lived here all my life, I have. I'll tend you now and then see to your young when they come." Jane looked her over. "Aye, his lordship did right by me after all."

Anne felt her cheeks glow. "I'll try to be deserving of your good service."

"Never mind, mum, you just let me take care of you and I'll be asking nothing more. I'll show you the castle, bring your meals, draw your —"

"You'll wear her out with chatter," Brennan scolded good-naturedly. "Go on and wait for your lady. I'll put her in your capable hands soon enough."

"Aye, milord," she said. "Don't you let him tire you, mum. He goes on worse than me."

"I doubt that's possible. Go on now, mistress. You may bend the countess's ear later."

Anne let out a sigh mixed with a chuckle when Jane had finally relented and disappeared. "It's almost as if I chose her myself," she said, smiling at her husband. "I will never be lonely again."

"You will pray to be lonely," Brennan added. "Ah, here is Sir Clifton. Sir Clifton, I would present the Countess of Ayliffe, my wife."

This handsome young knight bowed before her, but could not hide his stunned admiration from his eyes. His mouth stood agape as he confronted her dark beauty. Sir Clifton was perhaps Dylan's age, shorter, well muscled and thickset. She smiled at his look of wonder and he recovered himself with a slight blush. His square face, deep-set eyes, and thick brown hair gave him the look of a brooding little boy, but by the size of his arms alone his manhood was not in question.

Brennan slapped Sir Clifton on the shoulder. "My knight appreciates beauty as heartily as his liege lord, but he is an honorable man who will not let his appreciation of your loveliness disturb his duty. Clifton already faithfully protects what is mine. It is to his special care that Brainard is entrusted, and, serving me well and honorably there, you may be assured of his importance in this place."

Clifton lowered his gaze, hiding a glowering perturbance, but neither Anne nor Brennan noticed. Anne turned to her husband. "Where is Brainard, my lord? I would have expected him to meet you at the gate."

"He is riding, my lady," Clifton said. "I've sent a page for

him, and when he is properly attired, I will send him to you."
Clifton bowed again. It caused Anne to laugh lightly. Clifton
rose at the sound, frowning.

"Sir Clifton, your courtly manners are impeccable, but let us
save your young back," she said happily. "If you do not bow
each time you speak, I will not curtsey each time. May we agree,
for both our sakes?"

Sir Clifton's complexion darkened. The young knight's face
became stony and serious. "I am your servant, madam," he said,
almost bowing again before he stopped himself.

"I think we will be friends, Sir Clifton," she said, turning away
from him, dismissing him abruptly. She took Brennan's arm again
to continue the tour, oblivious to the fact that Clifton stared
after them for a long time, his brows drawn together as if a
serious thought disturbed him.

Weeks would be involved in just learning the hall and grounds,
much less meeting all the people. But there was a happy feeling
within Ayliffe Castle that made Anne's heart sail. It was a contented, clean, industrious place. Anne was especially delighted
with an elaborate pleasaunce called the countess gardens found
behind the hall, within the inner bailey. Water was allowed to
flow though two barred watergates in the outer and inner walls
to fill a small lake. Anne was amazed to see ducks and swans
and peacocks wandering about. Lush gardens, now in full summer bloom, surrounded the lake and bordered the paths, benches,
and fountains.

"Oh Brennan, I have never seen anything so incredible as this.
I cannot believe I will actually live here. Oh, I do understand
my mother's greed for this . . . and I now see quite clearly
why —"

She broke off suddenly, but he urged her to finish.

"Oh, it was a dreadful evening some time ago when you were
away from Raedelle. Madam and my sister took a notion to
taunt me because I had received so many new gowns and trinkets, and I was so hurt by their lack of love for me that I lashed
out at them both. I swore never to allow them forgiveness, nor
should they attempt to visit." She laughed openly. "I had no

idea what I threatened. I had no idea I should expect anything like this."

Brennan frowned. "You were wise to do it. I have not been comfortable with Lady Gifford's strange alliance."

"Oh, but they brought apologies and begged for forgiveness. They were only jealous, Brennan. Surely you know how hard a curse envy is to bear."

He touched her cheek with fondness. Each passing day he found it difficult to believe he could have such good fortune as this: a woman of such fresh young beauty, so devoted, so kind and good in her heart. "You are too forgiving sometimes, my love. You must learn caution."

"It will be easier to learn caution than to learn to live in this luxury, I assure you. I feel very much the simple wench when I look at these new surroundings."

He looked down at her slightly swollen middle. "This has gone on for long enough. Come to your bedchamber. We can spend weeks touring Ayliffe, but you need your rest." He deposited her in the richly appointed room that they would share. She had seen it earlier, but the shock was new as she entered again, unable to believe she would actually call this hers.

"I'm certain you understand that many things require my attention just now, with a home this size and having been away so many months," he said. How could she fail to understand? She was awed by the responsibility. She was not surprised when he did not return quickly, nor was she upset when an evening tray was delivered to her in the early evening. Although the sun was setting, Jane reported that Brennan was still involved in meetings with the caretakers of his demesne. Anne submitted happily to her private meal, bath, and chatter from her new maid.

"I imagine that's a young Forbes a-breeding, my lady. But, I'll not breathe a word of it before you allow," Jane promised after seeing Anne in her naked state.

Anne laughed goodnaturedly. "Those who have not yet noticed will quite soon. The child will be my Christmas present.

And Lord Forbes has already boasted of the fact to many of his friends at court."

"Aye, he would be proud. His lordship is proud, above all things. A good man, he is. There'll be babies here now, sweet babies for us to spoil."

"Do you long for babies, Jane?"

Jane laughed. "To have babies of my own I would have to marry and leave you. I have tended you for less than a day; are you tired of me so soon?"

Jane pushed Anne toward the dressing table and began to unwrap her hair to brush it. "Nay, mum, a lady's maid wants the lady's babies to come. Aye, there will be many children here now, for it is clear the earl loves you." She giggled happily.

"How old are you, Jane?"

"A score next month, mum. And missing no teeth, mum."

"My sister's age," Anne said almost sadly. In one day she enjoyed a warmer friendship with a chambermaid than she had in all the years she shared a bower with Divina.

"Ah, and you miss your sister, eh, mum. Don't you worry, there will be visits."

"My sister and I do not . . . ." She paused, looking in the gilded mirror. Jane pulled the ivory-handled brush through her hair, not meeting her eyes. "We are not very close," Anne mumbled.

"And how can that be? No fault of yours, certes. I knew at your first word you're a sweet young thing."

Anne was not listening. She absently heard Jane chatter about two married sisters, deceased parents, friends she had had since birth at Ayliffe. Anne was looking at her own reflection. All those years that she had thought Divina favored, had felt forgotten, Divina had been jealous of her. That jealousy had prompted Divina to betray her, when she could have formed a pact with her, protected her, and Anne would have reacted in kind, helping and protecting Divina. That door was closed to them now, for now Marcella had the upper hand. Divina must surely be suffering.

"Aye, if your sister loves you little, I'm not believing it's any fault of yours. Why you're generous and kind, mum. Lord Forbes wouldn't have no other kind, not him."

"It was harder for my sister," Anne said with a note of melancholy. "She expected so much, and was so disappointed. I expected nothing."

"Now isn't that just the way. You take what life gives you, I always say. And when it gives you the good, you give thanks, and when it gives you the . . ."

Although she was exhausted, both from her journey and Jane's chatter, Anne was determined to stay awake for Brennan's return, even if it meant staying up all night. She reclined on a stuffed daybed, thick down pillows surrounding her, and the comfort of a summer hearth lulled her into sleepiness. She wondered from time to time if Ayliffe was only a dream. Would she soon awake and find herself in a gray, cold castle, the more typical home of the English noble?

A sharp and impatient tapping at the door caused her to bolt upright and then, belatedly, she called out to the visitor to enter. A young boy stood in the doorframe. He wore man's clothing and he was quite large for an eleven-year-old, assuming this was Brainard. His hair was a russet blond, his eyes a blue-gray, and his build was stocky, almost chubby. There was very little resemblance to Brennan, but it could be no one else than Brainard.

It occurred to her for the first time that he had not come any sooner, and she stood in his presence, somewhat self-consciously. Her lightweight silk chamber gown was not the attire she would have chosen to greet Brainard, but, truth to tell, she had forgotten about him. She felt a blush form on her cheeks.

"You would be Brainard," she said nervously, painfully aware that she was only five years his senior.

"Of course. And you are my father's wife." He slowly appraised her from her brow to her toes and, if she was not mistaken, his expression was a sinister leer. "He wasted no time in mounting you."

"Brainard," she said, her voice trembling and stuttering a bit, "your . . . Lord Forbes is not here."

"Of course not. I saw him with the seneschal. I know where he is, even if you do not."

"I'm . . . I'm glad you've greeted him. He has missed you a great deal."

Brainard let go with a shrill, almost feminine laugh that did not match his stout body at all. "Really? I find that hard to believe. I doubt my father mentioned me much at all."

Brainard spoke more accurately than Anne. Brennan had not mentioned his son often and had never seemed concerned as to his welfare. For the first time she wondered about her husband's attachment, or the lack of it, for his son. But Anne attempted a polite lie, for, if possible, she would like to be on good terms with him. "Not at all, Brainard. He spoke of you often and lamented his time away."

"My mother has been dead not yet three years," he said with almost cruel indifference. "I am the heir to Ayliffe and you are not my mother."

Anne stiffened, shocked. This boy was nothing like his father. Was this jealousy and fear that would give way to acceptance once they were better acquainted? Yet the look in Brainard's eye told her that this was who he was, and it had little to do with the difficult adjustments of growing up.

"No one understands that better than I, Brainard."

"I'll count on that," he said, whirling about and leaving her room, slamming the door as he went. No special words of welcome, no greeting, no bowing and scraping. He meant to tell the countess the rules, and Anne had heard him clearly. She was distressed for a long while after his departure.

By the time Brennan returned to her, Brainard had been gone for two hours and she had dozed off. She roused from light sleep to Brennan's warm embrace and in the comforting circle of his arms reckoned that Brainard was only a spoiled little boy, the single flaw in an otherwise perfect setting. Yet the evil glitter in the boy's eyes haunted her in her dreams and she woke trembling in the night.

I am the lady here, she told herself. I need not fear a child. The others welcomed me warmly, happily. Perhaps Brainard will come around if I am kind and show him I respect his birthright. But sleep did not come easily. In her dreams she saw a tapestry scene of a glorious castle. The flaw started as a sliver and became a wide, gaping tear in near perfection. And the babe within her kicked violently, as if protesting their new abode.

Through the rest of the summer Anne spent very little time with Brennan's son, but it was evident that he was more than a little spoiled; he was demanding and inconsiderate. Castle servants could not easily please him and he indulged in childish tantrums that challenged the patience of the entire household, but Brennan did not take him to task. He seemed to ignore the problems his son presented. Anne knew that her skills as a mother would be tested, for she would not raise a child with behavior like Brainard's. And she saw that Brennan might be little help. Good in so many things, he seemed indifferent to fatherhood.

The air cooled and the harvest was being brought in. Anne's burden grew while she luxuriated in her rich home, getting to know the good people who faithfully served the earl. And then the Gifford banner appeared without the Ayliffe gates and Lady Gifford was admitted with twenty men-at-arms, six servants, and a baggage cart that held the furnishings of a bedchamber and a winter wardrobe. Anne knew then that Brainard would be the least of her problems.

Anne met her mother in the courtyard in the midst of many Ayliffe guards in addition to her mother's escort. "You're rounding out quite well, daughter," Marcella said, kissing Anne's cheek perfunctorily. She examined Anne's swollen form. "Your brother brought the news when he returned to Raedelle. Bart and Trenton have scurried off to do the earl's bidding. When is the child due to be born? Christmastide, Quentin says. No sooner?"

Anne lifted her chin and narrowed her eyes. She should have known that her mother would challenge her instantly. She felt overpowered by Marcella, a feeling made worse by the fact that she had to look up to meet her eyes.

"The earl must be very proud to get a child on you so soon."

"Indeed, madam, he is very proud. You should have informed us you were coming."

"Did I not? Oh, I write so many letters I was sure I told everyone in England and France and encouraged them to visit me here. The earl invited me. I assumed . . . ."

"Where is Divina, Mother?"

"Oh dear, I have been remiss. I must make tallies in the future. I was sure I had written you. She is with the sisters of Bury Saint Edmunds, dear. She is very happy with them."

Anne's face bleached of color. Her mouth opened in shock and she nearly swayed. "She did not want to go to the convent, Mother," Anne said in a stunned whisper.

"Oh, but she changed her mind, dear Anne." Anne gave a quiet and miserable moan as her mother looked around the courtyard, lifting a thin brow as she contemplated Ayliffe's richness.

"Is there any way I can assist, my lady?"

Anne found Sir Clifton standing beside them and she smiled in relief. This knight had developed a habit of being nearby when there was any need. Just when Marcella was most overpowering, there stood Clifton, his presence a show of strength. She gave thanks yet again that she had Brennan and his people. It was a great deal easier to face Marcella here, at Ayliffe, where she was a countess with so many strong helpers at her disposal. And Clifton had made it clear he would serve her most bothersome request and be grateful for the chance. She did not wonder where Brainard was as she took comfort in the show of allegiance. "Thank you, Sir Clifton," she said, smiling. "If you will direct my lady mother's escort to the cookery for refreshment, I will take her into the hall myself."

He nodded and bowed, backing away from her.

"Ah," Marcella sighed as she walked alongside Anne toward the hall, "it is good to be here; Raedclle had become so dark and lonely. It is doubtful the place will become cheery under Quentin's dominion, unless we can find him a rich wife. And, we must speak to the earl about Bart. It has been months since Edward was crowned and with all the attainted lands left by

Henry, surely we can fix him something now. I know you'll speak for him, Anne."

An uneasy feeling prickled up Anne's spine. She knew she must carefully balance her mother's power with her desire for more. Their tenuous pact, Marcella's silence against Anne's vulnerability, would be a challenging existence at best. *I must be stronger,* Anne thought. *Strong and clever enough to show her that I will not be shuffled out of sight as Divina was.*

"You will speak for Bart, daughter?"

Anne impulsively turned back toward the courtyard where Sir Clifton directed Marcella's escort by pointing toward the stables, the cookery, and other comforts they might indulge themselves in. Sir Clifton did her bidding quickly and efficiently, and the sight gave Anne a bolstered sense of might. She knew she had but to whisper a request to have services performed all over Ayliffe. "I will speak to the earl in good time, Mother," she said more easily.

The visiting troop of escorts dispersed to stable their horses and find food, but Sir Clifton stood staring at the hall where Anne had disappeared behind the door. Her smile still tickled his memory with desire, and there were times when he could not think clearly for hours after she passed him in the town.

"He won't be good for currying horses for an hour, now he's got her ladyship's scent," an Ayliffe knight said in jest.

Clifton's head jerked in the offender's direction and his dark eyes blazed with fury. "What did you say?"

A companion chuckled easily and slapped a hand on the shoulder of the first knight. "He meant no harm, Sir Cliff. It hasn't gone unnoticed that you're less often with young Brainard, but lingering about the doors, hoping the little countess will be passing by." Both men laughed. "You're not alone in your appreciation. I bet she's a lively piece for the old lord. Aye, for a *young* — "

Clifton's arms had tensed through the teasing and before the man finished he let out an enraged growl and flung himself on the two of them. Fists were flying as the trio landed in the dirt, the two teasing knights unable to escape Clifton's attack. Someone shouted when they were spied, and within moments a large circle of men gathered. But the match went quickly out of control as one of the knights escaped Clifton's hold and tried, futilely, to pull Clifton off the remaining knight. Sir Cliff sat on the young knight's chest and hammered his face mercilessly. A second, a third, and finally a fourth knight was required to pull Clifton from his prey. But for a trickle of blood at the corner of his lip, Clifton was unmarked.

Clifton's rage was slow to abate. He stood, breathing heavily and holding back the tides of his temper, while his victim was dragged to his feet, his face battered and bleeding.

"Christ, man, what brought that on?" someone asked.

"With Sir Cliff, he could have stubbed his toe on a pebble."

"Sir Cliff? I thought him the favorite? A temper like that guards his lordship's son?"

"He's different with his own kind, lad. Mind you don't make him angry."

Clifton might have answered that remark with another on-slaught of punches, but the crowd had grown and he would be badly disadvantaged. He whirled away from the group, stomping off toward his quarters. She brought him near madness with her young beauty, her sweet disposition, her soft, caressing voice. Even though he had become well known for his volatile temper long ago, he blamed Lady Anne for his sudden and dangerous outburst.

PART II

May 20, 1465

Chapter Nine

THE SHIP on which Dylan had sailed from Calais to England had belonged to his wife's father, but since his recent
death it was now Dylan's. He anchored off Plymouth, but did
not go ashore. It was too soon. He wanted to remember the
moment his foot was again planted on English soil, and he
wanted to touch ground on land he owned.

It was not to be Heathwick, but this would do nicely. If he
was ever welcomed at court, he would thank King Edward most
kindly for marrying Elizabeth Woodville. She would be crowned
in a few days, although Dylan would not dare go to London to
witness the event. He was still officially in exile until things
could be arranged. That he had actually returned to England
was the strictest secret. And this estate that he would henceforth
own and temporarily call home had been a part of his wife's
dowry. His wife, Raynia, God keep her, was the niece of Lord
Rivers, Queen Elizabeth's cousin.

Dylan had lived in precarious flight, often in poverty, for
most of the last four years. He used his warring skills as a
mercenary in six brief battles on the continent, never for loyalty,
never for the same duke or king twice. He had managed, along

with Cameron, to better his lodgings each year they remained abroad and even visited a few noble households, among them King Philip's in France. He made the acquaintance of Anthony Woodville, also in exile and, through him, met Raynia. They had been married now six months.

Dylan traveled with a few men and servants, but no one spoke as they transferred from the ship to a small craft. To reach his property it was necessary to travel through an inlet that went deep into the land, surrounded by woody hills, rocky cliffs. He pulled the scrolled map from inside his short mantle and studied it as the lesser men rowed. "There," with a pointing finger, was his only utterance. The modest castle, no more than a manor house really, was exactly as it had been described. It sat beneath a viny veil at the top of a steep bank and he could see that the brush and trees were kept cut back along a winding path from the beach to the house. A ship could not get in here, which kept it safe from sea attack. Access by land was said to be even more difficult, as there were many bogs and marshes, known by the residents, unknown to strangers.

He hesitated, but finally stepped into the shallow water, wetting his boots and hose, and walked a few steps to the beach. He sighed appreciatively, hands on hips, looking around.

England.

Anne.

The two thoughts had come simultaneously for four years. England and Anne, his two loves . . . and the two he could not have.

The six knights, former mercenaries who would serve him as men-at-arms when he was restored, and the four male servants began to carry parcels and trunks up the winding path toward the house. They remained quiet. On the voyage and before Dylan had told them so much about his home and his longing to have his country again, they held their tongues reverently while he acclimated himself. But he was oblivious to their efficiency, as to their courtesy. Tears burned his eyes.

Anne. Oh my beloved. Wed now, they say, and a mother. Would that you could have been the mother of my child . . . but an Ayliffe heir is impressive. I did not do so well by marriage, but Raynia is a decent young woman, if cool. And Anne, she did get me home. What will you say when you see me? That I am changed? I have fought more senseless wars; I took booty for pay. I robbed a baron of some mighty pretty stuff. Toughened. Perhaps I am only toughened. Perhaps my loneliness has not made me bitter or angry. Does it show, my Anne?

And you, my love? Ah . . . you could only be more beautiful, of course. And bedecked in glorious lengths of silk and sarcenet and jewels, not stolen by a mercenary soldier, but honorably earned by a noble close to the king — as it should be. You were born to be draped in the finest cloth, covered with glittering gems. And motherhood suits you well; I always knew it would. Your cheeks surely glow, your eyes, deep and brown and soft, show the warmth and tenderness earned by women when they nurse their young and rear them with that watchful, careful mother love.

I hope your marriage is good. I hope the earl is decent and kind and gives you much. Mine? Of course; my wife is a good woman. We are resettled, we two, long and far from our youth. Long and far from the gardener's tent at the fair. Far, far, from the cask room at Raedelle.

Am I so changed? My eyes only show the long distance I have traveled, that is all. I am not as old as I look, only seven and twenty. I have no sons, but I am only recently wed and my wife is . . . young. She is young. No, my Anne, not changed. I am not changed. *Nothing has changed, though I willed it.* I prayed for release.

I cannot see you, it is impossible for me. These passions have been barely controlled, though a sea has separated us. One look at your lovely face will bring all my secrets to my lips, to my eyes, and you will know that in my heart I am still the boy-knight who would have died for your love. Now and then, over the years, in a common place like a hall or shop or street corner, a scent would come suddenly and my mind would be filled with memories of you. Or a woman would pass and her back, or hair, or manner of step, would remind me of you and I would panic and run to see her face. There was always that hope, always that despair.

What will you tell me? Will you spill your heart's blood and admit it was the same for you? And will we then begin our sins anew, though now there are even more people we might destroy? Or, my only love, will you say you are content with the earl, and love me no more?

"My lord?"

Dylan slowly returned to the present. He swallowed back the threat of tears and turned to his friend, Markham.

"We'll take the skiff around for more of the baggage, if that's all right."

"Aye, Mark, my lad. Good work, and thank you."

"Glad to be home, my lord?"

"Aye. Praise Lady Raynia for providing a house. Is it a good house, Mark?"

"Stout and well kept. There's a caretaker who lives here with his family. There's a fine stock of wine, the woman will set the bread to rise, and I'm told the hunting is close and fat. We'll set an arrow or two and have a hot meal."

Dylan smiled. There were times abroad when he would have given much for a roof and a hot meal. He reminded himself to count mercies, not heartaches.

"Then let's settle in, Mark. I could kill a goodly flagon of malmsey. Perhaps we'll be forgiven and invited to Edward's court soon — once again duty bound and too harried to enjoy a good hunt and the quiet of a country house. Let's enjoy it."

Many hours of kneeling were followed by many hours of dining and celebrating. The coronation of Elizabeth made this Whitsunday a day of days. The streets were filled with both singing voices and rude jests. Jealous tongues wagged of her common birth, which was far from the truth, for her mother was the Duchess of Bedford. But, she was not a foreign princess, for which she would likely pay a high price with her subjects.

The Westminster galleries were filled with knights and nobles and King Edward had created fifty Knights of the Bath in her honor. Familiar and unfamiliar faces pressed into the halls and chambers and grounds for appointments, hopeful for conferences, even mere glimpses. Anne, Countess of Ayliffe, sat near the queen, exhausted. And anxious. The coronation would mark the end of a long winter in London. She craved Ayliffe Castle, and Brennan had promised her.

Lord Forbes, being one of Edward's favorites, had presented his wife to the future queen months ago, and if an appointment to wait upon Elizabeth hadn't come through Brennan, it would have come quickly in any case. Anne was taken with Elizabeth; she found her beautiful, quick, wise, and understanding. And Elizabeth was in like attracted to Lady Forbes, though she had never said the reasons. But the very first time their eyes met, there was a strong rapport between the two; a sympathetic, unspoken pull. Perhaps, Anne thought, the joy, pain, sorrow, and love shines in the eyes of all women who do more than just birth their young. Queen Elizabeth had two sons by her first marriage.

Anne had heard that Elizabeth Woodville, before Edward, had deeply loved her first husband, John Grey, who was killed at Saint Albans. Perhaps there was also a sliver of light, intuitive perception, that cut through the eyes of women who had loved and lost. Saint Albans had changed many lives. It was after that battle that Dylan had been driven away.

Anne stood behind Lady Scales, Anthony Woodville's wife, and a bit to the left. Still, it was a position of honor and more than Anne would have asked. She glanced across the large hall to eye Lady Gifford. While she was relieved to be included in the coronation festivities, Marcella would have liked to share Anne's close proximity to Elizabeth. Marcella still shook her head in confusion at the prospect of Anne's good fortune. She had never thought of Anne as deserving, only fortunate.

She felt an arm encircle her waist. "Lady Forbes is spent," Brennan whispered.

"Aye," she sighed. She laughed lightly and let her head rest against his side. "Not much longer, I pray."

"No more than two hours, lest they start to drink the river.

The queen will excuse herself shortly. The masses are getting drunk."

"The king himself is none the better for drink," she whispered, noting Edward reclining a bit more in his chair than a sober man would. "I marvel at her, Brennan. She has not flinched or trembled under the weight of that diadem, those robes. Some women, perhaps, are born to be queens."

"This queen was found in the forest under a great oak," he chuckled. "Excuse me to Lord Grange, my love. I will return for you as soon as I can."

Anne stood in proper attendance for another hour while man after man approached the queen, knelt to pay homage, and in some instances kissed her hand. Finally, Elizabeth stood from her dais and Anne snapped to attention with a gladness she could feel to her toes. She would attend Elizabeth to her bedchamber and then she would be excused. Each of the women approached their queen to curtsey low. In Anne's turn, Elizabeth held out her hand. "My lady, you need not, if you are tired."

Anne kissed Elizabeth's long, slender fingers. "I am at your call, my liege," she whispered.

To her amazement, she heard the queen stifle a laugh. "I saw, madam," she whispered. "Lord Forbes was nearly holding you upright." She smiled. "Attend your husband, my lady."

"Thank you, Your Majesty."

"To Ayliffe then?"

"Aye, Your Majesty."

"I will miss you, Anne."

"It will not be long, Your Majesty. God keep you."

She bowed away from Elizabeth and watched as many as a dozen high-flown noblewomen parade behind her. The evening would finally end. When Elizabeth was out of sight, Anne turned around. She did not see Brennan or any member of her family, but her eyes settled on a woman leaning tiredly against the wall. There was something oddly familiar about her, but Anne could not remember where they might have met. The woman's clothing was old though finely sewn, well kept, and clean, and she was about fifty years of age. Her auburn hair was grayed around the edges, but she had a slim, firm figure. On instinct and nothing more, Anne approached her. And the woman's eyes came alive.

"Madam," she said by way of greeting, "I am Anne of Ayliffe, Lady Forbes. I feel we were acquainted. . . ."

"Not actually, my lady," she said, smiling warmly and bowing graciously. "Although we have seen each other from across a wide expanse of lawn or field." Anne's brow wrinkled. "Daphne deFrayne, my lady, late of Heathwick."

Anne felt her cheeks grow hot. "Of course," she said in a breath. "Of course it is you." She wished to embrace her, but she knew the act of a Gifford woman treating a deFrayne woman thus would raise too many questions. And how did Daphne manage to smile? Did she not consider Anne the enemy? Marcella, despite everything, still harbored intense hatred for the entire family, although the deFraynes had lost everything and were reduced to impoverished flight. As thought of her mother crossed her mind, she glanced over her shoulder, but Marcella was not in evidence. "Madam, how do you come here?"

"By the gracious forgiveness of His Majesty. Anne," she said softly, smiling tenderly as if they were old friends, "are you well? Happy?"

Dylan had said his mother was sympathetic, but how much so was impossible to tell. "Aye, madam. I am well kept. And in good humor. How does your family?"

"We are all well, my dear Anne. I am in desperate hopes that I can gain an audience with Her Majesty on the account of my sons. I want to bring them home."

"They are fit?"

"It has been a difficult separation for us all, but yea, they do write me that they are well, growing stronger. Hard times do that for men, I think. For all of us. Dylan is anxious. Cameron is impatient. They have both married. It is through their marriages that I hope to bring them home. Dylan's wife is a cousin to Her Majesty and Cameron's Bess comes from good Yorkist stock."

Anne suddenly dropped her gaze so that Daphne would not

see her eyes. So, he had taken a wife. But of course he should. And a wise choice: a woman who could help effect his return. She found she was twisting her hands, looking at the long, thin white line on the back of her hand. Is she very beautiful? Anne wanted to ask. And does she adore him? Is there passion in their nights? Love in their hearts? Will there be children, sons?

"My lady, you tremble," Daphne said, pulling Anne's moist hand into both of hers. Anne could not still her shaking hand as Daphne looked at the hand with the scar. Daphne seemed to caress the hand, squeezing it gently. "An odd coincidence," she said in a near whisper. "Dylan has such a scar."

Anne slowly let her eyes rise to meet Daphne's, eyes the same glittering turqoise as Dylan's. They were rich with knowledge and compassion.

"My father said you were a woman to be admired," she said.

"Your father was a generous and gracious man. It is a terrible loss to us all, God rest his soul."

"Do you stay in London?"

"Aye, my lady. Until I can manage some residence."

"Let me . . ." She remembered Ayliffe. She longed for the luxury of Ayliffe. Another day? Two? "Madam, I will see the queen on your behalf, but I beg you, say aught. My family . . ."

"It is good of you, Anne."

"Do not tell Dylan, I pray you."

Daphne's eyes held the understanding glitter of lost love, recognition. "If that is your desire."

" 'Tis best. I shall leave shortly for the country. Patience, madam." Daphne still held Anne's hand, and Anne wanted to embrace her, kiss her, cry with her. "Please allow time. It may take time, madam."

"Anne, my dear, I do understand. You must run along and not be caught with me. But if you should wish to see me, at any time at all, I am presently in a comfortable house near the queen's residence, at Ormond's Inn — easily found. And there I shall remain until my sons can afford me a retirement. I do not plan to go into seclusion so soon."

Anne laughed lightly and squeezed the hands that held hers.

"It is good that you have made a prosperous life for yourself, Anne. You deserve happiness. You must be strong and happy, and raise many children."

She looked away uncomfortably. How much had Dylan told his mother? She felt tears threaten. She was so tired and had never imagined this meeting. Does he still love me? she wanted to ask. Does he dream that we are together, as I do? I have his son and I would cry it to the world. Each time I look at that handsome little face, those haunting eyes, I think of my beloved Dylan. I have worried about his safety every day . . . I cannot drive him from my mind. I love him still. I cannot help what I feel. I love. I love.

"Madam, I . . ."

"I miss him too, Anne. Go, darling," Daphne whispered. "Hurry now, before you make too much of this chance meeting. Be well. Godspeed."

Daphne released Anne's hand and gave her a gentle nudge, turning her about and facing her into the wide chamber, still filled with people. She saw Brennan not very far away and took two steps toward him. Then on impulse she turned back toward Daphne, but she was gone.

When she was again at Brennan's side she realized that Daphne had stopped her just as emotion was getting the better of her. Seeing Dylan's mother brought the memories, the loss, and the enduring love brimming up, almost to her lips. In another moment she would have burst into tears, perhaps clinging to Dylan's mother, weeping for joy and heartache all at once. She took a deep breath. Daphne is wise. It is better this way, she thought. We can never regain what we've lost. We must carry on. We must be strong. I must be stronger than I feel.

"Finally, my love." Brennan dropped a husbandly kiss on her brow. Happy marriages were rare. "Are you eager for your beloved Ayliffe?"

"Aye, Brennan, but it appears Elizabeth will detain me for another day, at least."

"That suits me, since I must remain for at least another fortnight. I do not rest well without you at my side."

"Then you must hurry to Ayliffe, my lord, where I plan to take my slumber through the summer." She smiled up at him. "You are so good to me, Brennan. Please, let's return to our lodgings now. I have never, ever felt so drained."

Brennan rode toward Ayliffe with the hot July sun pounding at his back. He was displeased with the time he had been forced to spend away from home, but there was trouble brewing. It was buried under still waters, unmentioned except in the shadowed corners of private chambers, but Brennan knew how dangerous the problem could be.

The Earl of Warwick was displeased with the king. Warwick had made it possible for Edward to become king and had intended to rule England through him. Edward not only defied him with his marriage to Elizabeth, but he was now surrounded by the enormous Woodville clan, which drove Warwick even farther away from that coveted dais. Warwick was the richest man in England. To whom did one pledge — the king, who owned the crown, or the powerful earl, who owned everything else? The answer was simple for Brennan, but not so simple for others whose fortunes might rest on choosing the most profitable side.

All Brennan had wanted was to be with his wife. He chafed impatiently at the meetings, and when other men were appreciative of the excuse to be away from their wives and were more happily occupied with their mistresses, Brennan only wanted to hold Anne in his arms.

He ached with the thought. Over fifty years old and as smitten as a lad, he thought. Once the notion that Anne could make him feel so young brought him pleasure and amusement, but now it only aggravated him. He remembered the passion he felt the first time he touched her silken flesh — he thought he would burst into a ball of flame from the sheer power of his lust. And it had energized him to feel so. These feelings had never quieted or calmed. He was still filled with a savage, rutting madness that he had to struggle to subdue so as not to ravage his own wife.

Any man would feel so with Anne, he reminded himself. Her fresh, clean beauty was stimulating in itself, but in addition she was smart, kind, and sweet. Early in their marriage he had been concerned that she was too sweet, too vulnerable, but in the past four years she had proved him wrong on that account. She could be quite firm as she managed the household affairs at Ayliffe, and he had never seen anyone, man or woman, who could spot a lie more easily. The people had come to love her, if not worship her. She was a woman among women: good, industrious, efficient, intelligent, beautiful. He had had two decent wives before her, but there was no denying the fact that Anne was the most perfect.

She did not, however, share his hunger. He almost flushed with shame as he thought it. He had no right to complain. She did not shrink from his touch. She did not avoid him, dissuade him, refuse him. She did not even relish time away from him; she seemed to prefer their life together and complained when they had to be separated. She saw to his every need, waited up long past exhaustion for his return to her, and rose early to be with him in the morning. But when he touched her, feeling the explosive passion surging inside him, she returned his touch only with warmth. His wife was not the hot vixen of his dreams, as he wished her to be. She was more his friend and ally.

Brennan's second wife had not been as domestic as Anne had proven to be. She was not pretty or even bright. She forgot things, could not manage well, and had a hard time with even the outstanding castle servants at Ayliffe. He had not even loved her so much when he wed her; he had still missed his first wife, though it had been many years. But in their common bed she had reached heights of ecstasy that had surprised Brennan. It was with his second wife that Brennan learned how much women could enjoy the act of love. In Anne he wished to have a combination of those two wives — the deep love he felt for his first wife and the ecstasy he could feel from his second. He wished for Anne to have that pleasure, that desire, and he tried to bring it to her. But while she allowed his every whim, she never once lost control. She did not yearn for him.

He passed through the Ayliffe gates, wondering where he would find her. In the pleasaunce? The cookery? Their chamber? He waved to the people he passed, his people, welcoming him home.

I do not wish to have her *fondness*, he thought in an unusually churlish mood. Nor her compliance, and I do not wish to be her *dear*, her *love*. I want her to rake her nails across my back in wild, desperate need. I want her to beg me *now, now, now!* I want to hear her soft purrs of yearning turn into screams of carnal pleasure. How does she not feel this, if she feels love?

He shed spurs, harness, and his tunic in the hall. He took a long pull on a tankard of cool ale, and a fresh tunic was brought to him. His wife, they said, was in the pleasaunce. Should she be called to him? Yea, he nearly replied. Call her to my feet after you have disrobed her, unbound her hair, and rubbed her body in fragrant oils.

But, instead, he went to the gardens. He saw her sitting on a bench with a tapestry frame before her. She was clothed in a yellow kirtle that set off the pitch of her hair caught under a simple net. Her fingers worked the design and as if she sensed his presence, she turned her eyes toward him. She smiled, her tender gaze resting on his face, stood and pushed the stand away from her.

"Brennan," she said, walking toward him. "Oh, how I've missed you. I thought you would never come."

Her full bosom bounced and pressed against him, straining at the fabric of her gown, and she looped her arms around his neck. He was distant, still churlish. Did her welcome give him invitation to take her down the garden path to a secluded place where he could rend her kirtle in a single tear and devour her? Nay. Again he met with her sweet compliance.

"You missed me?" he asked.

She looked at him quizzically, caressed his chest gently, and gave a little laugh. "Kiss me," she said. He obliged, covering her mouth in a searing, demanding kiss, thrusting his tongue between her teeth and embracing her with enough force to break her ribs. But her returned embrace was no tighter. He pulled back and looked into her eyes, and she smiled. "I know what you have on your mind, Brennan. Shall we go inside?"

So accommodating, he thought, still insulted that she did not share his aching, burning hunger. When she was a child bride of six-and-ten he had not resented the fact that she merely accepted his lovemaking. But now she was a woman, a mother, and he no longer wished to spend all his time trying to woo response from her. Acquiescence was just a breath away from indifference in Brennan's mind.

"What are you working on there?" he asked, pointing toward her needlework. He ground his teeth. He struggled to cool his unreasonable anger.

"I'm glad you asked me that," she replied, "even though I know it is the last thing you care about. I know what you want, Brennan. Can I have been your wife this long and not recognize that familiar light in your eyes? Come," she said, taking his hand and pulling him toward the tapestry stand. "We will meet your rutting ways in a moment, if you cannot await the setting sun."

"If you know my rutting ways so well, why — " He did not finish the question because of her soft laughter, a sound he loved.

"Brennan, if you did not always return to me in this condition, I would wonder how much gold you were spending to keep your mistress happy." She looked up at him, smiling, as though she not only understood him, but approved. He began to feel guilty. Many men had wives who abhorred their touch, and he complained because his own wife didn't claw his flesh to ribbons in wanton desire.

"It is only the beginning, understand, but it is going to be an enormous tapestry of many parts, and I intend to spend a fortune in making it." A devilish gleam came into her lively eyes. "You may scold all you like, but I will finish it just the same. Once complete, it will be a jeweled theme of this garden of Ayliffe, and I intend it for my heir."

He touched the small completed portion of her project, already quite pretty. Obviously this portion was of the lake. He chuckled at the enormity of her idea. "Your heir? Do you think Sloan will be moved by this?"

"No," she agreed quickly. "I expect Sloan would much rather I get him a good horse and any sharp, dangerous-looking thing that will suffice for a weapon. I intend this for my daughter."

"Oh, do you? Perhaps we should get started on that immediately, in that case."

"So we have," she said, looking up at him with that mysterious twinkle that belongs only to women a-breeding.

"You are *enceinte?*"

"I am a little disappointed in how long it has taken. It is certainly not due to your lack of interest, my lord. Just the same, I expected to have four children by now, especially since Sloan was obviously conceived with our first kiss." She remembered, all too clearly, how she imagined she was holding her firstborn in her womb almost by sheer dint of will until almost Christmastide. And he had been a large baby.

He touched her cheek tenderly. "You have longed for another child?"

"I was quite embarrassed that I had not given you one every year. I wondered if people thought we contented ourselves with long hearthside conversations." She rose onto her toes and kissed his cheek. "You put younger men to shame, Brennan. 'Twas no fault of yours that I did not come with child sooner."

"My God," he said, rebuffed. He embraced her carefully, tenderly. He couldn't imagine what had happened to him along the road. Thirst? Hunger? Heat? He looked at her eyes again. It amazed him how alive her eyes became when she was with child. "Are you well?" he asked, that other look beginning to rise in his eyes again. Anne laughed at him.

"I am in the best of health, my love. I will not be responsible for your surly moods for some time to come. Are you pleased?"

He swept her suddenly into his arms, kissing her lips swiftly in spite of her squeal of surprise. He carried her into the hall, through the galleries to the stairs. I am a brute, he thought. An oaf, a churl. To decry that which is the most wondrous gift of my life, this woman who sings her devotion for me . . . this woman whose eyes shine like black diamonds as she brings to life my seed. How did I *dare*? What would I have? Some hoyden of the streets? Some undignified slattern who hungered only for flesh?

This was the mother of his children; pure, good, and above all else, a woman who accepted him as he was, without complaint when she could have brought kings to their knees. He knew his demands tired her, that she lacked the hunger he felt, and still she never suggested that it not be she, she alone, to meet his needs. She never turned away from him. She was perfection. That he even considered trying to improve upon her was ludicrous.

It was unlike Brennan to be selfish; it was more like him to try to be the man she wanted. And he swore a silent oath that he would.

He tumbled her onto their bed. "Tell me you love me, Anne."

"Of course I love you, Brennan," she said. "You are a good man, and I love you very much."

Would you dare, he thought, ask that she tell you something more? What fool would trade this soft, yielding rose for a demanding thorn? What senseless moron would not try to be her perfect match? If this is not enough, he thought, there is not enough in all of heaven. He kissed her deeply and lovingly. And she took him in her arms, softly to her breast with tender acquiescence.

Chapter Ten

IT WAS NOT in Anne's nature to indulge idleness; the Countess of Ayliffe was not a pampered pet, but a dedicated and energetic noblewoman. After mass and a morning meal, she met with Mistress Kirsten to oversee the work in the hall and the meals in the cookery. She visited the town daily to appraise any needs there, saw her son all too briefly each morning while he was at play with his nurse, surveyed the nearby lands ripe with crops, and supervised a crowded evening meal in the hall. Her duties were many; her daily walking could easily equal twenty miles. There were looms in the town, sheep grazing in the fields, men-at-arms and squires practicing in the outer bailey, sometimes sick that needed tending, servants in need of training, and a multitude of other duties.

Anne knew she could do as much or as little as she liked. Though Brennan was often away, she could depend on Sir Wayne to manage the men's chores to her satisfaction and Mistress Kirsten to oversee the household duties and the needs of the women, but Anne chose otherwise. No doubt those two could function without her quite well, since they had before, but if the lady of the estate did not make her involvement felt, they might never learn to involve her. Because she was interested in every chore within the castle and town, the people grew to depend on her and respect her.

The work was hard, but Anne loved Ayliffe. The people were good, loyal and strong; the castle and towns and fields were luxurious and beautiful. She meant to keep it all exactly as Brennan had first presented it to her, if not improved.

Her personal court had increased in size. Jane was still her nearest servant, now her good friend after more than four years, but there were more women in her company now. The wives and daughters of knights and young serving girls being trained by Jane attended her. She stood as a witness for christenings, betrothals, and weddings. She sent well-trained tirewomen to other noble dames.

Sometimes Anne felt she was never alone for a moment, but she reserved an hour or two each afternoon to either write to Trenton or work her tapestry. Trenton was the only member of her family to send her letters, which she treasured. Quentin, Lord Gifford of Raedelle, communicated with Brennan and wrote short letters of report to Marcella; he had always been a man of few words. Bart, who had been awarded a barony, thanks to Brennan's help, sent frequent requests for improved posts or more available lands. And although she had written to Divina, had even convinced Brennan to increase the dowry for the convent so that Divina would be highly regarded there, Divina had never made contact with the members of her family. Anne suspected Divina blamed them all for her fate.

But Trenton wrote Anne long, affectionate letters, which she guarded from her mother. Trenton had grown into a fine knight, asking nothing of her or the earl, honored to be a part of a company of knights that helped protect the north on behalf of Ayliffe and Edward.

Today there was no letter to write or read, and Anne went to the gardens to work on her tapestry. Her desire for solitude was respected among the waiting women and tiring women, but not by her mother. Marcella was often in residence. She, too, loved Ayliffe. She had always liked luxury.

"You do not see to your brothers as you should," Marcella said.

Anne did not reply or look up from her tapestry. Marcella's fingers also worked brightly hued threads, but on a project of her own. Marcella had offered to work a piece of Anne's tapestry, but Anne declined. Marcella had intruded on enough of her life.

"Bart should have an elevated position by now," Marcella said.

"I warned you to be more patient, madam. You should not have pushed for a barony when you did; Edward's realm was still unsettled and there was little to give."

"There is plenty now. It is settled now."

"Aye, madam, I will speak to his lordship again. But I fear to make him angry with Bart's many requests."

"Humph, his lordship had a richer barony for Sloan before he was a year old than he has for your brother, who fought in several wars for Ayliffe and Edward."

Anne looked at her mother and sighed. "Two, madam. Two battles for Edward. And Sloan is Brennan's son."

Marcella smiled. "So you say," she said. "Perhaps you should speak to the queen about it when you return to court. When do we go?"

"We?" Anne asked. She looked up from her work.

Marcella met her eyes. "Do you ask me to stay behind, Anne?"

Anne did not like her mother's presumptuousness. Marcella's age was beginning to slow down her step, but not her ambition. Marcella had already acquired a pension from Lord Forbes, and Lord Forbes had used his influence to extend boundaries for Quentin's Raedelle and secure a barony for Bart from the king. In addition, she had made many new friends at court because Lord Forbes allowed her to accompany them. But the dowager Marcella was hardly satisfied. She constantly nagged and wheedled on behalf of Bart and Trenton. Anne suspected that Marcella would like to travel among four castles as rich as Ayliffe, making herself one of the most powerful and wealthy widows in the realm. She frequently made reference to the queen's mother and the king's mother, both living in style because of their children.

Marcella did not discuss their secret; never threatened, never screamed. But she was not above subtle comments that reminded Anne she had not forgotten and could use her information at will. She was extremely tiresome in her series of requests to Anne and Brennan.

"What of Raedelle, madam? Do you intend to spend any time there during the year?"

"I will visit in the summer," she replied. "In the following year."

"Visit? Madam, that is your home."

"Will you speak to the queen?"

"In good time, my dear. Let us not exhaust the queen with requests. She is with child."

Marcella cackled. "She is always with child. When do we go?"

Anne's needle stabbed the tapestry impatiently. She would have liked to have had this time to herself if Marcella could find something to do besides conspire to improve her lot. "I am to travel to the city with Brennan after harvest, but I'm afraid we are obligated to join the court at Eltham for a time. I am not sure how long. You are welcome to our London house; I'm certain you have already heralded a visit to my brothers." She doubted Trenton would travel to London; he did not seem to enjoy visits with his mother. Quentin would possibly go to court. And Bart would certainly be there.

"Wives, Anne," Marcella said. "Perhaps we should concentrate on getting them rich wives. The land can be provided later. . . ."

Anne did not quite hear what Marcella said, but it was unimportant. It was always the same litany. She needed retirement funds, or elevated titles for sons, or marriages — none of the Gifford sons had married yet, and Quentin was thirty. And there were always memorials for Ferris.

Anne did not hear Marcella, for in the distance she heard her son. Sloan, four years old, called excitedly to Brainard. Anne's ears strained to hear. Brainard was seldom tolerant of Sloan, but Sloan craved attention from his older brother and chased after him often despite Anne's advice to the contrary.

"Anne," Marcella said. "Bart should have a wife that will bring him his elevated station."

"Hush, madam," Anne said. "A moment, please." She plucked at the tapestry, her ear turned toward the sound of Sloan's voice as he called out to Brainard. The voices came closer to the pleasaunce. The boys did not see her because she sat in the very center of the garden under a tentlike drape. The brush and flowers were high this late in summer and they were concealed.

"Brainard, wait for me, please wait. Sir *Brainard!*"

She knew then where they were going, and what was happening. Brainard kept his favored stallion and all his prized battle accouterments in a small private stable beyond the gardens and near the far outer wall. Sloan loved to see these things, these implements of war. He adored the stallion, for he was young and was only allowed a rare, closely supervised ride on a pony. Brainard almost never let Sloan near his possessions and was livid with rage on those occasions when he learned that Sloan had sneaked in to steal a look or a coveted touch. Brainard, at sixteen, fancied himself an awesome, gilded knight — though he was not yet dubbed.

Instinctively, Anne pushed the tapestry away from her, ready to stand. For once Marcella was quiet. Where was Brennan? Sir Clifton? Brennan would be ciphering or writing. Sir Clifton, if he was faithful to his duties, would either be with Brainard or in the privy stable.

"Brainard, let me look, let me look just once, and I won't touch anything, I promise I —"

"Get thee gone, little cur, I have no time for you. You lap up my dust like a stupid little mongrel."

Anne began walking toward the path she knew they took. She merged with their route just as Brainard was approaching his stable.

"Brainard, please, I promise I —"

Anne lifted her skirts and took long, quick steps to catch up to her son.

Brainard whirled, red-faced, and with a gauntleted hand, struck the lad so hard that Sloan went flying backward, landing with a hard thump on the dirt.

"Sloan!" She screamed his name and ran. Brainard looked in her direction with surprise. Sir Clifton came from the stable, throwing open the doors to see the cause of the countess's scream.

Anne bent to the ground and cradled her son's head in her lap. She murmured his name several times, gently patting his unbruised cheek. He was completely stunned, his eyes teary, glassy, confused. His nose began to bleed instantly; his eyelid was cut and began to swell so that only one eye, void of understanding and filled with hurt, looked up at her. She drew up the hem of her light cream-colored gown to dab the blood away. "Mother?" he questioned in a quivering voice, looking up at her.

Anne kissed his forehead gently. "There, sweeting, can you sit up?" Half his face was red from the slap, the other half a sickening white from shock. Sloan struggled to sit, but his nose was pouring blood. Trying to be brave, he pushed his mother's bloodied gown away from his face, wiped at the muck impatiently with his hand, then pinched his nose as he had seen the older squires and knights do.

Anne looked at Brainard with a rage she had never before felt. Sir Clifton was beside Brainard by now, and in his eyes there was also fury. Anne slowly stood, her gown smeared with her son's blood. Her insides trembled and her eyes burned like a pyre.

"Maybe he'll leave me alone now," Brainard said with no hint of remorse.

Anne took two steps toward him, her hand flying with a will of its own. She slapped his face with all her strength, catching him completely by surprise. Her palm stung in pain. "Don't you *ever* lay a hand to my child," she nearly screamed.

Instinctively, Brainard raised his own hand to return the slap, but Sir Clifton was quicker and grabbed both of Brainard's arms, holding them behind his back. "No, lad, you do not strike my lady. Not ever."

Brainard was uninterested in Clifton's cautioning words and his restraining hold, though he did not struggle against the larger, stronger man. Instead, he vented his anger at Anne. "Why don't you just keep the little bastard away from me then? What do you expect, that I'm a nurse to play lackey to the little donkey?"

"Your cruelty knows no bounds, Brainard. He is your brother," she shouted back.

Brainard, still being held, spat at the ground. "I disclaim him. He is only the nameless cur you gave my father. Do not ever think that I will yield one portion of what is mine to that —"

Anne slapped him again, using the same hand. This time she brought a trickle of blood from his lip. Suddenly, Brainard smiled in irony. "Do you hold me for her assault, Cliff? Is that where your loyalty lies? Get her the whip that she might beat me properly. Does the slut own even *you*?"

Clifton made no reply, but gave his arms a jerk to show that he would, indeed, hold him fast against any further assault on his lady or the child. Clifton ground his teeth, the muscles in his arms aching to take Brainard to the ground and beat him senseless. This was not the first time he had had such an urge. He had always given Brainard his best, yet his young ward treated Clifton like a beast of burden, a slave. Brainard had always laughed at Clifton's demands for respect.

Brainard quieted, looking past Anne. Behind her, Brennan and Marcella both stood. Brennan must have run all the way from his closet to have reached them so quickly. It was quite obvious that he had either heard or been instantly summoned, for he stood in a short gown, opened at the throat and with sleeves rolled up, as though he had been hard at work when the disturbance began. He glared at Brainard and then stooped to look at Sloan.

"I'm sorry, Father," Sloan said, nearly weeping. "I didn't mean to make Brainard mad again . . . I only wanted to . . ."

Brennan stood, his eyes locked into Brainard's. He was not a large man, but in the rage that pinkened his cheeks and caused his eyes to blaze, he seemed enormous. Clifton released Brainard's arms and retreated, and Anne turned back to her son. The rest of this was between Brennan and his firstborn.

"I apologize for the misunderstanding, my lord, I —"

"Misunderstanding?" Brennan thundered. "How do you address my *wife*? Do you lay a hand to my *son*?"

Brainard rubbed his cheek, a disrespectful grunt escaping him. "I am likewise your son, my lord, unless you've forgotten. Do you naturally assume I am at fault here?"

"You are a man. You struck a child. And if my eyes do not deceive me, you would have struck my wife."

"It was natural. It —" He laughed in disbelief as he looked at his angry father. "I am your heir, but you place them high above me."

"God keep me safe and well, for you are not nearly ready to inherit my estates. When have you proven yourself capable of managing any part of this? Do you know how to pay the men? Do you know what sum is rendered for the household? Do you know the number of villeins, stock, the expected yield from the fields? Do you know which neighboring barons have pledged fealty to this county, or the sheriff's tally for taxes, or the tithe? Nay," he stormed. "You decry the countess's good name and strike my second-born son in a temper! Should I entrust their care to *you*?"

Brennan's fists were clenched at his sides, his face was turning purple with anger. He had ignored Brainard for too long. The boy was not developing any of the skills he would need to inherit this earldom; instead, he was playing with costly battle gear that had never seen battle or even a good tournament. He was swilling wine, wenching, and bracing arms with knights in late-night revelry, acting more like a base-born knave than a carefully reared young nobleman.

A thought came to mind and Brennan's temper cooled. "There is a property of mine in Wales, not too distant from Ludlow Castle. Ramsford Keep was your mother's, and she loved it. It is held on my behalf by Sir Baelfour. You will go there and prove yourself as an overlord."

"Ramsford? Father, that is a hovel, a wasted . . ."

"It is a stronghold for King Edward among the Welsh tribes. It serves its purpose and houses six hundred people, though it is not one-tenth of this. And mark me, before you take Ayliffe, you had better show that you can manage something."

"My lord, I was to go to Eltham Castle with you, to wait upon the king. . . ."

"That was before you disgraced yourself. I have thought better of it since. You are spoiled, Brainard, and if the fault is mine, I will rectify it."

"My lord, I beseech your —"

"There is no discussion," he boomed. "Gather your precious metals from your privy stable, find a suitable palfrey, and drag your destrier. You will not need a caparisoned horse or gold-plated sword there; you will need a sharp mind and a strong arm. The Welshmen will teach you the value of property and nobility. If you fail to learn among them, you will surely not live to get your booty here."

Brennan turned from his elder son to look at his younger. Anne was struggling to lift the stocky four-year-old, despite his protests and her early pregnancy.

"Sir Clifton, carry my son to his nurse for the lady."

He began to walk away from the disruptive scene, assuming his orders would be followed as usual.

"Once you've put the babe to bed, hie yourself back here, Sir Cliff. We winter in Wales."

Brennan stopped in his tracks, finding it hard to believe that Brainard would continue to push the point with insolence. He slowly turned back to him. "I will provide an escort," Brennan said with dangerous calm, "but Sir Clifton has suffered long enough under your brutish dominion. He deserves respite, as do the rest of us. He will stay in Ayliffe."

Brennan stormed off in the direction of the hall, leaving the rest of them behind. Anne knew it would be a long while before his seldom roused anger would cool. She stood patiently aside while Clifton wordlessly lifted Sloan in his arms to carry him into the hall. She attempted to follow, but her sleeve was snared by Marcella.

"Anne, we must finish our discussion about Bart."

Anne snatched her arm away, close to losing her temper with Marcella for the first time in years. "God above, madam, cease your demands while I see to my child! Bother me no more!"

She followed Clifton's departing back, lifting her skirts to keep up with his long strides, listening to Sloan's tearful protests that he could walk.

She had never brought complaint to her husband's ears in regard to his older son and frequently feared that Brennan did not notice Brainard's tyranny. Brainard's interest in the wealth and power of Ayliffe was confined to whatever money or possession or liberty his command would afford him. Anne was relieved that Brennan finally noticed Brainard's bad behavior, but the discipline was too late to help either Forbes son. Sloan would surely be hated even more.

Sir Clifton placed Sloan carefully on his bed, and Anne sat down beside him. She sent his nurse and two maids for water, cloths, salves, and clean clothing while she endeavored to soothe her child. His little face was badly battered by the blow and, once in the safe confines of his nursery, he began to cry.

"Why does Brainard hate me so, Mother? I am always careful with his things. I never touched without asking."

"It is no fault of yours, my little love. Brainard can be meanhearted and impatient." She placed a cool wet cloth over his eyes, brushing his light hair away from his brow. At times she could see so much of Dylan in him. His fair wheat-colored hair and bright turquoise eyes were so like his sire's. It was most fortunate that the resemblance went no further and that the Gifford family had predominantly fair hair and light-colored eyes. Sloan resembled Anne, too, in his mouth and quick smile. Some castlefolk even remarked that he looked like Brennan. But when Anne held and comforted this little lad, it was as if she could keep Dylan safe and loved.

She stayed with him until his nurse was able to urge her

successfully from his side. She found that Sir Clifton waited at the door, his eyes respectfully downcast, as was usual for him.

"My lady, I —"

"Say nothing, Sir Cliff. I know perfectly well that you did what you could."

"I have a request, madam. I fear to bring it to your ears."

"Let me hear it, Sir Cliff," she said, hoping it was not much of a request. She had been so burdened with her mother's constant appeals that she felt exhausted. She would gladly cede whatever would stop the begging for a while. In fact, it was Marcella's voice stilling ringing in her ears that prevented her from giving her full attention to Sir Cliff.

"I . . . ah . . . my lady, I know I did not prove myself a worthy guardian and teacher for Brainard, but given a chance, I would take on the training of young Sloan while he remains with you." Clifton raised his gaze to look into the eyes of the countess. He hoped she would not see how smitten he was. He longed to be within a step of her. Her sweet, natural fragrance caused his head to spin; her beauty gave him bothersome dreams. "I would do better by this one, my lady, or die trying."

Since coming to Ayliffe she had wondered where Brainard's problem was rooted; whether it was Brennan's lack of attention, Clifton's poor ability to train a young man, or perhaps even some trauma linked to his mother's untimely death. She was never sure; Brainard was impossible for anyone to manage, much less train.

"His lordship was wise to suggest Ramsford. I have been to Ramsford. The men are hard and hearty; Brainard will prove himself a capable heir . . . or not. It is a place of tests. Brainard wishes to rule, and rule he shall, though it is doubtful he will be successful. Still, he will not have much time to brood and complain. He cannot do much damage. . . ."

Anne's listening sharpened. She was thinking of Bart, who was not unlike Brainard in many respects. He did not fight or work hard, but he wanted much. His letters flowed to Marcella. Anne suddenly knew what had been bothering her, nagging her. Quentin could be respected for his fairness, and she loved and trusted Trenton. But Bart and her mother proved a worrisome combination. A wealthy and influential Bart could be worse than his constant begging. Sir Clifton, whether or not he realized it, offered a solution.

Impulsively, she reached out and touched Clifton's hand to respond to him, though she had only half heard. She wished to be finished with the knight so she could speak to her husband. She did not notice that he nearly trembled with delight. "I know you did not fail Brainard, sir. He is so unlike his father. He seems to wield a mighty sword — I've watched him practice at games in the courtyard — yet the knightly code of chivalry has eluded him completely."

Clifton dropped his gaze again. He might be punished for speaking out against the heir, but he could not hold his tongue. "He was born in wealth and indulgence, my lady, and thinks himself above all acts of chivalry. I swear, I did try."

"I'm sure you did," she said somewhat distantly, glancing over her shoulder toward Sloan. She had to protect Sloan somehow; she had to keep her son safe from Brainard's greed and her mother's interference. Sloan must grow up strong and decisive, and have compassion. "This son of mine cannot be reared with neglect for his code of honor," she said almost to herself. "There is more to building a lord than giving him a sword to carry."

"My lady, I would do my very best."

She looked at Clifton, finally giving him her complete attention. Anne had not heard much about Clifton beyond his knightly prowess, but she assumed his conduct in all matters befitted a knight. He seemed courteous. It seemed he did not take duty lightly. She wondered if his role as Brainard's lackey had been difficult for him; she had not heard that he complained. She had never seen him drunk, nor in a temper, nor taking any unfair advantage in a contest. She had witnessed for herself that he regularly bested Brainard, as well as many of the other knights, though he was not the largest among them. Brennan had said that Clifton was among their strongest and most loyal.

"To tend my son in his training would make you my right arm, Sir Clifton."

"My lady, there is no greater honor."

She sighed impatiently. It had been a draining afternoon. First Marcella and then Brainard. Lord, it made her almost long for Eltham, where she would have only to bear the titters of Elizabeth's waiting women and her small apartments shared with her busy, politically encumbered husband.

"I will speak to his lordship, Sir Clifton."

"Thank you, my lady. I will work hard to do you honor in my service."

"Just work hard to be sure Lord Forbes does not have to contend with yet another spoiled, ungrateful churl for a son. Ayliffe deserves more than that."

Anne allowed Brennan time to cool his temper, and then she visited him in his writing closet. He looked up, smiling, as she entered, and then returned his eyes to his ledger. She went to stand behind him, putting her arms around his neck and resting her cheek on the top of his head. His ciphering stopped. She saw a letter from Bart lying open on the stack of correspondence.

"Brennan, Sir Clifton said something about the way you dealt with Brainard that gave me an idea," she said quietly. "Bart is not unlike Brainard." She felt her husband stiffen as if his anger might return. "He wants a great deal, but he is not a very willing vassal. He is more interested in wealth than work. His ambition sometimes worries me."

Brennan disengaged himself from her arm and turned around, looking up at her.

"My mother is requesting brides and fortunes for her sons, and even though you have already given her much, she will not be still until she has everything she desires. Trenton is content to serve you, and Quentin, I think, is little interested in brides. The Earl of Raedelle seems to like his lot. But Bart . . . is much like Lady Gifford; he wants power, but he does not reckon its responsibilities. He wants a larger estate, though he barely manages his small one. And his loyalties seem not so fierce and firm as those of the other Gifford sons. He has been known to be unfair."

"What is your idea? What did Sir Cliff say?"

"Only that Brainard has what he wants in Ramsford. That he wishes to rule, and so he will, but there will be little time for brooding and complaining. He can do little damage.

"Bart has made no secret of the fact that he thinks his barony not large nor rich enough; he dislikes it and wants more. Give him more, Brennan. Petition to extend his boundaries, perhaps through a marriage, or ask His Majesty to declare an earldom and name you as his overlord. I know what has delayed you in settling with Bart; you cannot justify an influential seat for him because he has done so little with what you've already helped him accrue. But do you see, Brennan? Give him exactly what he requests, just as you have Brainard, and keep control. He will find himself working harder than ever."

Brennan laughed and gave her a quick kiss. "Your politics never fail to astound me." He pulled her onto his lap. "If I can help get Bart an earldom, what can Lady Gifford do but thank me?"

"Just a few weeks ago Sloan pestered Mistress Kirsten for a plate of marchpanes and she told him he might have one." Anne laughed at the memory. "He had a most fitting tantrum, for he wanted to eat as many as he liked. Mistress Kirsten told him he might eat one or the whole plate, whichever he chose — but only those two choices. Of course he is greedy; he ate them all. He was quite ill. He might have learned that to insist on having everything he desired has its consequences."

Brennan howled with laughter, giving his wife a squeeze. "Perhaps if mothers ruled the country, we would be better for it."

Anne smiled. "Lady Gifford would like that, Brennan. Will you suggest it?"

"I will learn to be less impetuous with my remarks," he said, sobering at the mere thought.

Lord Forbes wished to have his wife travel with him to London, but Anne excused herself. She promised to join him there within a few weeks, before the weather and roads became a hindrance. Brennan could not delay, for Edward needed him.

But Anne wanted to see the harvest in and her home settled before departing for several months. She knew she would return to Ayliffe with a second child, and there were things to prepare.

Lord Forbes had been away only a few days when a messenger brought a letter from Bury Saint Edmunds. Anne's fingers trembled as she unrolled it. She had hoped that one day Divina would respond to her. But the letter was from the mother superior, and Anne's trembling was of another sort. Divina was dead. The sisters could not name a disease that took her; they blamed melancholia. A broken heart.

Anne went directly to her mother. Marcella was immersed in letter writing, her favorite pastime. She had made friends at court who thought her wealthy and influential by way of the earl, and she enjoyed a great deal of visiting and letter writing.

"Madam, I have had a letter from the nuns of Bury Saint Edmunds. Divina, Mother . . ."

"What about Divina?" Marcella asked, not looking up.

"She is dead."

Marcella finally gave Anne her attention. Anne walked across the chamber to hand her mother the letter. Marcella took her time with it, shaking her head now and then. "Well, Anne," she finally said, "now there are only you and I."

"Madam?"

"Divina will not betray you. I suppose you are relieved."

Tears smarted in Anne's eyes suddenly. "Your daughter is dead," she cried. "Of a broken heart!"

"Nonsense. I assure you, if one could die so easily of a broken heart, many of us would be long since gone."

Anne stared at her mother in wonder. "You have no heart at all," she said quietly, the shock of her mother's indifference never failing to astound her. "My God, madam, do you not grieve for anyone?"

"Of course I am sorry she is dead, but what purpose will my grief serve her now?"

"I know you only use me," Anne said. "But once I thought you loved her."

"You speak so often and passionately of love, daughter. Was

it not your 'love' that made it necessary for Divina to go to the convent? Come now, you may admit to me that you are relieved."

Anne slowly leaned forward to place her palms on Marcella's writing table, her eyes so startled that she did not even blink away the swelling tears. "Had there been any love at all in our family, any loyalty between sisters or even between you and me, we would have all rejoiced that we were spared the consequences of a misdeed. But what we have instead is a pact of dishonor, silence for gain, secrets kept for largesse. My God, it cost a life."

"Be careful, Anne. 'Twas you who sinned against so many. Do not expect anyone to glorify your sin."

"Or forgive it, madam? You've made your purpose more than clear, you will protect me from disgrace as long as I make it possible for you to keep adding to your wealth and influence. You already have far more than you deserve . . . do you not even grieve for the daughter you sacrificed to this end?"

"It was for you," Marcella said slowly.

"Nay, you have never done anything for me. It was for yourself! You could not betray me because to do so would leave you far outside the earl's generosity. Oh, and he has been generous, though you are never satisfied. Madam, you are in a dangerous position, I assure you. You may find me willing to do without this luxury while you still crave more."

"I highly doubt that, Anne. Not while you are busy bringing your son into manhood."

Anne backed away from the writing table. Why did Marcella never say it? She meant to hold Sloan's birthright over her head like an ax. Sudden fury engulfed her. "It was a child you first threatened, madam, but I am a child no more. And you are correct; I will do anything I have to do to protect those I love. You had better hear this truth, though: your secret is valuable only as long as I keep it as well."

"As if you would tell the truth now," Marcella said, dropping the letter onto her stack.

"You may be assured that Lord Forbes would take my word

over yours, madam. I warn you, do not test the matter. You might find yourself without resources."

"When you think this over, my dear, you will realize how foolish your suggestion is."

Anger shook Anne so severely that she could not keep her hands still. Her face was red with fury. She struggled to keep her composure when she felt compelled to strike that indifference, that dispassionate countenance from Marcella's face. "You could have had so much more had you been gentle and kind, had you done things differently. All I ever wanted was your love. All Divina ever wanted . . ." Anne's voice cracked and she stopped.

"Had I done things differently, I would have a daughter wed to an exile, an enemy! It is easy for you to criticize, to begrudge me what little I request, while you live in such luxury. You should thank me."

Anne looked at her mother with fury. "I will never thank you," she said quietly. "I *blame* you!"

The hardest truth Anne had borne in her life came to her in certainty that day. She had tried to control her mother with a mien of cooperation. She realized her mistake too late. She should have robbed Marcella of the chance to pursue this conspiracy long ago. They would all be better off had she told Brennan the truth and refused to marry him. She would have been punished, exiled, perhaps sent to a convent to bear her child in shame . . . but she would not have found herself in these straits, with so many more people who could be hurt.

She would have to prove herself more clever than Marcella, or watch as her family, the Forbes family, suffered the consequences.

"I am going to have Divina's body brought here for burial. Her presence will serve to remind us both of the cost of this secret. And then I will join my husband in London. I desire that you stay here and even if you do not mourn Divina in your heart, you may act the part. And I warn you, madam, do not make the admission of my painful sin preferable to your devious manipulations."

"You will change you mind, Anne."

"You had better hope so, madam."

"I'm afraid it cannot be helped, my love," Brennan said patiently. "If I do not travel to Ramsford soon, I will be prevented from going at all. The winter winds will close the keep to visitors in another month." Anne sighed wearily in response. They had been together for only a month. "Perhaps I will find a new man in my son," Brennan went on. "Perhaps he has learned a valuable lesson and is ready to behave responsibly." He sighed and looked at his reflection in the mirror. He decided he was not an unhandsome man for his age. And his wife did not wish to be separated from him. Few men had as much. "More likely I will find the same surly colt I left; I cannot say where I failed with Brainard. I thought I did all a father could do."

"Brennan, I . . ." She paused and chewed her lip. At some point she had to confront him. She could not think of a more difficult issue. "Brennan, I am afraid of Brainard. I am afraid for Sloan."

"Sloan will have his due, I promise you that."

She patted her stomach, her pregnancy not yet obvious, but she was aware of the new babe. Conceived in June, the baby would come in the winter, in the city. She longed to give birth at Ayliffe, but unless she went now, before the heavy snows of winter, it would be impossible. "And if this is another son? How will you see to them all? I doubt Brainard will be docile while his estate is divided."

Brennan looked directly into her eyes. "I am a rich man. There is plenty."

She met his stare. Of course there was plenty, provided Brainard was generous, an unlikely possibility. It was unnecessary to explain this to Brennan, however. His eyes showed that he understood the unspoken worry.

"I will be gone only a month, my love. And if I do not find better behavior in my son, I will take steps to protect my other children. I will warn Brainard only once."

She walked across the bedchamber and stood before him.

She placed her hand against his chest and looked into his eyes. "Take very special care, Brennan. Brainard is a selfish, angry young man." Anne was more than a little concerned that Brainard might harm his own father.

Brennan gave her a light kiss on the lips. "I will hurry back to you."

"May I have your leave to go to our London house if the queen does not require me?"

"If that is your wish, but I cannot imagine you having time. Is it not your mission to find a lot of wives for your brothers from the queen's own stock?"

She smiled at him. He was so patient with the demands of her family. "I am more comfortable in our home. I would, of course, prefer Ayliffe."

Brennan's eyes became wistful and soft, as if in memory. He looked away from her face. "I wish my son cared as much for Ayliffe as you. I would rest easier, even with respect to Sloan, if I thought Brainard treasured the place. But he has no idea what he has in that beautiful gem."

"Brennan, it is a very rare man who does not become spoiled by such luxury. Just be very careful, my lord. Do not anger him any further."

In a month, Anne had not had a private audience with the queen, though she was often in her company with the other women. When Brennan had taken a small troop toward Ramsford and Edward had ridden out for one last good hunt before winter fell hard on them, Anne took a rare liberty. She ventured to the queen's chamber in the evening. She asked the guard to tell the queen she requested a moment and was informed that Elizabeth was with her brother, Anthony Woodville. "I will wait until she is finished with Lord Scales, if you will ask her to see me," Anne quietly requested.

Anne was not surprised that Elizabeth invited her in. She found the queen seated within a round of large pillows and Anthony nearby. It appeared to be little more than a social visit between brother and sister.

Anne bowed low, and Elizabeth put her instantly at ease. "Be comfortable, Anne. We will have music in a few moments. Did I hear the earl had some business abroad?"

"Aye, my liege, he is bound for his keep of Ramsford near Ludlow. His son resides there."

"Ah . . . that was it. I don't think I remember his son. What brings you to me at such a late hour, Anne?"

She glanced uncertainly at Anthony. He was a handsome, powerful man, gaining a strong reputation as the best knight in all Edward's domain. "It was . . . that is . . . I had asked Your Majesty . . ."

"You needn't be shy with Lord Scales, pet. He will keep our secrets," she said with a teasing smile.

" 'Tis not a secret, my liege, yet my kinsmen would wonder greatly at my part in this. It is for Madam deFrayne, late of Heathwick, that I make this request. Her husband and eldest son were killed at Saint Albans and her younger two sons fled the country in exile. Her homelands were taken and she has nothing, save her sons. They would swear fealty to Edward, if a compromise could be met."

"DeFrayne? My liege, I know the deFrayne knights," Anthony said. "I knew them well in Calais . . . and other places. They are good fighters, good men."

"I remember your request, dear Anne, but I did not find the time right to ask His Majesty to pardon more criminals." Elizabeth smiled then. "Yet, when he has been away a-hunting he hears many requests with patience. If Anthony will vouch for the men, I will speak to the king."

"I would speak on their behalf myself," Anthony said. " 'Twas I who set Dylan deFrayne on the path of our cousin, Raynia Blakely, Lord Blakely's only daughter. The little dark one. Do you remember her?"

The queen made a face, but did not explain her expression. "He has married quite close. That should help."

"In like, Cameron deFrayne wed a Neville cousin. Both weddings, I perceive, were managed for the sole purpose of returning the men to England."

"I will see to it, Anne. Anthony will help."

"I thank you, my liege. It is not for myself, but their family suffered grave losses, and they were once very strong. And if I may beg a courtesy — my kinsmen, most especially my mother, have little pity for them. They would mislike my aid to de-Fraynes."

"Nothing will be said, sweeting. Many survived Saint Albans to come begging this sovereign for help." Her blue eyes sparkled as she looked at Anne. Of course John Grey was killed in that battle as he fought for King Henry. And so had Anthony Woodville fled England on account of his allegiance having been on the wrong side.

Anthony laughed graciously. "We will mention Saint Albans as little as possible in this request, little one. Certes, if we mention any battle, it is only to praise His Majesty's great skill in fighting."

"Among us, not even His Majesty enjoys remembrances of that black day," Elizabeth said with a grimace.

Anne felt tears fill her eyes suddenly, an affliction she had not foreseen. She had been a little frightened to remind Elizabeth of this favor, and now she was overwhelmed at the thought of Dylan's return. She was assailed by joy, fear, and a multitude of conflicting emotions. She tried to cover her tears by kissing the queen's hands, but it was a clumsy and futile attempt.

"Here, sweeting, what is it? I bless you for your sympathy for Madam deFrayne, but my lady, why do you weep?"

Anne sat back on her heels before the queen and wiped self-consciously at her tears. "I . . . oh, Your Majesty, I find this happens to me often these days. I weep for no reason, or for some sentimental silliness. . . . I am *enceinte*, and sometimes I wish I felt ill rather than suffer this affliction. It mortifies me so."

Elizabeth's hand was gentle on her cheek. "Dear sweet, do not be embarrassed . . . not with *me*." With a finger under her chin, she forced Anne to meet her eyes. "Are you well?"

"Oh yes, my liege."

"You are so pleased for Madam deFrayne? Do you know her sons?"

"Nay, my liege . . . that is, I am pleased for her and her sons, but I am not acquainted. My family . . . their youngest, Sir Dylan, was a prisoner in our home once, but was released. His mother will be . . ." Her voice trailed off; her excuses combined with her undignified blubbering confused her request and diminished her courtly appearance.

Elizabeth sat back, studying Anne. "Perhaps you should not pursue the matter any further. Anthony will see it done."

"Aye, Your Majesty."

"You must be excused until you feel better. Leave the matter with us and go with a light heart. We love you so. You must stay well."

The suspicious look in the queen's eyes did not comfort Anne. Anne gave the matter serious thought. If she was driven to such extremes by mere mention of Dylan, how would she react when she actually saw him? She would see him if Anthony brought him home. She remembered the chance meeting with Daphne, and it caused her to shudder.

Once settled in the city, she embarked on her first errand with only her loyal Jane to accompany her. She knew that she must take a grave chance. She went to Daphne deFrayne, explaining first that Anthony Woodville and the queen had both promised to help.

"Madam, I am very frightened," she said, her voice trembling. "I must speak to you in confidence, and I beg you, keep my words in sacred trust. I suspect you will understand."

Daphne nodded, pulling Anne's hands into her own. But Anne could not look Dylan's mother in the eye.

"I am honorably wed to a powerful and strong man. He is very kind to me; he pampers me overmuch. I have a son and I carry my second child now. Madam, you must not tell Dylan that I have played any part in his return." She looked up. "Please, I must not see him. There was too much . . ."

Daphne hushed her and smiled. "Anne, my dear sweet, if my son is brought home through efforts of Lord Scales and the queen, you cannot avoid him for very long. As you wait upon the queen, and Dylan, by the grace of God and your generosity, works to prove his fealty to Edward through Anthony, there will be a time when you will find yourselves in the same room." Anne shuddered involuntarily. "You must be prepared, Anne. You cannot let all your feelings show."

"The longer such a meeting is delayed, the better for me," she said, praying Daphne would not probe too deeply. "My children, madam, need their mother's protection."

Daphne patted Anne's hand. "Come back to me in a fortnight, Anne. On this same day, at this same time. We will talk again. By the time you meet Dylan in a royal presence chamber, you will be controlled. I will help you all I can."

Chapter Eleven

JANE WAS Anne's closest friend. Though she had been brought
into the Ayliffe household by Brennan, the servant belonged
to the countess, in body and soul. After nearly five years they
had become dear to each other, very nearly confidential friends.
And Anne trusted her implicitly.

She told Jane some parts of her secret conversation with Lady
deFrayne, the significant truth being that her own family would
be appalled to learn she would even consider trying to help that
family. Of course, Jane was more than sympathetic, for Marcella
was a difficult woman to abide. As Anne also explained, she did
not want to involve her husband lest he, too, should oppose
her interference. Jane seemed to accept all this.

Jane was, therefore, Anne's only escort and companion to the
home of Daphne deFrayne. Two squires led their palfreys to
Knightrider Street, where the women left them and walked on
alone from there.

Anne frowned in concern when a man answered her knock
at the modest residence. He seemed to be expecting her and
asked, "Lady Forbes?" The man was not dressed as a house
servant; he was tall and strong, under thirty years, and wore a

knight's informal clothing of tunic and hose. She nodded in affirmation and stepped into the house warily, Jane following.

All her questions were answered with a rush of emotion. She saw him standing across the room and did not know what to do, her surprise was so great. Her eyes grew large and round, her hands began to tremble, and she simply stared at him, words failing her. He wore a plain linen shirt that was open at the neck and belted at the waist. His hair was overlong, his face tanned, his eyes glittering like the turquoise gems in her dreams. He wore boots and chausses and a leather jerkin, all the look of a knight at leisure, not an exile in trouble. She was silent and stunned for so long that Dylan approached her, a faint and reassuring smile playing on his lips.

"Is this your tiring woman, madam?" he asked.

"Yes . . . yes, this is Jane. She accompanies me everywhere."

Dylan gave Jane a brief, informal bow. "I am Dylan deFrayne, Madam deFrayne's son. I am sorry to surprise you, Lady Forbes, but my lady mother asked me to greet you. This is Sir Markham. He is in service to me and would take your tiring woman to the cookery for a modest repast." He chuckled as if embarrassed. " 'Tis modest, indeed, but will suffice to give your woman company and our meager hospitality while my mother and I confer with you."

Anne looked at Jane and nodded, indicating she should go with the man. She tried to smile, but kept her eyes blank so that Jane would not worry. In her breast a wild mixture of explosive feelings pounded and swirled as she fought for control. She had no idea which of her feelings showed in her eyes. He was married now, she reminded herself. They were both married to other people. Which marriage should worry her most? Perhaps he loved his wife deeply. Why was he here at all? Was this how Daphne proposed to help her? She had arranged something that could be either painful beyond words, or illicit beyond description.

Dylan seemed to have complete control. He took Anne's hand in a very decent and courtly fashion, leading her to one of only a few comfortable chairs in the central room at the front of the small house. He was quiet until he heard Mark close the door far to the rear of the house.

"You did not know I would be here." It was not a question, but a statement. Anne shook her head. In this humble dwelling there was very little furniture, but it was clean, and a fire lay blazing in the hearth. Still, she shivered. She uncovered her head, but pulled her cloak more tightly about her. "My mother is not here," he said. "She took the decision away from us, it appears. She planned this."

"Why?" she asked in a breath.

Dylan shrugged his shoulders but held her eyes. "In Madam's own words, 'The young woman's feelings shine in her eyes for all the world to see, as do your own, and if you do not have a moment alone to talk, to become reacquainted and lay your hurts and disappointments to rest, one of you will crumble into tears . . . perhaps in the queen's own presence chamber.' Would you have come, had you known?" he asked.

Again she shook her head, tearing her eyes away from his gaze. "How could I?" she replied.

Dylan was left to stare at her forehead, her eyes lowered. He judged the richness of the cloak and the ring on her finger, and it brought him no pleasure at all. He found his unselfish love had limits. "What feelings did my mother speak of then?" he asked. "Was it shame my mother saw? Nay, it could not be that. How could the Countess of Ayliffe feel shame? Is the countess ashamed of the earl's devotion?"

Anne looked up in surprise and engaged those eyes again. Never tell him, Dylan had warned. He will care for you and keep you safe. "He is good to me, Dylan. He loves me much."

"He dresses you well. I would have expected that much."

"You know such things have never interested me. . . ."

"I am told you have a son by the earl. That must endear you to him even more."

Anne's heart felt as though it would break. Your son, she wanted to cry. I married the earl to protect your son. But the temptation passed quickly. She had made an oath to bring Sloan into manhood with all the greatest of care, no matter what the personal cost. "I am with child now," she said quietly.

She noticed a flicker of emotion, and what might have been pain, cross his eyes. He looked at her midsection, then her eyes. The pregnancy did not show.

"It is early," she said, her hand going to her middle. "Do you have children, Dylan?" she asked.

"No. I have not done so well as you."

Anne began to tremble inside. Dylan's beautiful eyes held her. What was it? There was a hardness shining there that had never been there before; impatience and forced maturity. The boyish twinkle and the playful light were gone. Without even realizing it, she was examining the rest of his body, looking at his arms, hands, shoulders, thighs, ankles, feet, in much the same way she examined her husband when he returned from battle. Dylan was thicker abreast, his muscles more developed. There were lines creasing his forehead, smaller wrinkles at the corners of his eyes. He was still the handsomest man in the world, but he had aged. He looked older than he was. He smiled at her, having caught her studying him. His teeth gleamed white and straight and his eyes crinkled at the corners.

"Oh, I am whole, though it was quite a contest, the past few years."

"Will you tell me about it?"

"Only if you will tell me about your suffering over the past few years." He shot to his feet. He did not understand his own sudden anger; he had meant to hold her in his arms, comfort her, not lash out at her. But his anger was roused by the mere fact that she needed no comfort; she had thrived while he was in agony still. He began to pace. "Will your tirewoman tell your husband that we have met?"

"Jane? No, Jane is the most faithful in the —"

"Was there any misfortune over the cask room? He did not turn you away?"

She stared at his profile. He did not face her and she did not understand his hostility. "Misfortune?" she echoed. "Nay, as you can see, he did not turn me away. He believed some terrible half-truth and has always pampered me as if I am the purest —"

He whirled, facing her so abruptly that her answer was cut short. "I expected he would keep you safe . . . and well fixed. I can see that all my worry was in vain. I half feared . . . half hoped . . . Ah! You have not changed, Anne. I have. I am greatly changed."

"Dylan, I too worried," she said. "You must believe that. But everyday I was grateful that you had survived; escaped the rope. . . ."

"Flee with me now," he implored in a strained whisper. She stared at him in astonishment. "You said that if you could recall the moment, you would not hesitate. We can walk out of this house together, go by horse to Portsmouth and be in France in less than a week."

"Leave my son?" she whispered.

"Do you doubt the earl could raise him well? I would take this one you carry — come with me."

Anne nearly laughed aloud at the irony. If she did as he asked, she would be leaving Dylan's son with Brennan only to take Brennan's child to Dylan. She shook her head, a slight puff of laughter escaping her in spite of herself. "Do you know what you ask?" She stared at him; she saw his desperation. "Dylan, you are also married now."

"Aye. You said you would be my wife or my mistress; you would only be with me. Are our marriages any more of a hindrance than our parents were? Then a war was? Here is the moment, Anne. Come away with me."

"You have not recalled the moment, Dylan. I am married to a man who owns ten thousand men. You have wed close to the crown. How far do you think we could run?"

"Indeed, it is a mean life, and I have already lived it. Of course, my circumstances were very different. I was grateful to have life at all . . . and you . . . it appears your life has not been terribly difficult."

"You are angry . . . with *me!*"

"Anne, I . . ."

"What is it you wish to hear? That I lived in poverty and danger, as you did? That I will abandon my child and run with you now and enjoy that life? Once you only wanted me to live, to be safe. What has happened to you?"

"Tell me then," he said gruffly. "Tell me that you've made your life over . . . that you will *endure* your earl's wealth and devotion and —"

Anne stood, tears coming to her eyes. She stared at him for a long moment. He silently allowed this, but his breathing was labored. "I have endured, Dylan, and not in poverty. As far as gowns and jewels are concerned, there has been nothing lacking. And yes, my son and this child a-borning will have all of me until they are grown. I am sorry for all you have been through."

She turned away from him as if to leave, but before she had taken a step, he grabbed her hand. "Anne," he said in a breath.

"Please do not touch me," she whispered, a slight catch in her voice.

He pulled her into his embrace. She saw that tears wet his cheeks. "I have hurt so much without you!"

"Dylan, you must not touch —"

His lips covered hers and his arms encircled her. For a moment she suffered only surprise, but then quickly her memory was tossed and turned and all the desire and pain and desperation was like a vision behind her closed eyes. She moaned, almost a sob, and held him fast, her fingers locked together behind his head. She did not know if she kissed a memory or a man, but she let herself consume him even as she was consumed.

"Anne, my God," he groaned. "My love, my life. I have hurt so much without you. I have loved you. . . . A day never ended that I did not beg God Almighty for one chance to hold you, to tell you . . ."

"Oh, Dylan," she cried, her fingers tenderly touching his face, his hair, as if to be assured he was real. "I have prayed for your safety every day and every night. You must believe —"

"Anne, my Anne, I did not wish to hurt you. It is my own hurt that lashes out at you. How I longed to give you what he has given you — riches, children, love. . . . I love you. . . . I love you so. . . . It has never changed."

"But it is more impossible than ever . . . Dylan. . . ."

Before she could finish, before she could tell him all the reasons forbidding such emotion, such action, she welcomed his lips again, and again. Their kisses were wet with tears of joy and longing, their fingers greedily touching as if they might never touch again. The hunger had never waned. To be in his arms was like a miracle, to taste his mouth again was the answer to all her prayers.

"We are not meant to have each other, Dylan," she whispered.

His lips were hot and insistent on her neck. His hands crept under her cloak to pull her closer, to caress the rich sarcenet of her gown. "I cannot accept that, Anne. I have never accepted it, though I tried."

All time was lost for Anne. His hands on her again, his lips on hers, and she forgot where she was, who she was. Her fingers caressed his chest, his back. Over and over she sobbed his name, clung to him first in sheer relief that he was well, whole, alive, and then in passion both remembered and renewed. She forgot her lordly husband and her son.

Dylan lifted her into his arms, his lips holding hers. Against her open mouth he murmured, "Once more, my Anne. If you cannot come away with me, love me once more."

"Dylan . . . your man . . . Jane . . ."

"Markham? He was instructed to keep any servant attending you occupied."

"Does he know about us, then?" she asked.

"No. Nor will he ever inquire."

She shook her head, but he carried her to the stairs despite her wordless protest. The longing was as intense as ever. When she found herself in a second story bedchamber, she tried futilely to deny him, but his lips instead left her begging him to love her. She was famished for him; there was no stopping the waves of desire that overcame all good sense.

Dylan's life had been day-to-day, a constant struggle just for bread and wine, and through the tedious days and lonely nights he had thought of Anne. Daily. Sometimes hourly. It was difficult to keep this haunting desire secret. He had not told even Cameron. And other women could not draw his mind away from her. In his own strange way he was faithful to her memory, for he could not find satisfaction anywhere else. For her sake, if not for his own, he begged for release from this binding, everlasting love. It was as terrible as it was wonderful. But there had been no release.

Anne, too, had wished to be released from the torment of wanting him, trying futilely to accept her good fortune without longing for another, but it failed her. She had missed him as much in her luxury as he had missed her in his deprivation.

"Anne," he murmured. "Anne, I need you. The pain of wanting you is greater and stronger than I am. I want to come home to you."

"My love," she whispered in response.

There were only two rooms of state on the second floor of the small house. Jane was far away in the cookrooms behind the house. In less than an hour of her arrival Anne lay back on his bed, her eyes closed, and welcomed his touch, his lips. She did not think of her adultery, nor of how fleeting this moment would be. She thought only of the way he brought life back to a part of her she had thought long dead. She responded naturally, just as she had on those desperate nights so long ago.

It was the greatest luxury in the world, a down-filled mattress on a tester bed beneath them and their bodies together again after so long. The bolt on the door was in place, and there was no hanging scaffold in the courtyard. The pleasure that Anne had been lacking in her marriage and that Dylan had been unable to find in any quarter was swift and hot and pure. It was unlike those times in the past when they were so afraid, so tortured. Dylan was conscious of her delicate condition and was gentle, even in his haste, but the ecstasy was not lessened. His warm breath on her flesh, his roughened hands on her skin, his scent, the salty taste of his skin, all senses were sharpened to take him in. These were the things she had struggled to remember, but had been unable to retrieve. In his arms again, she was filled with a sense of being where she belonged. It was as if she had been born in his embrace, and was not quite alive without him. When she felt him moving inside her again it was like coming home for her as well, as if it had always been thus, and always should be.

The rapture came so quickly that they lay spent, entwined in each other's arms soon after Dylan had thrown the bolt on the bedchamber door. What Brennan had failed to bring her in almost five years, Dylan had commanded from her body in as many minutes. So right — so wrong. A low moan of despair left her and she wept.

"Anne . . .," he comforted.

"He will not have an adultress, Dylan. If forcing me to flee with you is your heart's desire, you can have it now. All you need do is expose me as the wanton I am and he will cast me aside."

He brushed the dark hair from her brow. "I want to love you, not cause you pain. My life has been —"

"But I cannot deny you, don't you see? Your life has been all of suffering and I have had luxury, but did you see any difference in the way one welcomed the other? Oh Dylan, my wanting has never been less than yours. But I had not wanted to hurt my son. . . ."

Dylan held her as she wept. Guilt at having taken advantage of her weakness turned the bliss of the moment into a shameful, regrettable abyss.

"I did what had to be done," she murmured, tears choking her voice. "My mother . . . I was caught coming from the cask-room that last night. . . . I knew the only way to await you was to go to Lord Forbes, for Raedelle with my mother was a dangerous place. And of course when he knew that I was not pure, my mother lied for me, to keep her association with Ayliffe through my marriage. Every day, every week, she threatens to tell him the truth unless I succor her every whim and want. Do you think your family can be restored if Lord Forbes learns that we were lovers? And here we are, lovers again."

"I was afraid you loved me no more," Dylan whispered.

"Are you still afraid of that?" she asked him.

"Now," he said with a rueful chuckle, "I am afraid of myself. Anne, I was so desperate for you, I . . ." He shook his head. He had never before been so out of control. "Will you forgive me?"

"For loving me? Or . . ."

"My hunger," he said, looking at her, his eyes deeper and more serious than she had ever seen them: "I have allowed my hunger for you to eat at me. Anne, I never wished to hurt you. Or shame you. Or . . ."

"Dylan, you are my heart; I could not deny you. I could not deny myself. But now Lady Gifford will surely have what she wants; she will see me stripped and stoned and thrown out of the Ayliffe gate. My son . . ."

"Nay, my Anne, my love," he said, embracing her and pulling her near. "Don't cry, love. We can keep this secret from Lord Forbes. When you return to him today —"

"He is not in the city, Dylan. He is with his son in Wales. But —"

"Then you are safe, my love. I won't hurt you. There is no tragedy yet. . . ."

She touched his cheek. "Fate is unkind," she said, stroking his hair. "We should be far beyond this yearning. We should have learned, by now, to accept what we cannot have. Yet we steal it."

"I only wanted to know that you loved me still. It is the only thing I have lived for. I'm sorry, Anne. I don't want you to be afraid of me; afraid of what I feel for you. If I cannot protect you, how can I ask you to love me?"

He lay on his back and she turned, bracing on an elbow, tracing his strong jawline with a finger, studying his face through tear-filled eyes. "Once I knew your eyes so well. Now I do not understand. You were so angry, then so —"

He closed his eyes as if he would block out her questions. "The past years have been difficult; I have become hardened and selfish. The boy-knight who would die for your love became a man who would tear it from you."

"But Dylan, my love is yours. You need not beg it, steal it, nor bargain for it. But I can give you nothing else. Lord Forbes would only mount his ten thousand and find me. He is not cruel nor evil; he treasures me, though I do not deserve him. In five years he has been tender and generous. But Dylan, his hand is more powerful than the Gifford hand ever was."

Dylan sighed, mortified by the fear he had caused in her. "To take you away from all our obligations is my heart's desire, though that kind of life is not what I would have for you. The existence is poor and dangerous. And I knew you were not a woman who could leave her children." His large hand covered her stomach, her pregnancy barely blooming. "Would that I could give you a child."

"You have a wife whose family ties gave you England. Tell me about her. Your wife."

"No. For you she does not exist."

"But Dylan . . ."

"I was certain you would tell me you loved him."

She closed her eyes against the threat of tears. "I do love Lord Forbes, Dylan. 'Tis not the same love I feel for you, but to hurt him would cause me great pain. He indulges my family, though they are mostly selfish. He keeps my mother in her place, when she would not hesitate to hurt me. And he raises an heir of Ayliffe . . . my son. I owe him everything."

"As do I," he said honestly. "The troop that rescued me, dressed in his lordship's livery, was my brother's troop. May the earl never know how much I owe him."

"I am afraid, Dylan. Afraid of you, afraid of myself, afraid of what this sin will cost us all."

"We have little, but it is a great deal more than I thought we would ever have. Anne, you need not be afraid. I will not allow you to be hurt by my own desperate need. I will take your love and let it make me strong."

"I did not foresee this day," she said, lying back in the pillows and resting her wrist across her eyes. "It was not the endurance of my feelings for you that I doubted; I just did not think I had the courage of an adultress."

"I think, my love, that it is more wrong for us to be forever apart."

"Dylan, this cannot go on. We cannot be secret lovers again."

"Perhaps not often," he replied. "If the time is right, we will be together, and if the time is not right, we will be content with a glance across a room. I, for one, feel grateful to know our hearts are still entwined. I will let that be enough. Can you trust me, my Anne? If I swear that never again will I force my feelings on you in such a way? If I find a way to prove that the light in your eyes will be enough? If I show you that your smile alone will — Anne, my love, please believe me; I ached to have those things I have been without — England and your love."

"Can you do it, Dylan? Can you force a smile when Lord Forbes puts his arm about my waist or kisses my brow? I am afraid. To see those angry, jealous eyes stare at me as if I have robbed you of something — I have only attempted to live the life I have been given. I only want to raise my children."

"I will prove I can do it. I have a wife, you have a husband. You have children now," he murmured. "I wish your children were of my loins, but I cannot change that. I know Lord Forbes is a decent man, and I would ever thank him, if I dared, for seeing to your needs when I could not, but I will not give you up, Anne. I cannot. If there is a moment when no one watches and I can hold you in my arms, I will."

"Secret lovers," she whispered. "Yet again."

"If you say me nay, I will leave you alone. I love you." He sighed deeply. "I do not want my love to hurt you."

"Would it not be wiser to go our separate ways, live our separate lives?"

"Undoubtedly. Can you?"

"Nay," she replied. "But while we selfishly take what we want, other lives might be damaged."

"We will have to do all we can to prevent that. Our moments together may be a precious few. But if we are cautious, they will continue for a very long time." He touched the curve of her jaw. To take her away from her child would destroy her; to shame her publicly would eat away at her love. To take her would mean giving her up. He knew it now as he had never known it before. "It would be braver to flee," he said. "But," he relented, "the world is not large enough to escape the mighty Woodville clan, nor one of the richest earls in England. Anne, I would marry you if I could, but I cannot. Still, I need your love, if only the memory of our last kiss and the knowledge that there will be a next."

"Things have not changed very much at all."

"Not at all; the choices are even the same," he said, somewhat sullenly. "The torment of having nothing and pretending our feelings do not exist . . . or this, however meager. Anne, I cannot help but feel you are meant to be mine. I will wait. Maybe our circumstances will change. God knows, they have changed enough in seven years, and I am still your slave. If you are ever afraid, you must tell me. But I cannot live without your love, Anne. It is the only thing I have had these many years. It is all I have now. I will keep you safe, whatever the cost. It has been a long time; can you trust me again?"

She kissed his lips. "I have to trust you, Dylan. If I cannot trust you, I am living a life of lies."

She knew this was not an easy thing for Dylan, for he had no idea the son she protected was his own. She smiled, and, strangely, she did not feel guilt or shame. What they did was wrong, but their love was right. Her body told her so. She loved him, and her love was good and strong.

She was happier than she had ever been. Since the day she had chanced to meet Daphne deFrayne at Westminster, she had feared losing control of her emotions. She feared that first moment when their eyes would meet. But having Dylan again, however briefly, had become the ballast in her unsteady life. She returned to his mother's house only twice more. Dylan was correct; their embraces would be few. But Anne thrived on those moments. She found she shared Dylan's opinion — a few stolen moments and the knowledge that their love was true and enduring were so much better than the torment of having nothing at all.

"Lord Forbes returns this week, Dylan."

He kissed her cheek. "So we will be apart for a long time. 'Tis well. The babe grows larger in your womb and you must not take these risks. But I will be waiting. Near."

"I wish I could be with you always."

"Someday, my Anne. I will be waiting for our someday. You have many blessings to account for. And I — I have more than I dared hope."

Late in January in 1466, four months after first seeing Dylan in his mother's house, Anne stood beside the Earl of Ayliffe in the presence chamber of the king and queen while Dylan and Cameron deFrayne, with their mother, made their first appearance at the royal court. Anne's burden was great and she expected to go to childbed in another month. It had been many weeks since she had even seen Dylan and their last meeting had consisted of only a few private words and a quick embrace encumbered by her growing pregnancy.

Dylan graciously moved through the introductions to the Earl of Ayliffe, the Countess, and many other people he did not know. Anne's eyes twinkled with pleasure. Selfishly, she was delighted to be able even to see him, to know he was safe and whole, to look at his handsome face again. She also believed his return would be good for England.

Later that evening, when Anne found an inconspicuous stool in a corner, Dylan approached her. There were many people crowded into the room, but the glow in his eyes was for her alone. He glanced at her enormous middle. "You are beautiful," he whispered. He passed her a goblet of wine.

"Thank you, sir. I was very proud to be a witness. Has anything of yours been restored?"

"Nay, nothing. But that is the least of my worries. You will have your lying-in soon, my love. I will pray for you."

"Dylan, I will go to Ayliffe in the spring. It will be a long time."

"Easier to bear now, I vow. I know the earl cares for you well, and I love you, my Anne," he whispered, barely mouthing the words. She was not able to reply, for she faced the room at large from her stool; Dylan's back was present to those who might discern his secret message. But her eyes shone with secret happiness.

Before another word could be said, Anne's eyes were drawn away as she saw her husband approach. Brennan joined them, placing a hand on Anne's shoulder as he spoke to Dylan.

"Anthony tells me you are old friends. If that is so, we are all glad you are home. And one day we must get deep in our cups and you will tell me the tale of how you managed the Ayliffe costume for your escape."

"I am not the one to ask, my lord, but the lady whose nimble fingers fashioned the garments from memory alone. My apologies," he said, bowing deeply. "But I thank you for my life, however far from your plan it was to save me."

Brennan laughed goodnaturedly. It had been five years, after all. And if Anthony Woodville's sister could marry the king, surely Dylan deFrayne could come home. "I suspect it was all to the good."

"Thank you, my lord. At the risk of being too forward, I would like to say that I have heard many flattering things about you. Your reputation is strong; you have a large force of arms."

"I have been fortunate," Brennan said. He glanced at his wife, and she placed her hand over his on her shoulder. "In many things."

Dylan chuckled, with not even the slightest jealousy. His restoration to England and his reunion with Anne had cured much of his anger and impatience. He was resigned. He had his country again, and Anne's love. The wait might be long, but he was determined that one day he would have Anne for his own. Until then, Lord Forbes was an able caretaker. "That is very plain to see, my lord. I vow to wait until we're better acquainted to tell you how much I envy you."

"You needn't sir. Every man in England envies me, and no one pretends otherwise."

"It would seem the good lady is making her last appearance, while I am making my first. I wish you both good health, continued good fortune." He bowed briefly, turned, and blended into the crowd.

"A pleasant young man," Brennan said. "It is good that he is with us again. Anthony says he is strong."

"Brennan," she said, placing a hand over her swollen middle, "please take me to my bed."

He looked down at her and knew instantly; her time had come. He whisked her away to their lodgings and sent for the midwife, staying with Anne and holding her hand as she labored with the anxious child who came early, quickly and easily. Anne and Brennan were given a baby daughter. The little lass was born with her father's reddish-gold hair, and her mother's dark eyes.

Joy and pride filled her. Two fine men love me, she thought. Should I be forlorn? Ashamed? I would give each what the other has if I could. I would give this kind and gentle husband the passion that is for Dylan alone, but it will not come. I would give Dylan this wifely service and loyalty, but it cannot be. Pray God I do not hurt either of them. Bless these tender mercies, and let me be strong.

The babe was named Deirdre Elizabeth Forbes and she thrived on her mother's milk and grew fat. The queen sent Anne silver plate, Lord Rivers sent lace from Calais to fashion a baptismal gown, the Duke of Clarence sent a tun of good Burgundy wine, and the deFrayne family sent a rich, ornamented tapestry portrait of the Divine Mother and Child created by Daphne's nimble fingers.

Marcella's letters had been frequent since Anne's angry departure from Ayliffe. To Anne's complete surprise Marcella had stayed at Ayliffe even through the Christmas celebrating, though her letters clearly begged for an invitation to court. Anne finally relented when Deirdre was born, knowing she would have to face her mother again eventually. She hoped Marcella had given serious thought to their conflict and changed, especially since Divina's death.

Deirdre was a month old when Marcella looked over her grandchild and the gifts that had been received. Her face turned chalk-white with rage. She turned on her daughter. "So, 'tis true. They are back and you helped them. It was rumored so; my friends write to me that my daughter did her part to restore them."

Anne knew at some point she would have to deal with her mother on this issue. She tried to remain calm. "Your argument with them is over, madam. Even Lord Forbes is glad to have the knights home."

"How pleased would he be if he *knew*," she threatened in hushed tones.

Anne struggled for composure she did not quite feel. "He would not believe you, madam. Be still!"

"Ah? And if I point out to the fine earl how like Dylan deFrayne his firstborn looks? Do you think you can hide it forever?"

"Sloan is Brennan's son," she said.

Marcella laughed wickedly. "You will perhaps betray your husband with success, daughter, but you will not turn on me so easily. I will find a willing ear unless you do as I say."

"Why do you pursue this?" she asked. " 'Tis done, Mother. Leave them be. They only wish to live, as the rest of us do."

Marcella fingered the beautiful tapestry, but her eyes were glassy with hate. "It was she, wasn't it, daughter? She made the costumes that were used to trick me. Well, it will take more than a skilled needle to trick me again. I will not let her win."

"Who, Mother? Madam deFrayne? Win? What more could you want? She has suffered enough, and for nothing."

"Get me Heathwick," Marcella said. "I know you can. I would be the Countess of Heathwick for my youngest son."

The color drained from Anne's face. She knew the deFraynes petitioned the king for the restoration of their family lands, thus far unsuccessfully. Sir Trenton Gifford did not yet have any demesne, but being unmarried still and the youngest of three sons, he had plenty of time. Yet Marcella's demand brought to light something Anne had never before considered. "It is so," she said in a hushed whisper. "All these years, has it been only Daphne deFrayne you truly hate?"

"That bitch has had more than I for long enough."

"That's absurd, madam! You have had far more than she! Of

everything; of wealth, offspring, influence close to the queen's ear. . . ."

"That's what little you know of it. I want Heathwick for my home and I will be silent."

"All these years I thought it was wealth you craved. It is more than that. You use me to —"

Marcella tore her wimple from her head, exposing her gray hair. "I am done with black. I wish to wear gems and colors . . . and I wish to reside as dowager countess in Heathwick Castle. Does she wear black? Nay. Do that for me, daughter — get me Heathwick and I will leave the earl to think he has a son by you."

Anne reached out to her mother. "Madam, why do you hate her so? What has she done to you?" Marcella only stared at her as if she would stare through her. She lowered her voice to a whisper. "Would you hurt your own grandchild, madam? Brennan will see to your comfort . . . but I fear you will lose all if you betray us now. He will have no place for you if he casts me aside. I beg of you, let this revenge die now. . . ."

"They may be home, these dastardly deFraynes, but I will not be silent while they are restored to their former wealth and influence and with *your* help!"

"Trenton will not want Heathwick; Brennan has better for him if he can be patient."

"I want Heathwick. I want to live there and wear jewels again. I have been in mourning long enough. *Daphne* does not mourn him."

Anne shook her head in confusion. "Who, madam?"

"Will you do as I say?" Marcella asked, refusing to answer the question.

Anne watched her mother's glittering eyes; she had seen this often enough. Marcella was fixed on an idea and would not let it rest until she had what she wanted. Why it was so important to take something away from Daphne, Anne had no idea. "And if I can arrange for your residence in that castle, you will cease in such demands? Do you swear?"

"Aye, daughter. But do not delay."

[208]

"You will be less often at court. . . ."

"I want to be dowager countess for my son, for Trenton."

"And if he does not want Heathwick?"

"I don't care," Marcella said firmly. "He will take it for me. I will not be still until it is done."

Anne used the six weeks before she was able to travel to Ayliffe to arrange her mother's strange request. She conferred with Elizabeth, who was barely up from childbed herself, along with Anthony Woodville. Then she spoke to her younger brother, Sir Trenton.

Anne felt confident of Trenton's loyalty to her in all things but this. He admired and respected Lord Forbes and she was frightened that he would be ashamed of her, that he would shun her and refuse to help. It was with great caution that she approached him, praying she was right to assume he cared deeply for her.

"Our mother wants Heathwick and title on your behalf, Trenton. She demands this."

"So?" he replied. "She has always hated them. She : . ."

"Trenton, the deFraynes have never been all the evil things that madam insisted. Lord Forbes welcomes the knights home and our anger with them is done. They are good men; they have suffered enough. But our mother will never be done with hating them. She threatens to tell Lord Forbes that Sloan is not his son." Trenton gave a short laugh of disbelief, but when he saw the serious expression on his sister's face, he quickly sobered. "She threatens to say that Dylan deFrayne was my lover while he was a prisoner at Raedelle and that I brought his child to my marriage."

"Anne . . . ?"

She lowered her gaze, for tears gathered in her eyes. "This is her threat, Trenton." She braved a look at him. "There is no question that madam would get the attention of the gossips if not the earl. Please, Trenton, take her for me? I have endured her for five years at Ayliffe, and she is a hard woman to please. I cannot change her mind. I cannot let her hurt my son."

"Anne, do you think it will stop if she has Heathwick? Soon you must answer to these . . ."

"She is determined to do whatever damage possible to the deFraynes, despite the fact that the earl respects them and would have the hostilities end. And she is furious that I used my influence with the queen to have the deFraynes brought home."

"Why? Why would you do that?"

She did not answer him, but only looked into his eyes, praying he would not hate her. There was a long silence. "She will hurt me, Trenton. She has never loved me."

A muscle moved in Trenton's cheek. He could not dispute that simple fact. He had seen his mother's behavior toward Anne often enough over the years.

"I do not understand how you have let this happen, Anne."

She shook her head. "Nor do I, Trenton."

He touched her hand. "I will not let our mother hurt you. But I do not want Heathwick. I did not earn it. I would do any chore the earl demands; I would act as his seneschal if need be. I am ashamed of the way madam uses your marriage with the earl." He sighed deeply. "As for the deFraynes . . ."

"Trenton, I beg of you, let us bury the hatred. Father wished it, Lord Forbes wishes it, and I wish it. Even if you cannot befriend any deFrayne, even on my account, you need not be enemies. Despite all that has happened, despite Wayland's death at Raedelle and Dylan's imprisonment there, he does not hate us all."

"How do you know, Anne?"

"I know," she said meekly.

"I will not let her hurt you," he said.

She smiled in relief. "For this, Trenton, you have earned your place in my heart for all eternity. Thank you. And thank you for not asking me."

"Don't thank me, Anne," he said, concern showing in his eyes "I did not have to ask."

"Maybe someday, Trenton my love, you will understand. For now it is enough that you love me and will help me."

Anne spoke to Lord Forbes, who did not understand, but

showed the same patience he had over the years. Finally, in a dark gallery at Eltham Castle, a few words were exchanged with Dylan. To her surprise, he only smiled. She had expected him to rage. "Silence her," was all he said. "She is old and mean. She will not live long. Poor Trenton."

The entire family and all the staff was occupied with packing for the move to Ayliffe, with Marcella present, when Lord Forbes brought a document bearing the royal seal.

"You are fortunate to have such a clever daughter, madam," he said to Marcella. "Heathwick will be your home, with a stipend of one hundred pounds a year for sustenance."

"Mine?" Marcella beamed.

"More or less," Brennan said, bending to his table to affix his own seal with candle wax to the thick vellum document. "Sir Trenton, of course, is the guardian, but you will gain the title you requested."

"Guardian, my lord?" she asked, confused.

Brennan looked up from the table, irritation creasing his brow. He did not like Marcella and never had. Doing anything at all to improve her wealth or status grated on him, for he felt she was not deserving of either. Likewise, he did not understand Anne's forgiving nature. He did not think his wife was wise to do so much for her mother. But he was unable to deny his wife's merest request. He sighed. "The Countess told me you have an idea to relinquish Raedelle entirely to Quentin without your interference, as you should, but you are not satisfied to take residence with your other children and Heathwick is your desire, though I can't say I know why. It is not a beautiful place."

"It was . . . in its day . . . ," she said, her voice weak.

"So be it; perhaps you can fashion something out of it again. It suffered a great deal from the battles fought nearby, but you have my leave to do what you can. And countess for Deirdre you shall be."

"For . . . *Deirdre*," she gasped.

"Aye," he said, frowning, "I secured the place from the crown's attainder for my daughter's dower estate, naming you and Sir Trenton as guardians of that estate on her behalf. The privy

[211]

title is only a courtesy, of course, but I concede you deserve as much, if only for your losses. I have given your requests due report, madam. Bart's estate has been increased by adding attainted lands to his barony and before the year is out he will be named the first earl. And I traded some gold for the honor of countess that you will wear — I do hope you appreciate it. I grow weary of bettering your estate at my own expense."

Marcella turned to look at her daughter, who had been supervising the packing of Marcella's belongings. Anne stood as tall as she could, still a head shorter than her mother. Anne had delivered Heathwick, but not without keeping her hands on it. Marcella's anger was boundless, but she was careful not to show it here, in front of the earl. Yet, as Anne read her mother's eyes, she knew the battle would continue.

Marcella looked back at the earl, her son by marriage, who was actually as old as she. "Thank you, my lord. You are most generous."

Brennan shrugged, frankly pleased that Marcella would not be residing with them at Ayliffe again, but annoyed that the luxury had come at such a high price. He would have considered Deirdre's dowry in a few years, and he thought Heathwick not good enough for her. He left the document on the table for Marcella and quit the room.

Marcella walked slowly toward Anne. She looked down at her and her voice was a whisper, for there were servants about the room engaged in packing the new dowager countess's belongings. "That's twice you have fooled me. There will not be a third time," she said.

Anne kept silent, but met her mother's eyes. She knew the route to be taken; she had to yield a bit now and then, but it was essential to keep Marcella's possessions in check. It was clear that what Marcella wanted — wealth, power, and some mysterious revenge on Daphne deFrayne — was all best sought through Anne. Anne, then, knew she had to keep her mother wanting, and keep control of Marcella's assets, so that Marcella would not risk abandoning her relationship to the earl. Anne knew better than to try to change Marcella. She wished only to outlast her.

"One hundred pounds a year is a grand fortune, madam. It should surely buy you the gowns and gems you desire. And that other thing you wish, to have Heathwick so that Madam de-Frayne may not, is also done."

"It is not enough," Marcella said, her eyes glittering. "I want sole possession of Heathwick; I want to be countess for my son, not for my granddaughter."

"Then tell him, madam. Hurry," Anne bravely challenged. "Perhaps you can catch the earl before he leaves. Once you finally use your threat, I am certain Lord Forbes will give you the moon and all the stars."

"You think you have outwitted me, don't you, Anne? Nay, I will not tell him today. I will find a better time, a better way."

Anne smiled courageously, though inside she felt tremors of fear. "When you tell him, you are finished."

It was not completely unexpected; Daphne knew that one day she would see the face she most feared. While she was allowed to return to court, Marcella's presence there could not be avoided for long.

She saw Lady Gifford enter the gallery from the other end. Daphne had just come from Lady Scales's apartments. The distance between the two women was great, but both paused at their respective ends of the long gallery. Daphne advanced with her eyes downcast, using her instincts alone to direct her. When she stood before Marcella she dipped into a deep curtsey. "Good afternoon, my lady." Then she bravely rose to look into Marcella's angry eyes.

"Our fortunes have greatly changed," Marcella said. "You have been told?"

"Aye, my lady." Daphne regarded Marcella's rich blue velvet, her sparkling necklace. Daphne herself wore a gown that was easily eight years old and modest by comparison. "If Heathwick is your desire, I am glad for you that you could attain it."

"How disappointing. I hoped you would be envious."

"I do not envy you, my lady," Daphne said softly. "I never have."

"Did you not love him, then? All those years that he longed for you and dismissed me? I told him you cared not at all, but he still gazed off in the direction of Heathwick." Marcella laughed. "Even from the grave I imagine his body has turned toward that estate. He will be surprised, then."

"My lady, though you are loath to believe it, I never took from you. I want nothing of yours now. Please, let it end. For your own sake."

"For *my* sake? Oh madam, all that makes my life pleasurable is watching your comeuppance. Your family may be returned, but I will do all I can to see that they are not restored."

"My lady, let us not hurt the children . . . it is not their —"

"You are not so haughty now, madam. Where are your title, your fine gowns, your highly sung heroes? I see you have been greatly reduced. Only two sons, landless knights, and no gems. I wonder if he would be smitten with you now."

Daphne lifted her chin. Marcella's cruelty was not startling to her; she had long known about the woman. She had been near to many conversations in which Marcella was discussed. Her heart was torn with pity. Marcella had acquired so much, and still she had nothing.

"If my poverty pleases you, my lady, then surely you will be happy for some time to come. My sons will be a long time in gathering prosperity . . . and you may rest easy in my home — the deFraynes will never have their former wealth and influence." Daphne smiled serenely and stood straight with dignity. "There is a portrait of Lord deFrayne in the gallery. Behind it, a closet. Within, gems that once belonged to our family and could not be retrieved before I could flee. If they have not yet been discovered by some warlord or castellan, wear them. They will flatter you."

Marcella's mouth opened in surprise. She looked down at Daphne deFrayne, speechless.

"Wealth is not important to me, nor to my sons. If I could

tell you where to find what you long for, I would do it. Good day, my lady," she said, bowing deep. "Good health; God's blessing." And then quietly and with dignity, Daphne turned away, moving slowly past Marcella and down the gallery.

Tears sparkled in Marcella's eyes. She had not cried in many years, and the ache in her throat was unfamiliar and painful. She stared at Daphne's departing form, her envy reaching heights she never dreamed of. Her lips moved in a trembling murmur. "How dare *she* pity *me*."

Chapter Twelve

CAMERON DEFRAYNE felt the deep insult of having his lands given away, but Dylan urged his angry brother to exercise patience and caution. Whether right or wrong, the deFraynes had supported the losing side, and to be allowed in England once again was something for which to be grateful.

With the sale of ships that had belonged to his wife's father, Dylan was able to buy a rich town house in London and send for Raynia. If Heathwick was no longer possessed by the deFrayne family, Dylan said, it was probably for the best. There were greater lands and keeps to own, and they would be owned, given time, when the deFrayne men once again proved their loyalty. Cameron settled in the north with his wife and young son, and Raynia moved to the city with Dylan and his mother. To secure this much had taken more than a year, but Dylan was grateful just the same. "Our fortunes will be replenished," he promised Cameron. "It was sworn to me by Anthony Woodville, and these things take time."

In this year Dylan saw Lord Forbes, but the countess remained at Ayliffe through the winter following the birth of her daughter. Anne's failure to join Brennan in London both surprised and disappointed Dylan. He grew impatient and tense. He wanted both land and a woman whom he could love. Life with Raynia was nearly unbearable. She was spoiled, sickly, and complaining. He did not frequent her bed, and she admitted she was grateful to be free of his affections. She found her wifely duty to satisfy his infrequent lust abhorrent. She had miscarried within six months of their reunion and did not recover easily. He pitied his poor mother, who carried the burden of her obnoxious daughter-in-law gracefully, caring for and indulging Raynia as best she could. He recognized Raynia to be his obligation, henceforth, and was appreciative that she was only a nuisance and not a dangerous or ambitious woman. They did not love each other in any fashion. Raynia loved no one at all except her ugly little maid, Jeannette. Dylan suspected the two women of indecent pastimes, but he held silent.

The summons from Anthony Woodville to meet in a private and secret place both intrigued and excited Dylan. He hoped his fortunes would finally change. He would like to see Cameron completely restored and his mother residing in more dignity than she did at present.

The ground was barely thawed from a hard winter as Dylan rode toward Raynia's house on the southern coast. He had told no one, not even his mother, where he was bound or why. He hoped the caretaker had seen the house through the winter without problems, and he was anxious to get there ahead of Anthony to be assured that all was in order. He could think of no better place and loved the hideaway for its secrecy, for its beauty, simplicity, and rustic comforts. He had given Anthony explicit instructions, in order to keep him safe from rocky protrusions in the inlet, or bogs and marshes on land, for Dylan did not know by what routes or means his old acquaintance would travel. They were not to arrive together.

Dylan saw the long, thin column of smoke rising from the house, and at first he was relieved to think the caretaker had already laid a fire in the hearth. But as he neared and saw horses tethered outside, his pulse raced. There were people already here, and he was unsure who they were.

With a stealth born of his experience as an exile, he crept into the house through the buttery, where food and drink were stored. His mouth actually stood agape at the gathering he found within. Four men sat about the hearth, apparently at their leisure. All four turned toward Dylan. He bowed in reverence, sheer wonder, and not a small amount of fright.

"Be at ease, sir knight," King Edward said. "I believe you are acquainted with everyone. Lord Rivers, her majesty's father, Anthony, your friend and best host, and Lord Forbes of Ayliffe. Sit, drink. This will not take long. Then," he chuckled, "your man says there is good hunting. We might enjoy the stay."

Dylan's face grew hot. He had no idea what this was about. Was he about to achieve some great importance within this elite group, or would he be quietly slain, never to be heard from again? A full tankard was brought to him by the caretaker's wife. Her hands trembled when she offered it, most likely from the excitement of entertaining the king and his closest friends and vassals, and Dylan's hands shook in spite of himself when he accepted the brew. He took a hefty gulp to settle his nerves, but had it not been for Anthony's confident and reassuring smile, Dylan would have wondered if Lord Forbes somehow knew about his love for Anne.

"We are moving toward troubled times," Edward said, without preamble. "Clever games are being played by others, and it is necessary to play some clever games of my own. I have enemies, it would seem, enemies who are richer than I am. My lord of Warwick is not pleased with me these days, and my brother the Duke of Clarence cleaves himself closer to the earl. My brother Richard of Gloucester is still mine, but I tell you this, there is danger ahead."

Dylan was speechless. He was to be let in on this privy council? These secrets?

"Anthony swears to me that despite the fact that I gave Heathwick to Lord Forbes for his daughter, you are sworn to be my henchman. True?"

"Yea, my liege. There are other lands."

Edward smiled. Dylan was in awe of him. He thought the

young king to be magnificent in both mind and body. Edward was actually younger than Dylan himself, yet he ruled England with cunning and power. Dylan lamented privately that he had not known Edward before Wakefield and Mortimer's Cross, for he would have seen that the crown should be pulled off mad Henry's head with haste.

"Other lands, indeed," Anthony said, "though you will earn them. The king has need of allies in enemy camps. I suggested it be you."

"Why would you choose me? I am only lately —"

The king cut him off. "Who else would be believed? Should I send the queen's own father or brother to pay homage to Warwick? Or Forbes, with his ten thousand strong? That would either alert them or amuse them. As to you, if you serve me loyally, you will earn yourself a handsome settlement, and if you betray me to them, you cannot do too much damage with your piddling few. I think it is an excellent notion."

"And what would you have me do, my liege?"

"You are a landless knight," Edward said, smiling conspiratorially at Brennan Forbes. "Give your services to my brother Clarence and stay close beside him. Warn me, if you can."

"Sire, why do you doubt Clarence?" he asked, shocked. How did brothers mistrust each other?

"It could be that George is a little lazy," Edward said sadly. Even when one was king and had an entire country to protect, a breach of loyalty from his own brother seemed to inspire more sorrow and pain than the blind rage Dylan would have expected. "Being the second son, George has always sought the simplest path to wealth and fame; he likes wealth and power a great deal. I thought to sate his appetite; I've been very generous with my brothers. But I cannot allow England to be ruled by the Earl of Warwick. Otherwise, I might just give George the whole mess and let him have his day." He looked between his friends. "Poor George cannot seem to drive from his mind the fact that I have no son of my own yet. He is the presumptive heir to England. A moving prospect for any man."

Edward sighed and gulped heartily of cold ale. "I love England, sir knight. But it is life I love most, and George would have to conspire with Warwick to murder me to get the crown. I should like to live a few more years."

"How do you think I can convince the duke to accept friendship and allegiance from me?"

"I will host a tournament in June. There you might prove your worth as a knight. After that, if what Anthony says of your skills is true, Clarence should be glad to have you."

Dylan glanced at each face. He saw something in each set of eyes and the curve of each mouth that he had not expected. He saw trust and confidence in him though he was only lately home from exile. He frankly did not know what he had done to inspire this powerful group to approach him, especially the Earl of Ayliffe. He finally settled on the king's face and smiled.

"I am honored, my liege." Each man present extended a hand to Dylan in brotherhood and conspiracy.

It was not quite by choice, more by necessity, that Anne had stayed away from the court for over a year. It was not difficult to convince Brennan that she should stay behind while he waited on the king. In fact, he seemed almost relieved. Their lives had become very complicated.

Brainard, still at Ramsford and still angry, created constant trouble for Brennan with hostile, demanding letters. Likewise, Brainard's host, Sir Baelfour, frequently sent letters about Brainard's occupation of Ramsford that worried and angered Lord Forbes. And the first Earl of Trelaine, Bart Gifford, grew restless and bitter. He had a large estate that was difficult to manage, and his frequent letters to the earl smarted with jealousy; had he known Heathwick could be gotten, he would have waited for that estate, which he perceived as richer. Anne could tell that Brennan was close to being finished with them both and that little would be required to push the Earl of Ayliffe to that end.

Meanwhile, the younger children needed their mother's attention. It was to nurture her baby girl in her first year and see to Sloan's training that occupied Anne while she remained at

Ayliffe, even though giving up her chance to be with Dylan was hard for her.

Sloan had become a large and handsome child. Anne realized, during Sloan's sixth year, how Brennan might have failed with Brainard. Brennan was a devoted husband to her, but his duties to his children fell to his wife and a group of nursemaids and tutors. Sloan did not suffer from lack of attention, for he had a mother who watched him closely and he was attended by Sir Clifton, who seemed to bear a single-minded adoration for the boy.

She knew she had to keep her son from the close scrutiny of both Brennan and Dylan, because he looked more and more like Dylan as time passed. She spent the entire winter looking for a noble household for Sloan's training as a page, finally sending her son off to Lord Todd near Yorkshire. She wept at her son's departure even though she was confident he was in the good care of Sir Clifton and she had the utmost respect for Lord Todd. It was a painful separation for her, for she knew she would not see him for many months. But her little lad did not cry; he was determined to be brave and strong. All too soon he would have to give up even Sir Clifton and face growing up. Anne was not yet three and twenty and felt as though she had been a countess, with all the rank's awesome responsibilities, forever. She welcomed the diversion offered by time spent in London.

The activities in London soon diminished thoughts of her son. A grand and festive tournament, the greatest tournament ever, threw the royal court and the entire city into a mood of frivolous celebration. The featured combatants were Anthony Woodville, Lord Scales, who was proclaimed to be England's strongest and most famous knight, and the Bastard of Burgundy, Antoine de la Roche. The lists were set up at Smithfield near the queen's town house and the streets were jammed with the populace, all trying to get a glimpse of the knights and the visiting nobility.

Anne's mother and all three Gifford men were in London for the festivities. Quentin and Bart meant to play the tourney, but Trenton seemed content to watch. Anne wished that she could have found a way to keep her mother at Heathwick and was in a nervous twitter the first day of the tournament, racked with worry that the presence of the deFrayne men would goad Marcella into some evil.

The four of them, Lady Gifford and Trenton, the Earl and Countess of Ayliffe, watched the jousts and melees from under the awning sewn for them in the colors of Ayliffe. Anne groomed herself with great pains each day, selecting her wimple or hennin with care, the color and style of her gown with prudence. She wished to be beautiful because she suspected that she would see Dylan. There might be nothing more than a glance, but even at a distance, she would meet with that faint glitter from those familiar turquoise eyes. In that much there was always promise.

The greater battle was between the two Anthonys, but for the purpose of arousing excitement and building suspense of the crowd there were other challenges and many smaller jousts for ransom and prizes. Anne tried to keep her face impassive as Dylan rode, fought, and collected prizes enough to draw some attention away from even the celebrated Lord Scales. It gave her great secret pleasure to note that Dylan was becoming rich in the lists. He won ransoms, men, equipment, and fame. Anne searched the crowd, when she dared, for a glimpse of the women who might be wearing his colors or cheering for him. She found Daphne, sitting tall and proud and alert, but there were no other women. She wondered why his wife did not give him tokens and kisses. She would die for a chance like that, to name her love, to show her adoration.

Lord Forbes did not ride in the melee, nor did he issue or accept any challenges. Through three days of jousting Brennan was quiet, and almost glum. Banners were flying, heralds were shouting, the crowd was screaming excitedly, but there was no mistaking the earl's discontent. She had begun to notice subtle changes in him that she could not quite understand.

"Do you mislike the tourney, my lord?" she asked.

"Why would I not enjoy the joust? When have you seen one more grand?"

She had heard similar snappish replies from him over the past year. He never talked of his unhappiness. Sometimes she thought he worked too hard, sometimes she thought he was ill. Sometimes she found herself wondering if he had ceased to love her.

The third day of the tournament dawned bright and clear and the contestants gathered again. A late challenge was issued by the Earl of Trelaine against Dylan deFrayne, and when the herald announced the contest, Anne's eyes shot to Marcella's face. She could not mistake the superior smile on her mother's face, though Marcella did not meet her eyes. She checked eyes with Trenton and was driven back in time; Trenton was the image of a younger Ferris. He had grown tall, strong, and broad. His dark, brooding eyes held a gentle strength for only Anne.

"This should be interesting," Brennan mumbled. "DeFrayne may get to own some of my land." It was the first time Anne had heard delight in her husband's voice for days. He clearly thought that Bart would lose, and it gave him pleasure. Anne was not so confident. Of her entire family only Bart and Marcella kept the hatred alive. And then she knew: Marcella had somehow driven Bart to do this.

Anne's heart pounded as the mounts were readied, as the herald read the rules, as the lines for the joust were drawn. The field was cleared as the steeds tore impatiently at the turf. The clarions were raised to begin the contest. The men lowered their visors and were told to take their positions. Dylan held his blunted lance firm and straight. Bart tipped his toward the ground and brought it up again.

"What is he doing?" Brennan asked as if thinking out loud.

The blunted end fell off Bart's lance just as the clarion sounded and the destriers charged. The contestants' visors were down, and the crowd rose as one, a common worry embracing them. Dylan could be killed by the sharp lance; he might not have seen Bart's movement. Women screamed. Brennan and Trenton both stood. Anne's hand moved unconsciously to her throat, sheer panic enveloping her. Only Marcella sat calmly.

Suddenly Dylan threw down his lance and dove from his galloping horse, rolling once, twice, and thrice to avoid the charge of Bart's destrier. But Bart, committed, rode past Dylan all the way to the other side. He turned his charger around, lifted his visor to see what had happened to his opponent, and stared down at his lance as if he did not know what happened.

The crowd gave a single sigh. Some, Anne suspected, would have liked to have seen a little blood.

"The fine will be a good one," Brennan said, disgust ringing in his voice. "I will not pay it. Bart will take it from his own purse and bear the weight. And he dare not ever ask another thing of me."

"My lord, surely it was an accident. He . . ."

"Accident?" Lord Forbes repeated, staring at Marcella in wonder. He turned his face back to the lists. Marcella sat beside Anne; the men sat on the other sides. "Nothing was ever more deliberate. He will find the price of his dishonor a high one indeed, for he is hereby out of my influence. He has had more of me than he deserves!"

"My lord," Marcella cried, half-leaning across Anne's skirts toward Lord Forbes. "Would you promote the deFraynes when they —"

Suddenly she was drawn back into her place. Anne turned her head. Trenton's hand firmly held Marcella's arm. Their eyes were locked. Trenton glared into his mother's eyes with barely controlled anger. "If you say another word in defense of Bart or to slander the deFraynes, I will take you from the lists if I have to carry you. And do not doubt that I can."

She blanched, as did Anne. "It is simple to see where your loyalty lies," she murmured angrily.

"Do not doubt it, madam," Trenton advised sternly.

Anne closed her eyes briefly, letting out her breath. Will it never end? she asked herself. And then a slow smile grew as she realized that Trenton protected her. It had been over a year since he had taken Heathwick for Marcella. It was apparent he had learned much about their mother's hatred.

Marcella properly cowed, Anne's attention returned to her surly husband. He now had good cause for his anger and churlish mood, but Anne still worried. He had been acting strangely for some time. His troubles could not all be focused on Bart and Brainard.

Late on the third night of the tournament, after feasting, dancing, and celebrating were finally done, Anne approached him again. "Is it me, Brennan? Have I done something to anger you?"

He looked her over, his eyes raking her from top to bottom, but his tone remained curt. "How could I possibly be displeased with you? Who has a more beautiful mate?"

Anne was dressed for bed in a long, flowing white gown, and Brennan was lounging in the room with a mulled posset that still steamed. Jane was pulling back the coverlet and pounding the mattress with her fists to soften it. She turned toward Anne when she heard Brennan bark at his wife. Anne inclined her head toward the door and Jane lowered her eyes and left them quietly. Anne knelt before her husband, her forearms resting on his knees, and looked up into his eyes. She had only seen Dylan at a distance and was filled with hope that she could speak a few private words with him, perhaps a quick embrace, a kiss. But first this trouble in her marriage had to be settled to her satisfaction. She had no idea what irritated Brennan so.

"Please tell me what troubles you, Brennan. Let me help somehow."

"And how would you help me, Anne?" he asked, with an impudent, churlish curl to his lip.

"I might try to correct my injustice, whatever it may be. Surely I cannot have done anything too terrible."

He sighed heavily. His hand trembled slightly as he touched her cheek. "Have you not noticed?" He gave a rueful chuckle. "You look as though you should be a passionate creature, but you are always the demure wife. Tell me the truth, Anne. Have you said nothing out of propriety, or is it that you have not missed my lovemaking?"

"Oh Brennan, do you wish for me to seduce you? You have never been shy, nor have I ever rebuked you."

"Did you notice? Did you even take notice?"

"That you have needed me less?" she asked, confused. "Of course," she said shyly. "But, my dear, the demands made upon you are constant — should I add mine? What would you have me do?"

His eyes seemed to fill with tears, but she did not know if it was sadness he felt, or something else. "I cannot blame you, no matter how hard I try," he whispered. "Anne, I did you wrong. I am old."

"Oh my dear, dear husband. What nonsense you speak. You . . ."

He pushed her gently away and stood, draining his cup and placing it on the table with a loud bang. "Anne, I have babies at home who should be my *grandchildren!* I have a young, passionate, and beautiful wife whom I cannot satisfy. And though I look at you and crave to taste your sweet flesh, I think a part of me has died. It was wrong of me to marry you. I did not know I would become old so soon."

She walked toward him and placed her hands on his chest, trying to keep the inevitable guilt and pity from her eyes. She had noticed that his demand for her body came less often, but she had not thought anything particularly wrong. He was a busy man, often away from her, and they still shared a bed, even if they shared little else. She had always counted Brennan as her dearest friend, but she never said so for fear of offending him. She knew that was not what he wished to be. And he was right; she had paid little attention because she did not hunger for his lovemaking.

She had been able to soothe him so many times, by a simple touch, a caress, her understanding. She hoped she could again.

"Brennan, please don't torture yourself over some nonsense that has no meaning. I love you! I have never thought you old!"

"I do not ride in the tournament for fear of breaking my bones on a chance fall. I rise stiff and sore each morning, and I do not have the strength I once had. My appetite is leaner, my nights longer, and I desire the comfort of a restful night over the comforts of your body."

She laughed lightly in spite of herself. "Perhaps the fault is mine. I have worried for so many years that you would be disappointed in *me!* You have always been kind and generous with me despite the fact that you have always wanted a more passionate bride than I. 'Tis my lacking, Brennan; a more skilled paramour would succeed in arousing you properly. Truly, if I were a better wife, you would have fewer worries. I cannot blame you if you love me no more."

"It is because I love you so that I am beset, my sweet." He turned away from her. "I wonder what problems I've created for you, when I could have let a younger man have you."

"Brennan, I did not want a younger man," she lied. The only other man she would have was not allowed her.

"There is no denying the fact that Brainard will outlive me and create troubles for you that will be difficult to quell. I cannot prevent him from having Ayliffe, but I can delay him. I have rectified the problem to a small degree — my will is with the king and states plainly that the order of widowhood is yours at your request. Ayliffe is yours until you die. Brainard will not inherit title there until after you are gone."

The issue was a large and important one, but Anne was less concerned with Ayliffe just now than with Brennan. What he had done suddenly brought the enormity of his problem home to her. She could not ignore what he must be feeling, if it drove him to drastic measures. "Wills? Order of widowhood? My lord, what do you plan? Do you willfully abandon me? Are you . . ." She couldn't even form the words; she was suddenly terrified that Brennan was suffering from melancholia and thought of taking his own life.

"I only say it is later in my life than you might think. I am withering away."

"Cease," she said almost angrily. "You are not suffering from anything other than self-pity. Truly, Brennan, it is not like you to fret over such minor things as morning aches or less passion in our nights. I will not hear of your fast-approaching death. It is too much!"

He smiled gently. "You do make me wish for my younger days," he said. "That's why I wanted you so badly seven years ago. You filled me with hunger; you made me feel like a reckless young lad."

"Come," she said, taking his hand and leading him toward their bed. "Take off your clothes and let me massage your back.

Perhaps you are only tired; Edward uses you too well and my family plagues you constantly." She helped him out of his tunic and knelt at his feet to remove his boots as he sat on the bed. "It is not always for the best when one stands in the good graces of the king. Brennan, you are only tired."

When Anne stood again Brennan pulled her toward him between his knees and held her on his lap. "Perhaps it is not my back that needs your ministrations, my love."

She gently kissed his lips and pushed him back on the bed. Her mind raced with worry. Poor Brennan, she had taken no notice that he was so beset. In recounting the year and several months since Deirdre's birth, she realized that he had touched her very few times. She strained to remember the last time they had made love and could not. Filled with remorse, she thought a better wife would have known more of her husband's troubles. Was it really over for him? She had never heard of such a complaint. She longed to ask him if all men suffered this way with age, or if this was some rare disease. There was rumored to be plague in the city; was he sick? She applied her gentle, caressing hands to Brennan's yielding flesh; she kissed his lips as passionately as she could. She employed all the clever and stimulating requests he had asked of her over the years. She had always hoped to please him, but now she felt it was encumbent on her to save him.

Brennan responded almost gratefully to Anne's efforts, but they were futile. Finally, with a groan of absolute despair, he rolled away from her. "It is useless. I am no longer a man." His voice caught pitifully.

"Brennan, nay, please," she said, desperate tears in her own voice as she pulled him back to face her. "Oh Brennan, my love, my dear love, it doesn't matter! Just hold me; just be close to me!" She clung to him, her torment completely for him. She had never yearned for Brennan's lovemaking, yet she had never resented his touch, either. She didn't need his passion, but she needed his friendship and devotion a great deal. And with this loss that he suffered, he seemed to withdraw from her. She became frightened. She felt as though she was losing her dearest friend.

"How can you accept me like this?" he asked.

"How can I *not*," she cried. "We have a family, children. I am your wife. Please, I would miss your touch, your body, but I need you. I do not desire more than your love. You are my husband, my lord. Whether ill or fit, whether rich or poor, we must succor each other. Please, Brennan, believe me, I love you *the same!*"

He touched her tearstained cheek, looking into her pleading eyes. "I know you do," he whispered. "I don't know if that is a good sign, or bad."

Anne went alone to mass on the sixth morning after the tournament had begun. She had not forgotten Dylan in the face of Brennan's troubles, but she had pushed him far to the back of her mind, so she was startled when she spied him in the chapel stall. With a mind that thought as one with his, she followed him through the quiet, dark passages of Westminster. A flight of stairs, a torchlit alcove, a door opened, and then she was in his arms.

"Anne, my beloved, it has been so long." His lips were hot and searing on hers, but she pushed him away. She was trembling. "Have a care, Dylan. Do not touch me, I beg you."

"What is it? What is amiss?"

"I had hardly noticed," she began, her voice quivering with confusion. "But the fact is this: my husband no longer shares my bed except for sleep. I beg you, do not tempt me overmuch; I am too hungry for your arms, your lips. Now, there would be nothing to protect me from being stoned for an adulteress if I should somehow come with child."

Dylan's brow wrinkled in sudden confusion. "What is this? He looks at you with all the lust and hunger that ever glittered in a man's eye."

She let her gaze drop. "But . . . he . . . cannot . . ."

Dylan whistled low. "How so? What ails him?"

"I don't know. Oh, tell me truly, Dylan, is this a common complaint? Brennan thinks he has become old; he believes himself near death. Is he ill, Dylan? Is it plague?"

Dylan gave a little huff of sad laughter. "Nay, my love, 'tis not a common complaint, nor is it a sign of sickness. Poor Forbes, a worse curse could not befall a man than to have so pleasing a wife and no will to use her."

"Dylan, is this my fault? I have never met Brennan in the passion he wished from me. I know that. I tried . . . I . . ."

"No, my darling. You must not blame yourself. I know you have been a good wife to the earl and have done your best to make him happy; I know you did not try to withhold affection, nor spurn him. He is a good man." He sighed and looked sympathetically into her eyes. His problem was not dissimilar. He did understand how she must feel, but he could not quite form the words. It was not something one could pretend. "Poor Anne." He squeezed her upper arms in sympathy. "Now your marriage will be more like mine."

"Yours?" she questioned.

"Never mind. Kiss me. I will give you no babe."

Upon his promise she yielded her lips, her arms, and more. Just to feel safe, however briefly, in Dylan's arms brought her familiar joy. Her body would always respond to him even when her mind willed it otherwise, and there was strange comfort in this. She had felt so burdened and guilty, as if there was something terribly wrong with her, as if she had harmed Brennan purposely, something she would never do.

She had not even known that the small closet in which they hid existed, nor did she know the way out. But his lips on hers and his hands on her breasts caused her not to care. There was so much life in his embrace. Once in a year, once in a decade, once in a lifetime — it did not matter. All else was forgotten when she was again with her love, her forever love.

She panicked suddenly when she felt her skirt rise as Dylan bunched it in his hand and pulled it up. She writhed slightly as though she would pull away when his warm fingers touched that willing, secret, dangerous place.

"Please, Dylan, do not . . ."

"Hush, my Anne. Let me. You will see."

Soon a low moan of release escaped her like trapped steam as her body shook with the secret splendor. She nearly collapsed into his arms as she felt the ecstasy of this lover's satisfaction, though Dylan did not enter her. His lips, hard and hot on her neck, devoured her flesh. He held her pinioned against a cool gray palace wall and remained still, supporting her for a long while as she slowly recovered herself. And then, understanding, she found him with her hand.

It was always clandestine, always less than it could be. Why, she asked herself, again and again. What would have been so terrible in having each other within the pure sanctity of marriage? Why could fate not smile on them? The touch of his lips filled her and she would recall the taste of his mouth for days and weeks. This was the only place she felt real, in his arms, in his care. And just when she began to think she could not live without him, it was always time to part. Each encounter was more dangerous than the one before.

An hour had passed when he cautiously opened the door and looked down the dark gallery. He found it empty and closed the door again, looking at her intensely. "If I am ever found out in this, I will be executed before cockcrow, but there is something you *must* know, Anne. Your word on your silence? Not even Jane —"

"Of course."

"It may be a long while before we are together again. Anne, my love, it may be years. I have entered into a dangerous conspiracy with your husband and others. The cause is the king's, I assure you, but if you wonder at what seems a strained friendship between Forbes and me and Scales and myself, it is for a purpose. I have been asked to join Clarence somehow."

"Clarence?" She whispered.

"I must not be thought to be on the best of terms with the Woodville clan, which by sheer proximity includes your noble husband. Trust me and do not doubt me, my love, no matter what you hear. I am not a traitor."

"Of course not. But do you go away?"

"I will always try to wedge myself near your company. I will steal whatever moment of your time I might, but this business of mine will keep me closer to Clarence. I only want you to know, to understand. If Lord Forbes acts as if he is troubled by me, it has nothing to do with you. You must not be afraid that we have been discovered."

"Be safe, Dylan. Be careful."

He kissed her once in parting, told her how to leave the hiding place, and sent her off ahead of him.

Ah, Anne. He leaned against the closed door. Had he shamed her by his desperate lust, by the way he manipulated her body? Her pleasure was his pleasure — he could not resist. When she melted in his arms in spite of herself, he was reassured. The response she could give no other she gave to him, though it was always dangerous. He had never considered reciprocal treatment; he had only wished to feel her response, bring her that carnal joy. An illicit hour with her sustained him for a while; it would be a long time before he would be racked with worry that she had somehow learned to live without him, that she did not love him anymore.

How did one become the recipient of this eternal love? How had they found each other? Why could he never forget her? Why, God help him, could he not live without her? It would be better for them both had they never met. But he shook the thought away. He had so little now. He could not live with less.

He sighed and left Westminster the same way he had come. He returned to his home, to his bedchamber. Raynia was at her bath, the odd little Jeannette sponging her skin in a familiar manner. He glanced at his little wife; she had the body of a ten-year-old girl: flat breasts, tiny, spindly limbs. Her skin was sallow and she was given to blemishes. She was surely the most homely thing ever born, but worse, she had the temperament of an asp.

"Jeannette, will you excuse us? I wish to be alone with my wife for a moment."

Raynia made an annoyed face, but Jeannette went quietly. The maid was a little ill at ease around Dylan. He could recall very few times he had even heard her speak.

"What is it?" Raynia asked impatiently.

"You have not been to any of the tournament festivities, nor did you see the jousting. I have won much. Will you accompany me tonight, or do I excuse you as ill again?"

"I have no interest in the English court. I told you that."

"I know. Your only interest seems to be in your maid."

Her eyes narrowed. "Do not accuse me, my lord husband, when the stink of the whore still clings to you in early morning. Mass, indeed."

Dylan grinned in spite of himself. Did Anne's perfume cling? Or did his odd little wife catch a whiff of the pleasure they had stolen? No matter. Perhaps if Raynia were moved to jealousy, she would behave herself for once, but he doubted it. She would go with him, in any case. This once, he would demand something of her.

"Wear your yellow gown. And the necklace I gave you for your homecoming. I will be here for you at noon."

"Noon? But   "

"There is plague in the city, Raynia. If you behave yourself, I will send you and your little maid to the country for safety." He shrugged. The plague was nothing. There had been only two deaths of which he was aware. "If you are difficult, however, I will keep you here with me and take you to court everyday."

"Plague? Are you certain?" He nodded. She splashed the water peevishly. "Why must I go with you?"

He smiled benevolently. "I think it is time those nobles at court see my wife. You are my wife, like it or not." He left the room quickly. He was uncomfortable even in her company, though he was uncertain why.

He knew Anne would at least partially understand when she saw the unpleasant little wench he had wed. He hoped, however, that Anne would not pity him; that was not his motive at all. He was better off with his peculiar wife than one who strongly desired him. Likewise, he was happy to be guiltless in betraying their union. It was for Anne that he forced Raynia's presence. They were *both* married. It was difficult for him to explain, with words, the sympathy he had for Anne's position. In spite of himself, even Dylan had come to admire and respect Lord Forbes. He was more than a little aware that Anne's burden was greater than his own.

Trenton had taken lodging for himself and his mother in the city and not with his sister. He thought it for the best. He had learned enough about his mother in the past year to know what mission had fallen to him. He could not undo the damage she had already done, but he could at least prevent her from doing more. He had listened to her rantings of past injustices and he had read some of her letters. He proved an able escort and keeper. It was the only thing he could give his father's memory.

The hour was late when he heard conversation in the next room. He went to the door and listened to the sound of Bart's angry voice. "You should have known the earl would do this to me! You should have known it would cost me everything!"

"Be still," she hissed. "I will give you a piece of gossip that will get you revenge on deFraynes, if nothing else."

Trenton pushed open the door. Marcella looked at him impatiently. "Leave us, Trenton. I must speak to my son."

Trenton stood firm and glared at them both. "Tell Bart there is nothing, madam. There is no revenge."

"Trenton, you must allow me to —"

"*Tell him*," Trenton's voice boomed.

Marcella was silent.

"Trenton," Bart said entreatingly. "If Mother knows a way to help me now, she . . ."

"Have you not learned by now that she only knows ways to hurt you? Go on, Bart. Her ideas for easy wealth and fame will only burn you the more." Bart stayed, hoping for a gain. "There is no gossip; there is nothing. Go."

Bart finally departed, anger still shining in his eyes, but his head down. Trenton turned to his mother. "Don't you dare," he said slowly. "Don't you ever dare."

Chapter Thirteen

BRENNAN FORBES went to some trouble to build a bed-chamber for himself at Ayliffe. The process was slow, for a wall had to be removed to enlarge the room to suit his needs and contain all the furniture he desired. Finally, two bed-chambers, the lord's and the lady's, were joined by a large common room and bath chamber. The Earl of Ayliffe had never before taken a room apart from his wife, nor had he slept apart from his two previous wives, even though separate quarters was more in keeping with the noble marriage custom. Some eye-brows were raised in curiosity during the construction of the chamber. Anne wept at the separation, but did so secretly.

"Some of the maids titter and gossip," Jane told her.

Some of the maids, Anne thought with a near laugh. Ayliffe had a force of weavers, seamstresses, laundresses, cooks, maids, bakers, and serving wenches that could rival the staff of Eltham or Pontefract Castle. This was without mentioning the local wives, daughters, harlots, and widows. "Let them be, Jane. Little enough happens that they find exciting."

"It rankles me when they suggest you are cold to his lordship's advances."

Anne looked into Jane's compassionate eyes. "It is better than the truth. Leave them be."

"But I know you suffer, lady."

It is nothing to his lordship's suffering, Anne wanted to say. But she held her tongue. She patted Jane's hand in thanks. The winter had been long and she was eager for spring. A rosebud, a violet would soothe her now. She had heard that Dylan was becoming rich; that he had estates now, and men-at-arms and soldiers. But she had not seen him even once during her winter in the city. When he had said it would be a long time for them, perhaps years, she had prayed it would not be so long. But since she had not even had the luxury of glancing at Dylan from a distance, she knew the separate bedchamber her husband chose was not because he suspected her of an alliance with another man. There had been no contact, and she craved the warmth of a lover's touch, an intimate word.

There was to be a homecoming soon, and she was making all the necessary preparations. Anxious days and nights preceded the event. Sloan would come home, but so would Brainard. Little Deirdre, her blonde-haired beauty, jabbered constantly and found mischief everywhere. Anne wished there could be more children.

In May the gates were opened to an approaching troop, and Anne, looking stately and majestic in her gown of Ayliffe white and gold, stood in the courtyard with the earl. She let her slim arm encircle his waist and she leaned her head against his shoulder. He dropped a husbandly kiss on her brow and she smiled up at him. At least this much had not changed. He still cared for her.

"Are you anxious, madam?" Brennan asked.

"I did not realize how I would miss him, Brennan. Why must we bear it? It is a mother's curse to send her sons away to become men."

"He is only eight years old, but his time for clinging to your skirts is over, Anne. You must not let him see how much you long to hold him to your breast."

"It shows so much?"

"In your eyes, in your trembling lips. Lord Todd writes that Sloan is stronger than the other boys his age, and smarter. He will make a fine knight, a brilliant noble. You must let him grow up and take his due. There are too few who deserve it."

"I hope you are proud of him, Brennan."

"Worse," he said somewhat sadly. "There is one thing I have always loved more than anything: Ayliffe. Forgive me, my love, if I slight you, but Ayliffe has had my life's blood, my loyalty, and all my energy. More than any other thing, I want Ayliffe to survive. And," he said, a note of melancholy creeping into his serious tone, "I am more proud of Sloan than Brainard. Sadly, Sloan is my hope for Ayliffe's future — for the future of my first love."

She gave him a squeeze. She dismissed the fearsome thought of what Brennan would say if she told him the truth: Sloan was her hope for the future of her first love. Dylan did not have children, but through Sloan he would live on. "Of course, Ayliffe will always be as strong and magnificent as you've built her," she replied.

He gave a doubtful snort, but placed an arm about her shoulders just the same. "That is all I've worked for."

Anne's eyes drifted down the long road through the village toward the outer wall. She could see them approaching — Sloan, Sir Cliff, and the escort of knights. Sloan struggled to keep a dignified expression as he dismounted before them. She could see his excitement and pride in his bright, glittering eyes, his handsome mouth that fought the temptation to laugh, to squeal with delight. But he dismounted and bowed before them as a man would.

"My lord. My lady."

How handsome and strong he was, how tall. Anne's heart ached. He was growing up so fast, he was nearly gone from her forever. Her arms trembled and finally she yielded to the urge and opened them to her son.

Sloan reluctantly entered his mother's embrace, gazing doubtfully at Lord Forbes. Anne covered his brow with kisses, raking her slim fingers through his thick hair. "Madam, I assure you I am well and clean."

"Anne," Brennan said, placing a firm hand on her shoulder, "enough of that now. He is not a baby anymore."

"Of course not," she said, sniffing sentimentally. "But I am still his mother."

"Come into the hall, Sloan, and tell me about your training. Let's hear what you've learned." Brennan did not succumb to the show of emotion, which disappointed Anne in a way. Perhaps that was what Brainard had been lacking. Brennan was distant; proud and friendly, but more like a lordly host than a father. "Bring me my daughter," he called when he was inside. "Bring me Deirdre." Once the little tot was seated on her father's lap, her most favorite place in the entire world, Brennan talked with Sloan about Lord Todd's estate, caressing his daughter's chubby arms throughout their conversation. He was not the least uncomfortable in displaying affection for his girl-child.

The children did not resemble each other much, Anne realized. Through all the preparations for Sloan's homecoming, she had half-feared that his strong likeness to his sire would reveal her secret in a glance. But as Sloan grew older, the resemblance diminished enough to give her ease. His blue eyes were bright, but his hair had darkened somewhat, and he had his mother's smile, which he used liberally. He was a happy child, and had a proud bearing that was at once Dylan's, and yet Brennan's, too. I needn't have been so afraid, she thought. Sloan had the strong seed of his sire, and the dignified and loving upbringing of her husband. He had the best there could be. And it showed in him.

Two days passed in peaceful reunion before Brainard's arrival, but in this homecoming the surprise was even greater. Brainard had been away from Ayliffe for three years. He returned as a man, fully grown, nearly a score of years. Anne stiffened in apprehension; Sloan hung back. Brainard, however, bowed as courteously as Sloan had done. His youthful petulance was gone. There was an adultlike disdain in his very posture, however. But he was decent and, thankfully, silent. Anne wondered, hopefully, if Brainard had finally learned something.

"Ah, Sir Clifton," Brainard greeted with ice in his voice. "How goes it with your new ward?"

Cliff bowed, unsmiling. "Good enough, my liege. We work hard, ride hard, and sleep hard. A knight's life, surely."

"Is he as good as I was?" he asked coolly.

Sir Clifton smiled, a smile which Anne attempted to read, but could not. Were they friends or foes? She remembered her first meeting with Sir Cliff when she inquired after Brennan's son and why he had not greeted them. She had seen a brief flicker of emotion cross Sir Cliff's features then — disappointment, anger, or something similarly unsympathetic. Later, Clifton had held Brainard back from striking her. Perhaps Cliff had always known that Brainard was not to be trusted, that he was not kind in his heart. "He stands a good chance at being your equal one day, my liege," Cliff replied.

"How politic, Cliff. I'll have to watch the boy and draw my own conclusions."

Brainard swept into the keep as though he owned it, but even Anne had to admit that he was mostly courteous. Brennan's watchful eye was on him, however. And it was a few days before anything was said to show Anne that only Brainard's manners had changed, not his principles.

"Tell me about Ramsford," Brennan said to Brainard during their busy, well-attended evening meal. "What news of Baelfour? How do the Welshmen fare?"

"Ramsford is not a rich keep, my lord, but you already knew that. The Welsh are for hard work and lean in luxuries, which seems an unnecessary waste to me. I did what I was asked, however, to the displeasure of your castellan. Baelfour did not like the way I doled out the money, nor was he in favor of the improvements I supervised to make the place stronger. I'm certain his complaints reached you — he was often writing letters." Brainard tore off a fistful of bread, chewed a hearty piece, and washed it down with wine. "The most heartening news to all of them and to myself is that I am done with Ramsford."

"Oh? I did not excuse you yet."

"I am aware of that, my lord," Brainard said with strained courtesy. "I am excusing myself."

"You will leave Ramsford when I give my permission."

"May we discuss this in private, Father?" Brainard asked with strained politeness. "It is unclear to me, and probably many others, whether I was given a nobleman's chore, or exiled from my home." He glanced at Anne, then slowly his eyes moved to Sloan. "The Welshmen are not known for their courteous ways, but I suspected that all you really wished was to have me behave after a courtier's fashion." He raised a brow and peered at his father. "And so I shall. You will see."

Brennan looked long and hard at his son. He removed his eyes to address his plate, completing his meal in silence, and, once it was done, he called for his daughter.

Anne was uncomfortable with the way Brennan seemed to substitute his baby daughter's presence for the comfort he had once gotten from his wife. Anne finally struggled to get the child away from Brennan, arguing that it was time for Deirdre to be put to bed for the night. She leaned close to her husband and whispered in his ear. She carried the child to her nurse, went to her chamber to dress for bed, and waited.

Brennan came late in the evening when the sounds from the hall had diminished. He looked tired; his age was beginning to show. She faced him with her chin raised. "Brennan, please stay in my bed tonight. Or let me come to yours. Please," she added quietly. It was the first time in nine years of marriage that she had made such a request.

"It's a little late for all that, isn't it, Anne?"

She shook her head. "I will not bother you with any fleshly demands, Brennan. I need you. Please."

He approached her and pulled her into a fatherly embrace. "What is it, little love?"

"Something is wrong," she shuddered. "I don't know what it is. I feel afraid, alone."

"All of our children are home," he comforted.

"They are a worrisome group. Please stay with me."

"You are not alone, my love. I am with you always."

"Will you stay? Will you hold me against the night? Just once?"

"What is it you fear most?" he asked, pulling her with him toward the large draped bed. He let her kneel and take his boots from his feet, and pulled off his vest and short gown. "Is it Brainard? Sloan? Me?"

"I'm not sure what I fear, Brennan. How different we've all become," she sighed, settling into the bed, into the crook of his arm. There was familiar comfort there. "Without you, I am nothing," she murmured.

He sighed deeply, pulling her closer. "That has never been the case, not even when first we met. You were very special then, and you become more special every year. You, Anne of Ayliffe, are remarkable and strong. I have grown to admire you."

Anne of Ayliffe. She marveled at the sound. Is that how Brennan thought of her now? Her life had changed so dramatically that she barely remembered who she was. The young girl who submitted bravely to the older, wiser, stronger earl was gone forever and in her stead was a woman, shaking inside from the fearful demands of her station, composed on the outside for fear that someone would guess how vulnerable she really was and, therefore, refuse to follow her commands.

No one knows me, she thought suddenly. No one at all. Her mother was jealous of her and thought her cunning. Brennan considered her independent and strong, not needy and weak, as she thought of herself. Dylan might know her better than any man, yet was near her so seldom. Sometimes, she felt she did not even know herself and that there was no one to help her discover who she was.

"Brennan, you molded me into the countess you wished to have serve Ayliffe."

"I did. And I will expect nothing less from you until the day you die. But remember you this; I chose the perfect person to be the Countess of Ayliffe. I will take only the credit I deserve. And that praise, for helping you use your womanhood to good purpose, I will take proudly."

"Anne of Ayliffe," she repeated doubtfully.

"Swear me nothing else, but that you will never abandon Ayliffe."

"Never. I love Ayliffe."

" 'Tis well. I could forgive anything but that. My wives before you loved Ayliffe, and they loved me, but differently than you do. They admired its wealth, its prominence. They were both good women; they tried hard to do well. Neither one was born with a gift to serve this place, to preserve its exquisiteness. You are different. You seem to know what it really is."

"Your other wives, Brennan," she began uncertainly. "Did they love you . . . very much?" Did they love you better than me? she wanted to ask. Did you love them better? Did I ever make you as happy as you hoped I would? She longed to tell him how hard she had tried, how much she had desired to make him proud, to please him well.

He was silent for a long while. When he answered, his voice was soft. "We all love in very different ways, dear Anne. This I have learned, finally."

Brennan had somehow resigned himself to the relationship molded originally by Anne. He was a strong arm to lean on, a friend to talk to, a courteous and generous lord. He no longer lamented nor complained that she did not meet him in passion. He was comforted mostly by Deirdre, who thrived on her father's attention.

"Do you still love me, Brennan?" she asked him.

"I do, Anne. In you, I see hope for Ayliffe."

"Do you love me for myself? At all?"

"Oh, my dear, I love and respect you for all that you are. All." And he dropped a paternal kiss on her brow and slept at her side. Anne felt a ripple of disappointment. The man who had desired her body, the man who had nearly lost control of his passions as she passed him in the gallery, was now calling her his "dear" and his "little love." She felt she had failed him. Her mind traced the years in a flash of brightly colored pictures. A great noble knelt at her feet and begged her good favors, wished to tumble with her in a frenzy on the grass, and she had blandly told him how fond she was of him. She had never been able to return his passion. The circle of their love had never closed; she had kept a gap open for Dylan. Her passion had always been for another.

For that one night, as she lay in her husband's arms, she believed she had done wrong. She felt, for the first time, deep regret. It was not her adultery that shamed her, for she could not deny the love she had for Dylan, but her failure to give Brennan what he most desired, what he willingly gave her. And now it was forever too late.

In the high heat of summer, when the crops were growing tall, the stock fat, and a good harvest was in sight, Anne heard the door of her husband's bedchamber slam. She looked up toward the stairs from the hall and saw Brainard descending, red-faced and furious. He looked at her as if he could kill her with his eyes. She shuddered involuntarily at his expression of loathing.

"A clever trick, my lady vixen," he accused in a harsh whisper.

"I do not know what you mean, Brainard."

"So the wealth of Ayliffe is to be divided? Among three . . . nay, *four!* I am no longer the sole heir here, unless I choose to accept some promise of title when I am an old, old man. We shall see, madam *slut!* We shall see!" He looked over the length of her as if she were a wench whose services could be purchased. He smiled wickedly. "Do you think I can't make my own way? One day, when you are still quite alive enough to see it, I will *take* Ayliffe!"

Sloan was just coming into the hall and Brainard rudely pushed him out of his way to take his leave. Anne followed his departure with worried eyes.

"Madam? Mother?"

She let her gaze drop to Sloan's face. She suddenly realized that Brennan's support was not enough. Her husband was aging before her very eyes, becoming melancholy, sentimental, worried. She had to keep herself and her children safe.

"Sloan, fetch me Sir Clifton. Right away, lad."

She knew of no one else to seek for aid. She needed strength and loyalty close to her hand. She thought it was essential to draw Sir Clifton closer to her needs, her troubles. She did not think it was a hasty decision.

Dylan housed one thousand soldiers and men-at-arms. Half that number equaled his farmers, smiths, servants, wheelwrights, artisans, craftsmen, weavers, bakers, and others. One thousand five hundred pledged. To whom? Only his right arm, Sir Mark, knew that their allegiance to the Duke of Clarence and the Earl of Warwick was only a fleeting, fancy trick.

He had watched his villeins bring in a good harvest, doubling his wealth. He had journeyed to the Scottish border with men and arms and drove back blood-minded Scots in an uprising, proving his value as a leader of armed warriors. The winter came down hard and fast after the celebrations for harvest and victory in battle. The ground was hard to break. He buried a baby son, born dead. And before 1469 was very old, he was informed of his brother's death.

Cameron was only five and thirty when a winter illness consumed him. Dylan could not believe it had happened to a man so vital, so strong. As Dylan's wealth and importance multiplied, so did his losses. He rode toward Cameron's demesne with a heavy, aching heart. They had been close in Calais. He grieved that Cameron had not been restored to his rightful position. He grieved for lost friendship, a lost son, a lost love.

Lady Raynia had not risen from her bed since the early delivery of her dead child at Christmastide. It was not the loss of the babe that caused her suffering. She had not wanted a child. Raynia would never recover from her marriage. She hated England, hated Dylan. She cried for the rich, sunny skies of Calais, her mother, her freedom from intimacy and childbearing. Dylan did not begin to understand how these strange things had happened to Raynia, nor why, but he knew his wife was sadly demented and tormented. She was only nineteen years old and had twice miscarried and once delivered her child too soon to save him. She had not wished to leave Calais, in any case, but her father had insisted upon the marriage, which looked to be the best prospect for his plain, poor-tempered young daughter. Raynia had hated her father as she hated all men. Then the old man died and Raynia was sent to Dylan, and to a cold, gray England.

Jeannette was Raynia's only solace, and their carefully tended secret was no longer safe from Dylan. He had found them together in bed, naked. "Is this what you prefer?" he had asked her, amazed.

Raynia had unshielded her heart, her tongue. Dylan, she accused, only forced agony on her with painful, disgusting acts, followed by the gruesome tortures of pregnancy. Jeannette was gentle, kind, soft, and loyal. Raynia begged piteously to be sent back to Calais. She hated everything in her life.

"I will send you back," he had said, gently. He did not love Raynia enough to be jealous or even outraged. "But I cannot soon. I need a wife. You must play the part. Keep your shame locked tight in your bedchamber. If the servants learn of your perversion, I will be forced into harsh punishments, and there will be no Calais. I don't care that you defy me, but you defy the church, and I cannot help you with that. When I can, I will send you away."

He knew he would find Daphne with Cameron's widow; he had not seen his mother in over a year. When she embraced him, kissing his lips and both his cheeks, his stoic mien crumbled, and he cried like a lad at his mother's breast.

Daphne stroked his brow, kissed away his tears, and held him. She had never broken. Dylan knew some secrets of his mother's private torment, of her own lost love. She had buried a husband and now two sons. Yet, she did not weep, but seemed to grow stronger. She whispererd the name of his nephew, Cameron's son, in his ear. "Justin, Justin."

Cameron had been laid to rest on his wife's dower lands, and young Bess wept honest tears of grief and loneliness when Dylan was with her. She had loved Cameron, given him a strong and handsome son, and was now left with the very thing she had begun with — a modest manor house on decent, but not rich, lands in the south of England.

"Give me Justin," Dylan said to her. "He is five years old and needs a father. I will raise him to be brave and skilled, and you may go to Lady Scales, Anthony Woodville's wife. He will visit you often, but I will petition the queen to find you a suitable marriage when your period of mourning has spent itself. We will do better for you than this. We will turn an eye toward a good man whom you can love. You are young and strong, Bess. You are lovely." He grasped his sister-in-law's hands. "I cannot otherwise have a son. Justin is all there is for me."

Dylan stayed a month on his dead brother's estate, feeling more comfortable and at home there than he did on his own lands. The estate he had conquered through tournaments and gifts did not feel like his yet. He kept it precariously balanced between an imaginary allegiance to George of Clarence, and a true, but secret, loyalty to the king. And Raynia was there.

It had not taken Dylan long to understand that Edward was wise to mistrust his brother. Richard Neville, the kingmaker of Warwick, who had helped Edward achieve the throne, had successfully turned the duke's head, and together they had begun to agitate small groups, creating minor uprisings, which raged in the countryside. Warwick's name was not mentioned by the rebels, but the skirmishes were fought with the battle cry of opposition to the king, calling Edward a bastard, degrading the Woodville family, and an attempt to usurp the crown was coming. Dylan did not yet know whom Warwick would crown, but the Duke of Clarence had been promised a position close to the throne. Dylan shook his head in wonder that the duke did not see that his link to power through his brother was more secure than a treasonous alliance with Warwick. Dylan sent frequent, secret messages to his king. Clarence was one day Warwick's good henchman, the next day, the king's true subject. It was a chess game of players that moved too rapidly to follow. But Dylan kept Edward very well informed. If Warwick, or, for that matter, the Duke of Clarence, found himself betrayed, Dylan would be executed most quickly.

The danger of the conspiracy, along with his loneliness and grief, was changing Dylan. His pain was so deep that he did not realize it was making him strong. Stronger than ever.

"I do not like this allegiance with the Duke of Clarence," Daphne said as they rode north to Dylan's demesne.

"Why, madam? The duke is a strong man; he is generous. He is close to Warwick — the richest man in England."

They had brought Justin with them. Daphne had agreed to live with them at least until Justin had adjusted to his father's death. He would need frequent, reassuring visits with his mother, and since Dylan could not provide motherly love in his home, a grandmother's attention was more than important. As they rode together, Dylan's eyes were focused ahead on some distant point. His future was out there somewhere. He knew it was beyond the estate that he had managed to win. Beyond the Earl of Warwick and the Duke of Clarence. Beyond his marriage, his nephew. It was still very far away. But he still hoped. He could not kill the hope, even though he wished it would leave him.

"What is it you think to gain in this alliance? Wealth? Power?"

"Aye," he said simply. "And a secure hold on my possessions for my family."

"What family, Dylan?" she asked. "Lady Raynia? I know Raynia is not long for England. If you keep her here very much longer, she will die of grief. A more unhappy lady does not live." Dylan was silent. "For Justin? Will you make him your son, your heir?" Still he did not reply. "For me? I do not need wealth and power; you are all I have left, you and Justin. Your heart is heavy and sad and all I ever wanted for you was your happiness. Dylan?"

He turned his head and looked into her crystalline eyes with his own determined eyes. He smiled vaguely, secretly. They were mostly alone. Justin was asleep in the litter behind them, the escort troop was far ahead. "There are only two women in all the world to whom I would trust the truth. You are one, madam. And I have been lonely long enough. Come into my confidence, Mother."

[247]

"Two?" she asked in a whisper.

"Anne of Ayliffe," he answered.

Daphne crossed herself and looked down into her lap as she rode, her lips moving as if she uttered a prayer.

"I mean to have her, Mother." Daphne turned to look at her son. She saw his smile. He appeared confident, almost serene. "I think you should finally hear it. You have gathered your knowledge from my eyes for long enough. Hear it from my lips. All of it."

Warwick's rumblings erupted into small battles in the spring of 1469. The uprisings were mainly in Yorkshire and along the Scottish border among splinter groups of commoners that protested the king's favors to his wife's family. None of the little battalions of ruffians wore any official noble name. It appeared the people of England had become disenchanted with their king and were rising in rebellion, just as Warwick had planned.

The Earl of Ayliffe was in London with his family and, as was typical of his visits, he was pulled into secret councils and meetings every hour of the day and night. He spent little time with Anne, which gave her far too much time to look around the gathered courtiers in search of a pair of turquoise eyes.

The element of intrigue in Brennan's life had become a matter of fact for them, and so a late-night interruption that pulled them from sleep was not met with any great surprise. A herald wearing the king's tabard was announced. Anne rose, as did Brennan, but she covered her nightgown with a chamber robe and left their bedchamber so that her husband could receive his message in privacy. She listened at the door of a small anteroom.

"You are a man of many costumes, Dylan," Brennan said quietly.

"Your pardon, my lord." His voice was anxious, strained, perhaps frightened. "A courier of mine was captured on the road. My message to the king was intercepted, and the messenger was executed. In a few days I will know if he spoke my name." There was a heavy sigh. "I'm certain you will hear, by way of gossip, whether I am done of this service."

"I'm sorry, Dylan," Brennan said. "You knew the risks."

"Aye. Never mind, I have faced this before and will again. The king must be told these facts. There are many small groups inciting rebellion, but there is one to watch closely. There are bandits who run with Robin of Redesdale; he is not a champion of the people. He is Warwick's man, and his army is large and will converge on Edward."

"Who is Robin, then?"

"I am not sure. There is talk that it is Sir William Conyers, Lord Warwick's good man, and that he has sixty thousand now. I have seen factions of the army; you may be assured these are not the unhappy artisans and serfs of York following their local hero. And the demands they make will sound strikingly like his lordship of Warwick's own vendetta. The names of those whom Robin would remove from the king's personal favors will be Warwick's enemies. This you must tell His Majesty."

"And George? Where does he stand?"

"Today, with Warwick. He seems determined to marry Warwick's daughter Isabel. It is true, though, that he has never mentioned wearing the crown of England himself. It is only that Edward's brothers hate the Woodvilles."

"Gloucester, too?"

"Richard of Gloucester refuses to be drawn into Warwick's camp. He is hard for Edward. But, my lord, he hates the Woodville family every bit as much. Be wary. Richard is young still."

"Do you know their plans for attack?"

"Nay, my lord, but I was told by the duke that I would be called. My forces are not great and we will be . . . delayed. All this, of course, if I do not hang before the week is out, for my betrayal of Clarence."

"Flee, Dylan. The king will understand."

From behind the closed door Anne felt tears come to her eyes. Flee, she wanted to cry out. Run, Dylan, run. She pressed her fist to her mouth to keep herself silent. The struggle to contain her emotions was almost impossible. She had not even seen his face in two years.

"Nay, my lord. I swore to see it through and I will. I said I would be the king's good secret man, and so I shall be. I vow this is only the beginning and there will not be a peaceful settlement until Warwick is dead." There was a long silent pause. Anne imagined them looking at each other, their eyes deeply locked. "Tell my king that I remain loyal in his service."

"His brave and loyal man, sir. I will be called to arms for His Majesty while you sit close to Warwick's forces. Should our plans go awry, see to Ayliffe, I beg you."

Again there was silence. "You do not know what you ask, my lord. I cannot —"

"There are few whom I would trust," Brennan said.

There was a soft chuckle from Dylan. "You seem confident that I will live long enough. I will take it as a good sign, but one thing, my lord — tell at least one person that you have made this request of me, lest your ten thousand cut me down as I near the gate. Ayliffe, I know, is strong for the crown, and my reputation is set in another direction."

"Aye. We remember Towton and Saint Albans well. Rest assured, you would be admitted. Thank you, Dylan. I will carry your message to Edward's household."

She imagined them shaking hands, but had she looked through a small crack in the door Anne would have seen something far more startling. The Earl of Ayliffe opened his arms and the men embraced fiercely, like committed friends who might be parting for the last time. She heard the chamber door open for Dylan's departure.

"My lord, I cannot leave without telling you this. It pains me deep and I pray you believe I have no personal stake in the news. I saw only a small faction of these rebels as they gathered for Warwick. Your son, Brainard Forbes, rides with Redesdale against the king." Again there was a long silence. "I'm sorry." Dylan's voice came in a breath.

"In a way," Brennan said quietly, "he has been driven to it." There was a soft rueful laugh. "How can I pity myself? The king's own brother betrays him. Such is the world; our labor is painful, our rewards are few. Ride hard, Dylan. Go with God."

The chamber door was hardly closed when Anne came out

of her small writing closet and ran into Brennan's arms. He saw the path of tears on her cheeks. "You heard?"

She nodded solemnly. "What does it mean, Brennan?"

"It means, my dear Anne, that my king and my beloved Ayliffe are in severe jeopardy. I imagine we will see battle soon."

"Brennan, you must not go. Send troops, money, anything, but do not go to battle. Your life is more valuable than Ayliffe, than the king's cause."

"Are you afraid for me, my love? I am flattered, but my first call is to protect my country and my home. All will be well, given time and good fortune." He looked down into her frightened eyes. "At least you do not betray me. I will reward that loyalty someday."

She tore her gaze away. She could not let him see the conflict shining there.

Chapter Fourteen

AFTER DELIVERING the message about Robin of Redesdale to King Edward, Brennan Forbes quickly moved his family to the stout castle of Ayliffe and returned to his king with a large troop of men to join with Edward's forces to drive back the rebels. Lord Forbes expected the confrontation to be brief and glorious for the crown, but he was never more wrong. Rebel forces, small and scattered factions of various armies that had been gathering steam over a year, surprised King Edward's armies. There were executions and captives were taken: King Edward was a prisoner of George Neville, Archbishop of York.

King Edward was not long unseated. Warwick had managed to eliminate some of his enemies, but in the end he could not raise an army without a king. Therefore, he grudgingly released his captive. Edward was yet king, but the countryside was in turmoil. It was far from over. There was more war to come.

The respite after the king's release was brief, and Lord Forbes was now fully conscious of the magnitude of the conflict. Upon his return to Ayliffe for replenished numbers of soldiers, horses, and ordnance, he made serious changes in his own household that he hoped could help Ayliffe sustain a long and difficult struggle. He sent Sloan to acquaintances in Calais, hopeful that the deputy there was King Edward's man and would not fall in with Warwick. The much-used ruse of getting heirs away from their property brought the enormity of the trouble home to Anne; Sloan was being protected so as not to be killed in an overthrow and for the eventuality of returning and avenging his family's loyalties. Male heirs were often executed; women were merely fined and ousted.

Next, Brennan knew he would have to take many of his best men with him, leaving Sir Clifton as the highest ranking officer to remain to protect Ayliffe's walls. Sir Cliff was brought into Brennan's confidence and was instructed to beware of Brainard and keep the countess safe. The knight, proud of his new post, did not seem to realize he was the only one left; rather, he thought the earl had honored him.

Through the fall and winter Brennan only visited his home. He and his army stayed mostly on the road, quelling this uprising in the south, that rioting in the north. He came home for new troops and all too brief rest for himself. Each time he returned, Anne begged him not to leave again.

The summer of 1470 was hot and steaming. Apprehension and lack of information caused the tension to mount throughout Ayliffe's walls. There were few whose confidence and courage could be considered dependable. Down to the last washwoman there were short tempers and nervous titters. The watchmen strained their eyes to survey the land accurately, and everything was in readiness to defend Ayliffe against a possible attack.

The Countess of Ayliffe and her chief officer, Sir Clifton, moved through this frightening summer with a fortitude that neither of them quite felt. Anne often surveyed the troops with Sir Clifton in her husband's stead. Her mind was turned away from household chores and toward castle duties. She began to manage her husband's accounts, for she could read and cipher as well as he, and it was essential that Ayliffe remain the stronghold it had always been. As for Sir Clifton, he answered to no one but the countess. Together, through long days and many late-night conferences, they ruled the great demesne.

She touched his arm once, partly out of respect and also because she was grateful to him. "I would be lost without you, Sir Cliff."

She did not seem to notice the hot light in his eyes, the trembling her meager touch caused. "By the grace of a most merciful God, my lady, you will never be lost."

Anne and Sir Clifton sustained themselves on rumors brought by monks and traveling merchants. They could not verify the truth without opening Ayliffe's gates and sending out riders, a tactic that had been strictly forbidden by Lord Forbes. In mid-October of 1470 a messenger arrived, a remnant of the Ayliffe troop that had left with Brennan months before, to bring them the blackest news. Lord Forbes had ridden north with the king to drive back a rebel group, and during this sojourn, Warwick had landed with an army. The king and his ministers and advisers, among others, had been chased and had escaped by leaving the country.

"Lord Forbes instructed us to ride hard for Ayliffe and bring you the word to keep the castle. He was alive when I last saw him, my lady."

Anne swooned against Sir Clifton, but she did not faint. She steadied herself with the help of Clifton's strong and eager arm. For Brennan to lose and flee into exile after a year of fighting was almost more than she could bear. She feared she would never see her husband alive again.

"And the devil, Warwick?" she asked.

"He has taken mad King Henry from the tower and crowned him."

Anne knew in her heart that Ayliffe would be next. If Warwick had the power of the crown, he would quickly take all the greater holdings into his possession. Ayliffe sat northeast of London, close enough so that any troop of Warwick's that was dispatched could reach them in two days, yet she felt as though she lived thousands of leagues away from the action. There were stories of riots all over the country, sometimes London was said to be in celebration because of the restoration of the pitiful, senile king; sometimes it was said that the city was being torn apart by rebels.

Letters came slowly to Ayliffe. Quentin was killed while fighting for Edward's cause in the south, leaving no heir. Bart took Raedelle on King Henry's and Warwick's behalf, finally close to a chance for quick power. And Trenton, Ayliffe's and Edward's loyal vassal still, pledged to unseat his own brother. Marcella wrote from Heathwick, her tone accusatory; Anne had turned brother against brother by making Trenton her protector. Anne shook her head in confusion. She had only meted out her mother's many requests. Though she felt little loyalty for Bart and, indeed, was often worried by his ambition and lack of honor, there was still a deep ache in her heart as she dispatched one hundred of her best soldiers to aid Trenton.

It was November, a year after their struggle began, when word finally came that Brennan was alive, safely out of England and with Edward at the Hague. She had not even seen him since June. She greatly feared she would never hear his comforting voice again. When she was not walking the wall, commanding the men with Sir Clifton, her head was often bent in prayer. For her people she kept up a courageous and positive front, but there were two people who knew she was often afraid and wept for her husband's safety: Sir Clifton and her friend Jane. To trust Jane to this degree was common for Anne after so many years, but it was only the wars and the fighting that brought her this close to Sir Cliff. She began to trust him; she certainly had no other man she could depend on as much. She did not, however, consider there could be danger in this trust. Sir Clifton struggled to conceal the fact that he was deeply in love with his lady, his countess. He tried to appear duty bound, but he prayed that Lord Forbes would not return to Ayliffe.

As the winter winds began to descend on the countryside and doors were frozen shut, a troop bearing the banner for King Henry gathered outside Ayliffe's gates. The residents and guards panicked, certain the day had finally come; Warwick would claim Ayliffe for King Henry. If Ayliffe, with her enormous garrison of warriors and powerful ordnance, was pulled into Warwick's cause against their own lord, Brennan Forbes might never recover his home.

Sir Clifton forbade his men to fire until a herald was heard. Anne thought he was acting out of resourcefulness and prudence; she was confident of his skill as a knight and his loyalty to Ayliffe. She did not know that he secretly hoped that Lord Forbes would be prevented from ever reclaiming his earldom. The gates were opened to a lone rider.

Anne listened to the messenger, and a slow smile grew on her lips. How did God deliver her, in the darkest of days, after all she had done in defiance? The dispatched troop, sent from London to read the charges against King Edward and announce the restoration of King Henry, was led by the Duke of Clarence's loyal servant, Lord deFrayne.

She tugged on Clifton's sleeve and whispered in his ear. A flicker of disappointment that Anne misread as suspicion crossed the knight's eyes. "Open the gates," she shouted. "Lord deFrayne brings word from Parliament. There will be no battle today."

She watched him enter her demesne. Her heart lurched like a ship on a stormy sea. She had not seen him in over three years. Over two years ago she had heard his voice in confidence with her husband. No one, not even Jane, knew that her tears and prayers were often for Dylan.

He was more handsome than ever. His face was strong, his chin firm and held high, his arms had grown mighty. As a lad he had caused her heart to sail because of his good looks, but as a man, two and thirty years now, he was like a god. As he dismounted she filled her eyes with the sight of his powerful thighs, his magnificent hands, his steady and determined stride as he approached her.

He unscrolled the vellum document and read the words, surely Warwick's words, delivering the message to the people of England that Edward had been declared a bastard and deposed. King Henry would rule. She heard the moans of disappointment all around her as Dylan read, turning full circle to address them all. Behind him, still astride, were only forty of his men.

Dylan finished reading the missive he had delivered and faced the Countess of Ayliffe. He held the parchment high, his hands locked into the top. He looked deeply into her eyes with a vague smile playing on his lips and, in a dramatic gesture, he slowly tore the announcement from Parliament down the middle, rending it into two equal pieces. Anne, understanding perfectly, grasped her skirts on each side and bowed low before Dylan. From behind him, his own men led a cheer for Edward that was quickly joined by the Ayliffe troops. Dylan's days as a spy were nearly over. After sending word to the Earl of Warwick that he met no resistance at Ayliffe, he would hold the mighty estate until the return of Lord Forbes . . . and his king, Edward.

The Ayliffe gates were slammed closed behind Dylan's troop and the bridge was raised. Dylan extended his hand to Sir Clifton. "Will you give this troop rest and food, sir? It appears we will be unable to return to London soon."

Sir Clifton was astounded. He not only had seen Dylan on more than one occasion, but he had heard a great deal about the man. Dylan's prowess in tournaments and in battle were well known. "But . . . I thought . . . that is, my lord, you are said to be . . . I thought you were for Lancaster?"

Dylan smiled brightly. "As you were meant to believe, sir. How else do you think King Edward would know his brother's and Warwick's moves so well?"

"You are . . . ?"

"Surely my secret is safe here?" Dylan asked. "Until His Majesty comes home?"

Sir Clifton smiled in understanding. He was not too disappointed in the news. He did not wish to serve Warwick. Indeed, he felt privy to a royal conspiracy and was excited by the prospect. This was not Lord Forbes, come home to take Anne away from him. This was a young warrior sneaking behind the mighty Warwick's back. And there remained the chance that the earl would never return. Sir Clifton hoped for a good, long winter . . . with his countess. "Welcome, my lord. We are your grateful hosts."

In January Brainard rode on Ayliffe, carrying the Lancaster banner. He was met by an impressive emissary in Lord deFrayne, who rode out to greet him with a substantial troop at his back. Brainard was informed that the castle was already held for Lancaster and that the king's strictest orders were that no one, friend or family, was to be permitted entry. Brainard foolishly launched an attack and was sent flying down the road by an army twenty times the strength of his own.

Sir Clifton could not resist the urge to give chase, and took a force of two hundred knights in pursuit. He returned a day later, late at night, his cheeks flushed from excitement and the cold, and converged on the countess in the darkness of night to give his report.

Anne sat in her bedchamber and listened patiently while Clifton told every detail of a two-day chase that drove Brainard far to the west. She nodded and smiled, more disgruntled than she dared let on. "You are my good servant, Sir Clifton," she said. And, "We would surely be conquered without you." He rambled on, and she patiently replied, "Lord Forbes will reward you well. Get thee food and rest, sir knight. I bless you for your bravery." But still, he rambled on, taking more than an hour of her time, in the middle of the night when the fire had burned low. Before leaving he fell to his knees and kissed the palms of her hands, swearing to keep her safe always. She thought she would never get him out of her bedchamber. Finally, with a heavy sigh, she closed the door behind him and threw the bolt.

The door from the common room slowly opened. Dylan stood shivering in his hastily donned chausses, wearing no shirt. He went to stand near the waning fire to warm himself. He looked over his shoulder at Anne and whispered, "Your good and stalwart knight not only interrupted my hard-earned pleasures; he nearly froze me to death."

"Come, my love, and let me warm you properly."

Dylan stirred up the fire for the benefit of the bedchamber and by the time he turned away from the hearth Anne was already in the bed with the quilt drawn back. He was pleased to accept her offered warmth. The winter had been good to them. They were careful not to look into each other's eyes when they were in the same room. Dylan rarely even dined with the countess, and kept quarters on the north side of the castle, far away and reserved for guests. During the days he kept his attention strictly focused on the knights and Sir Clifton, becoming close to the earl's men and remaining a good comrade to his own. For all eyes he was merely a vassal of the earl's and frankly uninterested in the countess. He was courteous, but distant. He even caused a little gossip by flirting with castlewomen, but he was cautious to stir no jealous, curious blood among the wenches. And late at night, almost every night, he crept through the halls to be let into Anne's bedchamber by Jane.

They lay back against the down pillows, the quilt drawn up high, and Dylan encircled her with his arms. "You have so many strong men who would die for you," he teased.

"And then I have you," she countered, "forever sneaking around, appearing in so many disguises, and putting me at grave risk."

He laughed low in his throat and gave her a squeeze. "The wolf guards the hen. Sir Clifton would explode if he knew." He turned his head and looked down at her. "You do know about Sir Clifton, do you not? You do not fool yourself. . . ."

"I know," she said. "I try to discourage him as politely as I can, but I do know, Dylan. Yet, what am I to do? Without him I would reside in danger."

"Just be careful, my Anne. Watch him. Do not allow your dependence on his strength to put you at any disadvantage."

"I will be careful. While he serves me loyally I can think of no reason to replace him with another. There seems to be no more able man in Ayliffe."

"Would that it could be I, Anne."

"Do you ever worry, Dylan — that we will be . . . punished for this stolen pleasure?"

"Punished? I worry that we will be caught, but punished by

God? By the angels?" He kissed her forehead. "I have been deep in love with you for a dozen years, and somehow I cannot believe 'tis the devil's curse. I see it as a gift; the only truly important thing in my life. Do I delude myself?"

"Nay," she whispered with a smile, snuggling closer. " 'Tis a gift, surely."

"Perhaps I should relieve Cliff and move in here to keep you well for the old earl."

"Lady Raynia might find it amiss," she teased him.

"Ah, Raynia, poor creature," he sighed, mention of his wife causing him to become serious. "Bless her frail little mind, a more odd, unhappy woman has never lived. I cannot even hate her, I pity her so."

"She is no better?"

"Worse each year, my love. I shall have to send her back to Calais for at least a long visit. She loathes England, me, everything in her sight." He thought for a moment. He had told Anne almost everything, but some things were too private, almost embarrassing. His ugly little wife still had her ugly little maid.

"She will have none of you? Even after losing her son?"

"She does not wish to be burdened with a husband. So . . . I give her whatever comforts she requests and I allow her sanctuary in the country where she feels safe and left alone. Raynia will not complain that I am too long away."

"And Justin?"

"Bless Lady Raynia, she does not deny me that pleasure. She gives him none of her love, but she abides his presence politely. My mother nurtures him well and I give him as much time as I can. He will be a strong man one day and carry on this deFrayne family for my brother's sake. I confess, the boy makes me proud. And I am glad that he is too young to understand this business of mine; if he thought me a traitor, it would hurt me deeply." His eyes gazed across the room, his voice became wistful and distant. "It is just as well that I do not have a devoted wife, but I cannot pretend that I don't feel cheated. Every man wants a son."

Her heart ached for him. "Oh, Dylan, perhaps you can convince Raynia . . ."

"Nay," he laughed, but his eyes were somewhat misty. "There will be none of that. I will act as a guardian to my nephew. That will have to do."

"Had you ever given a thought to what might happen if I conceived your child?"

"You know I have, minx," he said, giving her a squeeze. "We have taken every possible precaution, sometimes to our own displeasure. Thus far no one has noticed how I give thanks to every saint in heaven when you announce the flow of your monthly blood. In two months, we have been fortunate. May our luck continue." He chuckled to himself.

"What would you do, Dylan, if I came with child?"

"Given our present circumstances?" he asked. She nodded, looking up at him. She saw his eyes come alive a little. He smiled as he thought. "I would pray first that the earl mistook it for his own, but you would have to perform some pretty witchcraft for that, since the earl, God bless him, does not make use of you when he is home. But . . . if it could be, if he could believe it was his own child, I would watch you round out, if possible, and wait patiently to hear the news. I would be near if I could, but you are wed to a man boasting ten thousand soldiers, so discretion is the word." He chuckled, in spite of himself. "And I suppose I would offer to train the boy, to have some influence. Barring that, I would simply content myself with watching him grow handsome and strong and good in his heart. You would raise him to be good in his heart. He would perhaps inherit Ayliffe, more than I could ever give him."

"You would not like that," she said, her heart beginning to beat wildly. "You are too proud to watch a child of yours raised as another man's heir."

"Oh? Think you so?" He laughed. It was all only a story to Dylan. She felt herself grow increasingly warm in the cold bedchamber. "You are wrong, my Anne. Just to know that a child of mine lived would fill me with uncommon joy. Just to know that you nurtured my seed and brought it to life, that would be glory. Perhaps when he became a man, if we were friends, I could tell him of my love for his mother, of my devotion, though carefully distant, to him. Perhaps I could convince him that had I claimed him, it would have cost him, and my silence while he grew into manhood was the better part of my love. If he grew to be someone who could feel love at all . . . he would surely understand."

Hot tears stained her cheeks. He felt the wetness of her tears on his arm.

"There now, my love, do not weep. It is only a notion; you forced me to become carried away. I will be careful. I know it can never be."

"You almost make me believe you speak the truth, Dylan. I wonder. Perhaps if I birthed you a son, you would begin to speak of flight again."

"Do you think me a coward because I gave up the notion as easily as I did? If I thought something could be gained by running away with you, I would risk it. The danger is too great; I cannot, in conscience, subject you to possible death. I know this is not much, my love, but it is a great deal better than we would have by running, hiding. Nay, there is no day of flight ahead. This is the most we are likely to get. And I have resigned myself. I will never have a son."

She thought she might choke on her own tears. "Is it really so important to a man? Just to know —"

"That a portion of himself will live on? That a man never really dies when a child of his own breathes the air long after he is dead?" He gave a little huff of air. "What more is there?"

"Many nobles have bastard children. There is a country full of pretty wenches who would gladly . . ." She could not finish.

"Ah, yes, the wenches. But, my Anne, my thoughts never fail to turn to you. I want no other woman. Not even my own wife." He squeezed her hard and kissed her brow. "Do not weep. I have a little bit of you; I have your love and carry it with me when we are parted. I will manage without a son."

"Dylan, do you speak true? If the earl mistook your child for his own, would it truly please you, yet keep you silent?"

"Anne," he said suspiciously, "you told me all was well." He sat up straight and held her away from him. "Did you lie to me? Do we have some trouble?"

She shook her head and wiped at her tears. "Dylan, forgive me, but for all the reasons you named . . ."

"What?" he insisted when her voice trailed off and her tears began anew. He gave her a little shake.

"Sloan," she wept.

"Sloan? What about Sloan?"

"Your son, Dylan. Sloan is your son."

He stared at her in shock for a long moment, his eyes wide with surprise. His eyes moved absently about the room, as if in search of an answer, almost oblivious to her though he still held her in his arms.

"Conceived . . . in the cask room," she whispered.

She could see that he was concentrating, counting in his head, thinking carefully of the past. Then he slowly slackened his grip on her arms and pulled her against his chest, embracing her. A slow smile grew on his lips. His arms tightened about Anne.

Someday, if we are friends, he thought, I can tell him that my love for his mother was pure and good, even if our circumstances were sad ones. I was about to die, I will tell him, and I had loved her so desperately. The love never waned, never faded, not for a moment, not for a day. But our families wed us far from each other and ours were only stolen moments. Still, we never gave up hope. Never did we tell, so that our son could grow into manhood without the stigma of being born a bastard. If ever there was a child conceived in love, nurtured and protected for his own sake, it was Sloan. A son. A son. A son.

He bent his lips to Anne's. He stilled her weeping with kisses. He thanked her for her courage, her loving attention to his son. He swore to keep safe and secret the truth of Sloan's conception. He blessed her for telling him. Now he might watch his son become a man, even if it would be from afar. There was *a son!* There was another someday for Dylan. His heart soared.

He made love to her, filled with a new excitement, a glow that would not be dimmed. He forgot that she was wed to another, as was he. Nothing mattered to him except the moment, the glory, the eternity of living on and on. He had the woman he loved in his arms, and out there in a world that had given him little a part of himself grew strong. His son would have children of his own. All burdens seemed to fall from his shoulders. Fate was kind, he had a son. He forgot everything. He was less than cautious, and he failed to notice.

"Stay in your rooms then, if you cannot see me to the gate without betraying your feelings. You may believe that this is the moment we have been waiting for; our true king will rescue England from the hands of a greedy earl and a mad ruler. Your husband comes home, my lady, and my life rests in his hands. If you grieve my departure and give away our secrets, Edward's only reward for my years of spying will be a hangman's noose."

"What will happen now that Edward has landed?" Anne asked in the early predawn hours.

"No matter what you might hear, be assured he has come for his kingdom, and Warwick will die. Many will die. Edward is more clever than he lets on. He will not be fooled again."

"You will finally ride with the king," she mused, snuggling closely, knowing it would be a long time before she would be near him again. She refused to think that this might be the last time ever.

"I am certain he will keep me busy, resettling his domain, while the traitors will be confronted. They have gone too far. Spies will be most unnecessary." He tilted her chin, kissed her lips. "Among the traitors, not only King Edward's brother, the Duke of Clarence, but your brother. Forgive me, my love, if it is my own blade that slays Bart. Believe it is for England, not for some old feud."

"I cannot help Bart now," she whispered. "He was never loyal to anything but his own wanting. I'm sorry for him, that's all."

Finally the hour came for Dylan to depart. He kissed her and held her one more time. "I love you. Remember that." He beamed a smile as he crept from her chamber. "Thank you for Sloan." And he was gone.

Dylan took many of Ayliffe's men with his own troop toward Yorkshire. Edward had let the word be that he came to pay homage to King Henry and only wished to reclaim his duchy of York. And then he rode toward Coventry, collecting troops along the way, and held a public reconciliation with his brother George, the Duke of Clarence. As Anne heard of this she remembered Dylan's words — no matter what you hear, Edward is home for his crown.

March grew old and messages came from the Earl of Ayliffe. Edward's army faced off against Warwick's, but there was no battle. Edward pressed his forces on London, returning mad Henry quickly to the tower. Word came by way of travelers that Edward's army was enormous and once London was secure, they would move toward Warwick for a final confrontation.

Riders bearing the Ayliffe arms rode to Anne to tell her to prepare the hall and slaughter meat. The battle had been fought at Barnet on Easter morning. England was Edward's again. Many had fallen, Bart among them. Warwick was dead. And Brennan was coming home.

When he arrived, Anne ran into his arms and wept copiously. She hoped, as he comforted her, that he would assume her tears were only the grateful rivers of emotion that flowed from her for his safe return. But, she had lost her love again. This time, however, she was not pleased by the notion that he might have left a part of himself with her.

Chapter Fifteen

THE EFFECTS of many battles, intrigues, and months of tramping the continent in search of military allies showed on Brennan Forbes. He was nearing sixty years of age. He was still a formidable looking man, tall and lean, and his voice still issued command convincingly. But his hair was almost entirely white and the lines on his weathered face were deeper. And when he finished dealing with a castellan, servant, or soldier, his shoulders slumped in exhaustion. Faced with his weakening constitution, Anne briefly forgot her own troubles.

His five-year-old Deirdre was still his greatest comfort, though he had brought eleven-year-old Sloan home with him. The earl's health was suffering; he was too old for such battles. And too old for the hard work he forced on himself. He let only a day of rest pass before he began to interview those people who had held together Ayliffe with his wife in his absence, and started to look over the pages of accounts she had kept.

She took his praise of her good work with mixed feelings. "Brennan, please, everything is in order; you need not strain yourself. You should rest."

"Don't worry about me, my lady. I am only old, not infirm yet."

"Let me rub your shoulders, bring you a posset, something."

"You have done a fine job, with Sir Clifton's help. But then I never doubted you would. I knew that Ayliffe was yours the moment I met you. In my heart, I knew it."

She sighed heavily. "I fear you are becoming befuddled, Brennan. You are too sentimental. Rest, I beg you, or Ayliffe *will* be mine."

"A wiser lass would be anxious for the old man to die. I half believe you are trying to keep me alive." His head was bent to his work and he did not look at her.

"Brennan Forbes, do not toy with me. I have commanded these troops in your absence, though it would insult Sir Cliff mightily to hear me say that, even to you. If you do not stop and relax with your family and villeins, I shall call the guard and have you carried from your work."

He looked up and raised a curious brow at the sound of command in her voice. He chuckled pridefully. He laid down his quill. "I half believe you would, Anne of Ayliffe. Very well. Get Sloan and Deirdre. Sloan plays the rebec beautifully. I don't believe you've heard him. Perhaps Deirdre will sing. Let us have music, then."

Brennan was relaxed in his hall, holding Anne's hand now and then, while the children entertained them. She told herself over and over again that he was only tired, that his remarkable energy would return. Late in the evening when they climbed the stairs together, Anne raised on her toes to kiss his cheek. He paused meaningfully, looking deeply into her eyes. "You seem tired, lass. Has the strain been too much?"

"It is only worry, Brennan. I think you do not take care of yourself as you should."

"You do not beg me to hold you through the night. . . ."

"Oh, please," she said, changing her expression for him, "come. . . ."

The youthful twinkle in his eyes disappeared as quickly as it had come. He chuckled in spite of himself. "It was just a fleeting memory, my dear. I am too tired for all that. I am old. I need my lonely bed . . . and rest."

"I will be still," she whispered, longing to make him happy. She was a little afraid that she might be losing him; not his love, but . . . him. He might be dying.

"My Lord deFrayne, did he do well by you? By Ayliffe?"

She shrugged and looked down. "Sir Clifton managed our men; Lord deFrayne kept mostly to himself. He did send away your son, however."

"Aye, Brainard, waving Lancaster's colors. But he is only temporarily gone, I'm afraid. He sent a message immediately. He wishes for me to receive him. I imagine he would like to be forgiven." Brennan laughed somewhat cruelly. "By now, with Edward's enemies being hanged one by one, I'm sure that the meagerest portion of Ayliffe appeals to Brainard. It is amazing, is it not, how a little war can curb a man's greed?"

"Brennan, do not let him hurt you."

He patted her hand. "Don't worry, lass. He can't hurt me. Not really."

"I am afraid of him, Brennan. He is not steadfast."

"In a way," he said softly, "he has been driven to that."

The words caught in Anne's memory and she almost gasped when she heard them a second time. But Brennan was not willing to say any more. He went to bed alone and rose to his chores again. Anne watched him warily. Her husband was becoming frail. There was no doubt anymore. She would not have him long. And she did not know what she would do without him because she knew that, still, she could not have Dylan.

Lord Forbes was home for less than a fortnight when Brainard arrived. Anne had alerted Sir Clifton that he was coming. She made a grand show, herself, of donning her Ayliffe costume, her blazoned gown of white and gold, and an elaborate hennin that gave her height, and met Brainard in the courtyard. Sir Clifton stood at her side.

Brainard wore an insolent smirk as he dismounted. He nodded

toward them both. "Your mother, the Countess of Heathwick, sends her good tidings," he said.

"My mother?" she questioned. "How do you know my mother?"

"When Lord deFrayne sent me away, I thought a visit to a friendly noble home was in order. Your mother is a gracious hostess when your brother is away fighting for King Edward." He chuckled slightly at her reaction. "At least you have the good grace to blush, my lady."

Brainard made to pass and she reached out and snared a piece of his sleeve to detain him. "Brainard, your father has suffered this past year. Do not hurt him, I beg you."

"I do not intend to hurt *him*, madam," he returned snidely. He pulled his arm away roughly, gave his short cape a meaningful swirl, and strode into the hall with great purpose. Anne stared after him in a state of shock. Could Marcella really have betrayed her now? Like this? After all these years of keeping silent?

"What does he mean, my lady?" Clifton asked. He grasped her elbow gently when she did not reply immediately. "My lady Anne," he whispered urgently, supportively, "what does Brainard mean?"

She turned and looked into Sir Clifton's eyes. She swallowed bravely. "He means to make trouble for me, Sir Cliff. Any way he can."

She saw fire come into Clifton's eyes as he clenched his jaw. "I will kill him if he hurts you in any way, my lady. I swear."

"You will do nothing without my approval," she told him sternly. "But thank you," she said more quietly. And she left him standing in the courtyard while she went into the hall. She could almost feel the stones pelt her naked flesh.

Through a long afternoon and early evening Anne sat unmoving in the chair before the hearth in her room. Deny or confess? she asked herself over and over again. Do I answer these accusations that will surely come with truth, or do I pretend 'tis only the unkind slander of my enemies? My own mother, and my husband's son. The eerie combination chilled her to the bone.

To have hurt Brennan with her actions filled her with remorse, for he did not deserve such betrayal. His punishment would be easy to bear, especially if it gave him any relief at all from the pain he must surely feel. If only she could have known the consequences of her actions. If she lost her children through an act of adultery, the pain would be unbearable. Sloan and Deirdre needed her. How could she have indulged herself at the expense of so many people she loved?

Oh Dylan, she thought, we were wrong. Dreadfully wrong. How did we manage to convince ourselves it was right? What was it we said, that our act might be wrong, but our love was good and pure? That our strong passion was a gift we carried with us when parted, to make us strong? That to have a small, secret part of each other was better than nothing at all?

Jane, who had allowed Dylan to enter the countess's private chamber night after blissful night, did not know how deep and long the love affair had been. The tiring woman, so dedicated and true, pitied her mistress's chaste and celibate life and was swept away by some romantic notion when she considered a brief, safe alliance with the handsome and reknowned Lord deFrayne. Even though Jane had accompanied Anne to Dylan's London lodgings three times, she had not known that there was more to their conferences. And since the nights they shared when Brennan was away were never discovered by anyone, Jane had no idea that there was trouble.

It was quite late when Brennan came to Anne's bedchamber. She had refused an evening meal, had refused to be dressed for bed, and was, in fact, numb with worry. She could not face the gathering at the evening meal, nor could she find the strength to leave her own chamber and chance Brainard's accusing remarks or his superior sneer. And then Brennan entered and she wondered why she had expected him to arrive screaming, purple with rage. His anger had never been turned on her, not once. The only sign of a brewing storm was in his red-rimmed eyes, his furrowed brow.

"Poor Anne," he said. "I fear you have been indiscreet."

A bowl of frothy syllabub had been left for her hours earlier and Brennan dipped into the flat, stale drink, filling two goblets. Her eyes were glass, her lips still. She could not respond. She had no idea to which accusation she would be responding.

Brennan handed her a goblet of the drink and sat down opposite her. He stretched one leg out in front of himself and leaned back in the chair tiredly. She had heard nothing all through the day and early evening. No yelling, no fighting, no accusing.

"The battle, it appears, is really between you and Brainard. I sent him away, but I think in all my efforts to protect you, I did not help you at all."

She took a swallow of the drink, lifting the goblet with trembling hands. It did not quite go down, but seemed to sit, thick and painfully, in her throat. "Please tell me what has happened," she requested politely. She braced herself to accept a beating, or at least a berating, but Brennan's expression and indeed, his posture, did not hint at anger. Not even the pain of betrayal. His gray eyes were sad, but almost sympathetic.

"What has happened," he repeated. "Do you realize that in little beyond a month, I will celebrate six decades of life? Almost everything has happened to me. I lost my own father and was created an earl in his stead when I was a young man. But I was ready for the title, the responsibility."

Anne frowned and took another drink, hoping the brew would stabilize and quiet her inner turmoil. Brennan went on.

"My first wife's name was Elizabeth. She was seven and ten; I was five and twenty. Our betrothal was written when we were children, but we had a passion for each other that rivaled the passions and lusts in the court of Arthur. Ah," he said, in a melancholy voice filled with nostalgia, "it was Elizabeth, really, who showed me the depth and intensity of true love, and how long it could last, proven so because our marriage was not long; she died in childbed, poor lass. Ten years passed before I stopped crying out for her in my sleep. Sometimes, I still long for her warmth beside me."

A tear collected in Anne's eye and slowly traced a path down her cheek. Brennan's pain was her pain.

"I never forgot Elizabeth. I searched for her in other women, but there never was another, not even you. I did marry, however, because earls must marry, must beget sons. So a utilitarian wife I did take, a rich young widow named Charise. She was neither pretty nor smart. She exercised no power in my home, nor did she come with child. Do you wonder what Charise did give me? She adored me. Charise was demure in the hall, wanton in my bed. A rather amazing woman. And in all her adoration for me, she forgave my every indiscretion; indeed, she excused me completely if I was inattentive, unfaithful, or even cruel."

Anne had asked brief questions about his wives, but never had they had a conversation like this one. Never had Brennan bared his soul. Another tear came to her eyes, but she kept silent.

"And I met you. Well," he laughed, "I saw you. You resemble Elizabeth in a small way. Your slight figure, your black hair and dark eyes. It stirred first a memory, and then a youthful fire in me. I had not felt that way in some years. And I did love you most passionately for a man of fifty years."

"Brennan, I . . ."

He held up a hand, warning her not to speak yet. He drained his cup, made a face at the taste, and dangled the goblet in his hand.

"I loved you passionately. Your beauty and tenacity refilled this dented old cup with fresh wine." He smiled at her. "And for a long while I was angry that you did not share that passion. I thought that as I played your body with my expert skills, you would grow addicted to the joys of our intimacy. That you did not feel what I felt was a disappointment to me. But it was to your advantage, my dear, that I was not a young man, because in my age and experience I could not overlook all your other qualities. Oh, I have been aware of your devotion, your love. I have felt it as you knead the pain from my sore arms, as you see to my home, raise the children with dedication and deep love. When you run into my arms when I have been a long time away, I have been assured that you truly missed me, that having me near is good for you. I do know that much, Anne.

"What I wanted, though," he continued, "was for Elizabeth's loveliness and Charise's talent in bed. I wanted you to embody the best of my two former wives. It was unfair of me. And," he said, shaking his head, "impossible."

She inhaled a sob and her shaking hand came to her lips as tears flowed down her cheeks. She tried to control her weeping, but it was too late.

"Do not let any of this overwhelm you, Anne," he said patiently. "This conversation is long overdue. We have some small troubles to overcome. Of course, you must never see him again."

She swallowed hard and wiped impatiently at her wet cheeks. She steadied her goblet with both hands and brought it to her lips. The stale brew caused a wave of nausea to flow through her, and she shuddered.

"You need not be afraid. Not of me, that is. I am old enough now to be both understanding and forgiving. We have all had our, well . . . sins. But some of us manage to escape without being exposed."

"Brennan," she said, her voice quivering, "what did Brainard tell you?"

"I'm afraid I've failed my son again, *chérie*. He did not surprise me, but I certainly surprised him. You see, he fully expected to enrage me and I imagine he licked his lips at the prospect of seeing you stripped and nailed to the wall for a stoning. But his little piece of gossip did not move me greatly. I have known of your love for Dylan deFrayne." He paused meaningfully, watching her eyes, but she struggled to keep them blank. How long? she wanted to scream. When did you know? How did you say nothing of my betrayal? "In part, I asked him to see to Ayliffe for your sake. You deserved a reward. For . . . your good and faithful service to me . . . for giving me Deirdre, my only legitimate heir."

Anne could not suppress her shocked gasp. Her eyes grew round, startled and a little afraid. Her stomach jumped. "What . . . what are you saying . . . ?"

There was an impatient look that suddenly darkened his gray eyes. She could not tell if it was denial, disappointment, or anger. She immediately regretted that she had not argued the parentage of Sloan instantly. Brennan was done with story-telling. He stood abruptly and went to the anteroom that separated their bedchambers to summon Jane, though the hour was quite late and she might have been asleep on her pallet. "Bring us wine, hot and spiced," he demanded. He turned away from the anteroom door and began to pace.

"I was not always a proper man, Anne. While I was married to Charise I got a woman with child. I meant to settle her with a knight of my household and have her moved away, but Charise, who had not managed to give me a child, begged me to let the woman give birth in seclusion, and give Charise the child to raise as my son. Charise would do anything for me. Anything. And so we went to Charise's dower estate of Ramsford with my one-time mistress and came back to Ayliffe with a child of our own. Brainard is not a legitimate heir.

"Brainard came here to tell me that Sloan and Deirdre are products of your long love affair with Dylan deFrayne. I suspected Sloan's parentage, and after a while it was quite obvious whose child he really is. I recommend, for Sloan's sake as well as your own, that you do what you can to keep him away from Dylan deFrayne. Despite what Brainard says, I know Deirdre is my child of our wedded union. I gave you that child, and you gave her to me. She was not conceived in a moment of ill-directed lust, but of love. Nay, not a passion that you could not resist, but *love*. No matter what happened before or after, it was only we two, and there was *love*."

"Oh, Brennan," she sighed. She shook her head. Did nothing escape him? Was it true that he endowed her with Dylan, out of gratefulness? Did he mean to slight Sloan?

"I would like to write a document and have it posted. I would like to cast the ungrateful Brainard to his betters in Ramsford. It does not bother me that he has no respect for me — but that the surly colt does not appreciate what Charise did for him, what she did for all of us, makes me angry. Perhaps I am not

[274]

worthy of my son's respect; perhaps it is true that children inherit the breeding of their parents — and his mother was not a virtuous or decent woman.

"And, yea, I would like to send Sloan to his father and be done with him, even though it is no fault of Sloan's that he was conceived as he was. Even though he is a good lad, and loyal. And he loves me and calls me Father with respect, a thing my own son never did. Aye, I admit it would feel rather good to make a clean sweep of it all, and give Deirdre Ayliffe."

There was a light tapping on the door and he whirled about to admit Jane. He took the tray from her hands, closing the door again, and poured the steaming wine from the flagon into two ornate crystal chalices. He gave her one and took a large swallow of his own. "Not hot enough," he grumbled. He worried over his wine? She nearly choked on the brew, which to her was tasteless.

"I won't, of course," he said, sitting down opposite her again. "Disinherit Brainard and Sloan, that is. It would not be good for Deirdre. And, all this talk of bastardy is rather incidental. When a king can be driven out of the country and declared a bastard by Parliament, then return to revoke his bastardy and kill his enemies, well, I imagine it's pointless to carry on about it." He laughed suddenly in a short snort. "Especially in King Edward's case. He looks remarkably like his father."

"Brennan, why have you never — "

"Confronted you? Why? I know that your first intimate association with young deFrayne was born of that young love we have all felt. In fact, I still marvel at the strength you displayed through that entire event. I remember quite clearly those weeks; your grief, your fear, your lies. You were very young, yet unbelievably brave. And, of course, deFrayne was out of the country for a long while afterward and I know I had you to myself. It would have been better if you had been able to forget him . . . and deny him. But, when I realized it was he, I already knew him. If you were my daughter, I would wish for you to have such a man. In many ways, you never lost that fatherlike image you had of me. I wish you had, but you did not."

"Brennan, that is not what I felt for you. If you believe nothing else, please — "

"I know that you loved me, Anne. I've said so. I would have to be blind not to realize it. In your own way you were loyal. Now, we must move ahead with caution. You must not see him again, now that Brainard thinks he has a secret to tell. You must not look into his eyes at court, you must not watch him play the tourney. He has done a clever piece of work for the king, and eventually it will gain him considerable fame and wealth, but you must remain distant; you must not notice him. You've had your moment, you've had a few months during which I imagine he crept to your bed and gave you what you craved most, but it is done now. Over. For Deirdre's sake."

Anne looked down into her lap. Oddly, there were no tears. Brennan was her dearest friend in all the world. She wanted to tell him how it was with Dylan, how he made her feel, how their love had survived so much. Her passion for him was like a melody that could not be forgotten, like a poem that never ended. Her love for him was like a bird that flew and flew and could not descend for rest. It did not diminish what she felt for Brennan; her love for Dylan was something she simply had never been able to change.

Was she to understand, now, the strange comfort that Brennan seemed to feel when he held his daughter? Was it because Brennan held no illusions about Anne's feelings for him that he seemed not filled with pain? He said he had known for a very long time.

"You should not have sent him here," she said quietly.

"I thought you would thank me."

She slowly raised her eyes to look at her husband. "I am with child now."

A brief flicker of shock held him motionless. He was like a stone statue, his mouth slightly open, his eyes blank. "I thought . . . Ah! I thought Dylan was more clever than that. That is unfortunate. It will have to be taken care of."

She stared at him, bracing herself for the final blow. Again he stood from his chair, pacing, thinking.

"I have a little business for the king — it shouldn't take long. I will not let it take long. Do not tell anyone your circumstances and keep yourself thin, if you can. We will be going away. I'm afraid, my dear, that you will not be able to keep this child. You may give birth in seclusion and I will lend a tidy sum to have it raised in decent surroundings. Do not beg me to send the child to Dylan; do not even bother. I have been gone away from here for many months. There is no passing it off."

She blinked hard, trying to control her wild thoughts. She could not concentrate on this child now; that would have to be confronted later. She had only just come to terms with the fact, had told no one, and was in the midst of something a great deal more complicated than the birth, still many months away.

"This business with Brainard?" she asked.

He shrugged. "Nothing has changed except that he has been informed of his own, ah, mistaken birthright. It is a draw, you see, and puts you in the middle of the battle. Brainard thinks he has a cunning piece of news in Sloan's illegitimacy, but it is balanced quite evenly with his own. If Brainard goes to Ramsford to verify the news, he will find it is true.

"My plans for Ayliffe are the same. You shall remain the countess, in fact. Heathwick, now there is justice," he laughed. "Heathwick, plus a fortune in land and gold, is for Deirdre. Sloan has his barony and I have drafted a letter to Parliament and the king; I recommend that Trenton, who was always loyal to me, have Raedelle when my daughter is married and has a husband to take to Heathwick.

"As for you, my dear wife, I suggest you have someone taste your food and never go abroad without a solid guard, for Brainard should surely wish to slay you. He would like to have this earldom, uncut by my wishes."

"Did you confess Sloan's birthright?" she asked with great hesitancy.

"Certainly not. I denied it. But Brainard thinks he knows, and if he can somehow manage to get you and the rest of his own dreary past out of the way, of course he will use his information. If poor Sloan continues to resemble his father, it will be useless to argue his parentage. You will not have an easy life of it, Anne."

Sheer wonder caused her to shake her head. "I expected you to banish me . . . after a beating . . . and worse. . . . I did not dare imagine what I had done to my children."

He looked down at her, a very paternal concern showing in his eyes. Again she wondered how she had gleaned this much, this compassion from a man she had wronged with such a terrible sin.

"You have many fine qualities, Anne," he said softly. "Among them, you are a good mother. Deirdre will have the best." She looked into her lap. Her shame could not be more intense. "I wish," he said softly, "that it had all been different."

She raised her eyes and stood from her chair to approach him. Her hand was half raised. She had so often laid a comforting hand on his chest and asked how to please him, asked to ease his aching body or troubled mind. "Nay," he said, backing away from her. "Don't touch me — don't even think it. I could endure much, I have even given you a few nights with your lover; you had little enough of each other through all your uncanny, long-lasting desire, and I had, after all, failed you in bed. But now that it's out, never touch me in a wifely fashion again."

She backed away as though her hand were a knife that would cut his heart out.

"In fact, tread cautiously on my mercy, my generosity. Keep yourself quiet and small while I attempt to resign myself to the fact that for Deirdre I must take you away and get rid of your bastard. Pray God, Anne, that no one ever finds out. And resign yourself — you will never have deFrayne. *Never again.*"

He turned away and filled his goblet from the cooled flagon. He gave her a short bow. "Good night, my lady wife. Rest easy now, assured that you are spared."

"I'm sorry," she said, her voice humbled and trembling.

"I do believe you are. 'Tis sad that you were not more wise, not more cautious. I imagine your suffering is as great as mine."

He quietly quit the room with great dignity. She stood numb

and afraid, unable to move for quite some time. She had so many thoughts that no single issue surfaced long enough for her concentration. The only notion that did arise was that she *was* spared in order to raise his daughter. She had no idea what great performance of strength and mother love she had given to convince Brennan that she, she alone, was the proper parent for Deirdre. Another man in such a position would have carried away his adulterous wife, murdered her, and returned to the greatly prized child with the news that she was orphaned. Why did Brennan forgive her? Would he change his mind and clear her presence away in one impetuous, angry motion? She could hardly blame him if he did.

Nausea choked her. Brennan had said that now, reconsidering the events surrounding Sloan's conception, he marveled at her strength. Odd, how that thought came to mind as she leaned over the basin at her bedside and vomited up the bad wine, her insides racked with pain. Her head began to pound and she became cold and dizzy. Perhaps it would be unnecessary to go away and birth Dylan's child in seclusion. Could she carry the babe through this crisis and give it life? Her whole body shook with fear, despair, chilling pain. She held on to the furniture and the wall as she moved toward the anteroom to rouse Jane. She walked on trembling legs into the large room that separated her chamber from her husband's.

Jane was sitting up on her pallet, her face white and her eyes red-rimmed. Anne approached her loyal servant, one hand pressed to her mouth, one hand clutching her stomach. Jane knew. Jane had heard all. It was etched on the woman's frightened, tortured face.

The sound of crashing glass came from Brennan's chamber and both women's eyes flashed toward the sound. Following was a loud moan of grief and pain. And then, a man's sobs echoed through the room. Anne had stood through war, execution, and a multitude of events in her life that required courage and a show of strength, but never before had a sound ripped her heart from her as did this sound — the painful tears of a good man who had been greatly wronged.

Suddenly, she knew the truth, Brennan had not been sure before today, before her lack of denial. If he had indeed accepted Anne's adultery, there would not be sobs of anguish coming from his bedchamber now.

With Brainard's slander, however, given to him by her mother fact by fact, Brennan had been able to see the years in a day. As she had waited bravely in her chamber, Brennan had probably recounted in his mind each time Dylan and Anne had been in the same city. He had not sent her lover to her as a reward. He had just discovered that he had been betrayed by his wife and a young man whom he had trusted and admired.

Brennan was not the cool, calculating man he wished her to think him; he was only proud. And she was not the perfect mother he had declared her to be. Yet she was spared. Because he was unselfish and good; because he loved her. Still.

"Help me to bed," she said weakly.

The call to arms came by royal messenger in the early morning. Perhaps Brennan Forbes welcomed it. There did seem to be a faint look of relief in his tired, bereaved eyes. He instructed Anne, very quietly, to prepare for travel while he was away. He would ride to Edward's cause and, upon his return, they would journey to the continent.

Margaret of Anjou had landed with troops brought from France, and still more were being collected in the name of King Henry. Another forceful opposition was pressing into England. Edward had finished Warwick, and the senile king was again a prisoner in the tower, but the crown was not yet secure. Margaret and her son, the last representatives of an old Lancastrian reign, must be finally killed. And then, Brennan said, we will clean up our messes and get on with our lives.

He rode away with two thousand soldiers. One week later, on a warm May afternoon, two hundred men wearing the bloody Ayliffe tabard over dented armor returned. Anne stood in the courtyard, pale, drawn, and weak, to hear them. At Tewkesbury, in a victorious battle for Edward's crown that left the meadow red with blood, Lord Forbes had fallen. He was dead. Anne, Countess of Ayliffe, swooned. The world went black. She vaguely felt her head strike the ground, heard the strange, muffled voices and felt the vibration of the dirt beneath her as running feet struck the ground, but she did not try to rise.

"Take me," she muttered as she was lifted into strong, capable arms, but she was not instructing a servant. She was talking to God. And she wished to be taken. From life.

Chapter Sixteen

SIR CLIFTON WARNER had no illusions about himself. He knew his station, his skills, his gifts, and his limitations. He had come from decent country gentry and he was not nobly bred. He had applied all his energy to become a strong knight; there were none stronger nor more astute in battle plans or in the defense of a stronghold such as Ayliffe. He did not wish for more. He was not a scholar, he spoke only one language, and he would never inherit great power or wealth. He did not even want it; high-flown titles were for others to bear. As to money, he had the respect of a legion of trained soldiers, which he preferred. The devil take the crown or the House of Lords, Ayliffe was a good, solid home filled with strong fighting men, many of whom had been groomed and trained by Sir Clifton. It was a place of plenty. All he wanted was the woman.

He had pieced together Lady Anne's story without being told directly. He had carried her to her bed and between her babbling, weeping, and Jane's additions to the cryptic tale, he surmised that Anne, long without physical love, had succumbed to the amorous attentions of the confident noble swain, Lord Dylan deFrayne. Although Clifton was very surprised, he decided he should not have been. He wished he had known much sooner that the countess had longed for a man's touch. And why would she not? The old man had not slept with her in years, and Anne was a beautiful, sensual young woman. But the fool, deFrayne, had left her with child. Had the truth killed Lord Forbes? Or was it the bloody meadow?

Sir Cliff was cautious with his proposal. He did not wish to tarnish his own image with the truth that he was filled with desire for her. He had been in love with her from afar for a long, long time. He would kill Brainard to keep her safe. He would raise her bastard as his own. Had he not taken the earl's son, Sloan, under his wing with a father's pride, a teacher's zeal? True, he had done it to be near the countess, but it was not unpleasant duty. Clifton needed very little. He wanted to command his troop, practice arms, enjoy the plentiful bounty of Ayliffe. And . . . he wanted the woman for himself.

"I do not see that you have any choice, my lady. You have to marry immediately, and you should wed someone you can trust."

"There is so much you do not understand," she sighed. Since the word of Brennan's death was delivered four days before, she had not been able to rise from her bed. But the tears had stopped. And the sickness had ceased. Instinctively, she tried to clear her head. Survival had become second nature to Anne by now.

"Then tell me what you think I should know," Sir Cliff entreated.

"I have already been told that you and Jane, no others, tended me through delirium. I suspect you know more than I would have told you freely. My husband, whom I loved deeply, learned of my adultery just before he died. I carry another man's child. These are not small burdens. And they are not your burdens, Clifton."

"You cannot hide the fact that you have been unfaithful. Think, my lady. Is it not better the world assume your tampering was with the commander of your troops than with deFrayne? His lordship of Ayliffe was a long time away. We did not know for months if he was alive or dead. You committed only the sin of the woman's heart — you desired a man to ease your loneliness." He paused and took her hand in his. To touch her in such a fashion of courtship took great courage. "I would claim the child."

"Clifton, do you believe that would be accepted?" She laughed sadly. "Brainard traveled here to accuse me of adultery with Lord deFrayne. My own mother planted the seed in the young heir's ear, for Brainard has been hoping for a way to secure Ayliffe without sharing the estate. He hoped to discredit me enough so that his inheritance would be uncut by my children."

Clifton shook his head in irritation. "Lord deFrayne should have let *me* send the bastard away. He would have had nothing to say if he had not known deFrayne was here. You would have had to admit nothing if deFrayne had not given you the babe."

He does not know, she thought. He knows Dylan well, he has been Sloan's friend and teacher, and yet he does not know. It was surprising, yet she recalled what Brennan had told her about the incidental blabbering of bastardy. A Parliament could call a king who strongly resembled his own father a bastard, then recall the statement. Then, at will, they would do it all again. It had long been the way of the English government. Brennan was correct; the gossip would start and stop. Parentage was a fact that could never be proven. Marriage and birth, however, were recorded events.

"Think, my lady. Think of Jacquetta of Bedford."

The story was well known. The Duchess of Bedford was early with child when the Duke of Bedford, who had been a long time away from his wife, was killed. Bedford was a rich seat, and the widow's marriage fell under the dominion of the king. Heavy with child and with guilt, she threw herself on King Henry's mercy and begged to be allowed to marry a common soldier of her husband's house, the man she loved and the father of her unborn child, one Richard Woodville. Henry, gentle and compassionate, and not yet insane, fined her for her disobedience and allowed the marriage. Rumor was that the wedding

preceded the labor pains by mere hours. The babe arrived —
Elizabeth Woodville, now the Queen of England.

They snickered and called the queen baseborn, for the Woodville family could trace their ancestry only to country folk. But
Elizabeth held her head high, as did Jacquetta, and their brood
grew strong and proud. It had happened so. She felt her shoulders shake with silent laughter in recounting the story, for it
strongly resembled her own. But it did not spell out a solution
to her. Dylan deFrayne and Anne of Ayliffe were the noble
parents in this case, and Dylan was already married. She had
not tampered with her soldier. She had never desired him.

"Think, my lady Anne. Who, of your own household, would
not accept that it *was* me?"

"Let me think," she whispered. "Give me some time."

Taking a grave chance, Clifton leaned forward and gently let
his lips touch her brow. "I am sworn to serve you. My word is
my life. DeFrayne had his moment, but he cannot relieve you.
Let me save you."

"At your own expense?" she asked with a cynical lift of her
brow.

"To be at your side is an honor. To stand beside you in
wedlock would not shame me, but fill me with gladness."

"How can you be sure?" she asked quietly.

Clifton gave his head a sharp nod of determination. "A good
man, deFrayne. I honor myself to call him a friend. But, had I
only known how lonely you were, how sad, I would have helped
you. Twas wrong of him to be the one; he being unable to help
you now, in this time of trouble. And, I have wanted to touch
your hand, kiss your lips, for many years."

"Oh, Clifton, you should not —"

"Admit my lust? Better it is out. If you do not let me save
you from the mire of this circumstance, I shall leave your estate.
I am your loyal servant, my lady, but I stand hard on honor. I
would never touch you against your will. Nor, after this, can I
command your men if you choose to share your pallet with
another, because I have wanted you for myself."

[285]

"And what of love, Sir Cliff?" she softly asked.

"The man you have claimed to love is dead," he shrugged, his eyes focused on hers. "I want you, and you have depended on me, respected me. That is enough to make a better marriage than most."

"But . . . will that always be enough?"

He gave his head a sharp nod. "I have Ayliffe and my men, a plentiful table, a solid bed, and my work. If I also have you, in wedlock, I have everything I want. Think about it, my lady Anne. You will agree."

He went away from her then and did not press her. She half expected him to visit her often, to pursue her with his outrageous proposition, but instead he stayed clear of her chamber.

Anne's remorse was complete. She had tempted fate and the gods and if she did not, henceforth, take complete control of her life, she, Dylan, and her children would suffer greatly. She would bear the pain of destroying Brennan for the rest of her life. No amount of guilt or confession would restore him. She hoped that from his place in eternity he could see into her heart and know how deeply she loved him, how desperately she had always wanted to please him. And, most, how sorry she was. Her feelings for Dylan had long been beyond her control, but that she had acted on those volatile feelings was now only a dull ache in her breast.

For all the years she had kept alive the flame of love for Dylan, she knew now she had to douse the notion with the cold reality of her position. Until such a day as they were both free, she could have no part of him. Not even the smallest part. As Brennan had said, not a glance, not a look of longing. She owed them both this much, that the children should have good lives and good fortunes. The truth would gain them nothing. Dylan could not help her. He already had a wife.

The idea of going into hiding to bear her child crossed her mind, but she knew it impossible. Ayliffe was second only to Warwick's possessions in importance and wealth. And what had been Warwick's, the king would quickly divide to his advantage. Anne would not be left in widowhood long, not with her fancy title, her wealth, and her stronghold of many soldiers. A good monarch would marry her off to one of his friends or vassals. She remembered with great personal concern the time when the newly married king had brought the Woodvilles to court to find places for them. Marriage was the best route, always. One of the arranged marriages was notoriously diabolical. John Woodville, one of the queen's brothers, aged twenty, was married to Katharine Neville, Duchess of Norfolk, aged eighty. It was more than reasonable to assume King Edward capable of another such political performance. She knew many of the unmarried noblemen at court. There were few she thought she could abide.

"There's no more time, my lady," Jane said. "You'll have to do it; Sir Clifton is the only way."

"No one will believe I have dallied with him," Anne replied. "All of England will laugh. And I fear to give Clifton such power over me. He does not seem capable of the weight."

"Did he not tell you that he's been smitten for years, mum? Lord above, look at the man — he's not touched you once, yet he's been a-wantin'. I take it as a sign."

"A sign of what?"

"He stands by you, he's clean, he does not disgrace himself. . . . I know he's not half the man Lord Forbes was. Mary Jesu, where will we find such a man in quick fit. Mum, if you don't get a husband fast, we'll be in bad trouble. He's not smart as you, but he'll stand firm for Ayliffe."

"I should take the children and run away," she said.

"And give young Sloan what inheritance? Run, and Ayliffe will be gone from your children this fast." Jane snapped her fingers. "Marry, mum, and hold the castle against Brainard. For yourself and your young."

"You approve of him, then?"

"I know of no other."

It had not been her intention to test Sir Clifton, but she did weigh his response to her request heavily as a means of knowing his true colors.

"I have considered your offer of marriage, Sir Clifton, but I have a very unusual request. I can promise you all my wifely loyalty in return for a favor. I can be faithful, I assure you, for no one has learned the tortures of adultery better than I. But I should like to tell Lord deFrayne the truth. I would tell him that the child I am carrying is his, and that the child will be raised as yours."

Clifton's eyes registered the shock. "To what purpose?"

"*Jesu*, the baron can surely count," she said impatiently. She quieted her emotions. She had been a countess for too long. She must not treat this man, likely to be her husband, with a ruling hand. She sighed and looked at him closely. "His wife cannot bear him children. Privately, he lamented that he can never have a child and told me, in confidence, that only to know a part of himself lived on would fill him with gratitude. He is an honest and discreet man, Clifton. He has labored hard for the king's cause, at great danger. Let me give him this single gift. Let me tell him the truth."

"If he would know by counting on his fingers," Clifton said with a shrug, "what purpose in a conference, in a confession?"

Anne wondered if there was some mistake close at hand as she recognized in the strong and determined knight a childlike confusion of the facts. In commanding armies he was gifted with almost instinctive prowess. But in life? He lived by a short set of codes, a minor list of behavior rules. He was not, she realized, terribly intelligent. But she shrugged off the feeling of impending danger in this fact. She had ruled a mighty castle boasting fifteen thousand residents, sometimes beside her mighty husband, sometimes alone. Some of her most faithful, hardworking people were also the simplest. Sir Clifton was not a man of deep vision. He was a soldier. Simple, rugged, and, so far, honorable.

She touched his hand. "I could not have taken Lord deFrayne to my bed on a whim and a craving, Sir Cliff," she patiently explained. "I was lonely, true. And saddened, true. But I am not a wanton, a slattern begging for fleshly pleasures. I have known Dylan deFrayne for many years. He worked closely with my husband. I respect and admire him, and I assure you, he is a good and honorable man. He longs to know that a child of his lives; he confided it is his single hope. Sir Cliff, allow me to give him an explanation. He will understand."

"Very well," Clifton said instantly. "If that is your desire, I can afford you that much. But if I am to be your husband, my lady, you must grant me this. First, let us not seek the baron. When he is in our midst, whether in a fortnight or a decade, will do well enough. To go to great pains to find him and confer with him will cause people to wonder. I will not be slighted by such an action, by the wagging tongues.

"Second, I will gladly take you, even full with his offspring, because I want you and because you need me. But once vows are spoken, I will not share you. I am hard in this concern, my lady. You must swear."

She smiled. He extracted her word in the same way he would pull fealty from a group of young squires. "If you are to be my husband, Clifton, you should call me Anne . . . especially in our private bedchamber." She leaned toward him with eyes half closed, an invitation to be kissed. He did so clumsily, but she was not concerned. She knew that now that she was done with Dylan for the sake of sheer survival, she would never again find passion in her life. She hoped Clifton would be a gentle spouse, and craved no greater gift than that. She was more than a little grateful she need not bear Dylan's child in seclusion and abandon it. "I swear," she said. "Will you go with me to Heathwick to deal with my mother? She needs to be silenced."

Elizabeth had borne King Edward a child while the king was abroad in exile and the queen hidden in sanctuary. The child was a son — he would be Edward V. The riots and smaller battles raged on. There were revolts in Kent and Thomas Neville, called the Bastard of Fauconberg, had led a fleet of ships up the Thames into London. But a son and heir had been born. Queen Elizabeth, with a son who could be king and a husband who was a victorious ruler, was soft in her heart. And she loved Anne. She need not be reminded about her own birth and her mother's dilemma so many years before.

There was no fine and, indeed, no censure. Elizabeth promised to speak to her royal husband, thanked Anne for coming to her first, and warned her with loving condolences that there would certainly be plentiful gossip in the court, but it would be stronger than Anne only if Anne allowed it to be. The title, fitted so perfectly on Anne of Ayliffe, bequeathed to the Earl of Ayliffe's firstborn, could never be Clifton's. He would remain a knight.

Dylan deFrayne was not in London, although Anne carefully inquired. She felt only a moment of unexplained panic when she spoke the vows with Sir Clifton in a simple ceremony in Westminster.

The people of England were still unsettled, some shires and towns swept away in a spirit of riot begun by the year-and-a-half-long struggle for the crown. Clifton took five hundred men to protect them on their journey. He did not hurry the journey from Ayliffe to London and on to Heathwick. He was courteous and careful in his treatment of Anne, but he did quickly claim his conjugal rights. His hunger far outpaced Anne's expectations, but Clifton did not seem to notice that Anne was not swept away with the same passion.

She suffered from his amorous appetite while they traveled and knew that her marriage to Clifton would hold this nightly ritual. She had also quickly learned that it mattered not at all to her new husband whether she liked it. He thrived. He had a possession of which he was proud. He would likely be good to his word, his rules and codes, and he would undoubtedly protect her with a vengeance. Marcella would be properly cowed. She regretted she had not dealt more harshly with her mother before.

Heathwick showed the glow of attention one hundred pounds a year had afforded, plus the good, hard work of Sir Trenton as castellan. When Anne embraced Trenton after a long separation, she felt suddenly weak and frail. The tears began to swell, for she began to wish she had not tried to be so wise. She could have abandoned Ayliffe and run to her brother for protection. All the wealth would be gone from her children, but she knew Trenton would try to keep her safe. She fought for control. She introduced her husband, to Trenton's shock, and asked Trenton to let her deal with Marcella alone.

Anne asked a servant in the hall to announce her. Marcella awaited Anne in her chamber, not at all pleased by this surprise visit. She did not wear her colors and jewels, but black for Bart and Quentin. Still, Anne did not pity her at all.

Anne knew better than ever that a show of force was necessary now. She entered the chamber as if she owned it, which in fact she did until her daughter was suitably settled.

"You have finally done it, madam. You loosed your tongue and now all your power is gone."

Marcella's face went white and she half stood, returning to her seat before even completing the rise.

"You fell in with Brainard, who brought the rumor of my adultery to his father. Fortunately, Lord Forbes did not believe him. But my husband was killed at Tewkesbury; no doubt his vision was clouded by your treachery. I have already remarried." Anne took note of her mother's surprise. "I married the captain of my guard to keep Ayliffe safe for my children."

Anne waited a long, silent moment to study her mother's face. It looked much the same as on that day when they learned the Duke of York had been slain; all her aspirations were crushed.

"It is over — you could only use your secret to hurt me once. I warned you . . . so many times. I told you again and again that to betray me would gain you nothing, but cost you everything. Don't you see? I am safe and better kept than ever." Anne clenched her eyes and swallowed the threat of tears. Life without Brennan would be difficult at best. Burying him had been a painful ordeal. But before her mother she would not show weakness. "I am the Countess of Ayliffe until my death, madam. My husband, Sir Clifton Warner, strong, loyal, and honorable, is a knight. There is no longer anyone to gainsay my authority . . . not even a husband. I can have you banished, if I choose."

Marcella stared at Anne. Her eyes began to sparkle, but Anne doubted it was shame or remorse that caused the threat of tears. Finally, Marcella showed her teeth. "So, you have ruined me. I imagine you are pleased. You always were a bad child."

"Bad?" Anne looked around the rich bower. "Did a bad child give you this? Nay, madam, you were a terrible, terrible mother; no love in your heart for your children, no loyalty, no compassion. You have only two of us left, madam, and we will not succumb to your cruelty. You should be ashamed of the useless death your meanness has caused. But I see you are not . . . you still manage to blame me. Somehow, that surprises me even now."

"So, you've another lackey to do your bidding, eh? You always manage somehow, don't you?"

Anne shook her head sadly. "I have never understood why you hate me so."

"You're just like her, though I didn't see that right away. But you are . . . just like Daphne deFrayne. You should have been born to her."

"It is I and Daphne deFrayne you hope to hurt. Yet . . ."

"I was his breeding mare, nothing more. All those years I tried to comfort him, succor him, gain his love. He wanted *her!* He tried to marry her, did you know that? But her father was quicker, taking her to Lord deFrayne to make her a countess." Marcella laughed. "Just like you, daughter; playing the simple lass, protesting that she did not want to marry a rich earl, satisfied to have both a rich husband and a handsome lost love pining for her. Just like you."

"Father?" she asked weakly.

Marcella laughed. "You thought him so good and so noble; you thought I was a bad mother. I gave him five living children and nearly died birthing you. But did he come to my bedside and thank me for my courage? Did he ever tell me he loved me? Not once in our many years together. He cast me aside like soiled linen, but bounced you on his knee and called you pretty and sweet. I could never look at you without hating you. Until you were born, I at least had my hopes!"

Anne felt the tears come. "Madam, I . . ."

"And then I saw the whole thing happen again before my very eyes. You captured yourself a rich earl on your first outing; he adored you. How did you reward that adoration? By falling in love with a deFrayne. You cuckolded old Forbes with a deFrayne, just as my husband wasted my life as he longed for *her.*

"And you, Anne, so high and mighty, lectured me about love, and how I might have done things differently. You, who have never been without a legion of men to love and want you. Look how fast you replaced Ayliffe with yet another loyal steed." Marcella cackled suddenly. "So you will banish me, daughter? How will you punish me? As if my life has not been punishment enough."

"All these years," Anne said, "it has only been jealousy. Madam, you sent a good man to his death doubting me. How can I forgive you for that?"

"I do not require your forgiveness! My life has been hard! I wanted only to see my children rich . . . richer than her children. And I wanted to watch her suffer . . . as I suffered. You always accused me of greed. My desires were never so grand as you thought. I just wished to live long enough to see all the pretty little maids fall . . . all the little demoiselles like Daphne . . . and you . . . who never asked for the dozens of men who begged for your favors, offered to die for your smile . . ." Marcella began to cry, but they were not the tears of sadness. Rage encompassed her. "You complained so much about my interference, my poor mothering. Life was always so easy for you . . . you had everything any woman could want and still you spoiled it, adultered for lust. Was no man's love good enough? I would have given my heart's blood for one good man's love!"

Anne's eyes closed and she leaned her head back. The truth of it struck her hard. She *had* had much, and she had somehow squandered it all for one love. Was it worth it? she asked herself over and over. She could not help but pity her mother.

"Poor Divina!" Marcella cried.

"Your tears come late," Anne chided though tears of her own. "You wasted too many years on being jealous of pretty women who were lucky. You could have taught Divina the beauty of a good heart; you could have taught yourself. You hate anyone who seems to have an easy life, but you cannot see the truth. Madam deFrayne has suffered enormous pain, but you still think she is luckier than you. And how do you look with envy at what I have endured? Oh madam, I pity you, but not for what you have suffered. I pity you because you have never looked at another's misfortune with any compassion at all. You could have embraced me long ago," she said softly, "and found in me a daughter willing to do much for you. But rather, you cast me aside because I reminded you of your own unmet desires. Did it never once occur to you that you failed to win what your heart longed for only because you were so selfish?"

"Anne," Marcella said, smiling though her eyes were red and her cheeks wet with tears. "Do you school me on love yet *again?* Spare me! You have had your share!"

"You will spend out your days in loneliness, for you are not welcome at court again," Anne said, dry-eyed now. "And only the acquaintances Trenton approves will be admitted. 'Tis sad that I cannot trust you at all and must protect my children at the cost of your imprisonment." She turned to go, knowing that she would never meet minds with her mother, knowing she would never see Marcella alive again.

As her hand touched the bower latch she heard her mother's voice. It was the softest her voice had ever been. "May you never know, Anne, how it feels."

Anne resisted the temptation to look at her mother again. "I will accept that as your wish for my happiness, madam, and count it as the kindest thing you have ever said to me."

She found Trenton and Sir Cliff in the courtyard still. "I beg your forgiveness, Trenton, but I must leave at once. I cannot stay the night here."

"Anne, you've been crying. . . . What did she —"

"It is of no bother. Suffice it to say that my mother does not wish me well. I will write you a long letter when I am home and settled. Perhaps I can find a way to explain. Until then you must guard her carefully; do not ever admit Brainard Forbes again. Madam is likely to be spinning tales where she thinks it will do her good. For Deirdre's sake, you must keep her for me."

Trenton glanced at Cliff. "Anne, this marriage. So quick and —"

"Ayliffe is rich," she said dispassionately. "Believe me, I was in danger of being thrust before the priest with one of King Edward's lackeys the moment Lord Forbes died. And my husband . . ." Her voice caught and she struggled for control. "My husband only asked one thing of me — that I keep Ayliffe safe and strong."

Worry creased Trenton's brow. "Are you sure, Anne? You can stay as long as you like. I would lock her in her chamber for you."

She laughed almost happily at the sound of his loyalty. She sniffed and brushed the remaining tears from her eyes. "No, my dear, I must return to Ayliffe. But I thank you. I love you."

Anne rode quietly away from Heathwick. There was little doubt in her mind that it was all true. She wondered if her life resembled Daphne's. Had Ferris been plagued by his one true love? Had he crept around dark, unlit halls for a brief embrace? Had they been kept apart, or did they, too, meet secretly? For an instant she wondered if her father had sired any of Daphne's children, a horrifying thought, but she quickly pushed the possibility away. The three deFrayne brothers resembled each other too strongly. But the fact she could not ignore was that she had not been the first to suffer this denied longing. Poor Ferris. Poor Daphne.

She tried to explain to her husband that the root of evil lay in Marcella's unreasonable jealousy of Daphne deFrayne. "So that is how it is with her," Clifton finally said as they rode home. "A woman's jealousy bites harder than anything. It is a pity that Lord deFrayne happened to be the one. It lit a violent fire under the wicked old woman. She saw her chance to defame her rival."

Anne sighed. Sir Clifton was not very smart. She was very grateful. She would try to be of good service to him. "It is over now," she said softly.

"Nay, not yet. There is Brainard. When you are safely returned to Ayliffe, I will take an impressive troop to Ramsford."

"My lord, you must not," she said in a panicked breath.

"I will," he answered firmly. "I will not be bothered with him through all the years of our life together. But do not worry, Anne. I am stronger than Brainard."

Which of them had the most brute strength was not Anne's worry, but what would be done to Clifton if he should kill Brainard. Anne had no idea where King Edward would stand on such an issue. But the worry was short-lived. Clifton returned to her a mere fortnight after he had departed. He had taken one thousand men and pulled cannon, battering rams, and other fancy ordnance. He had not been able to finish Brainard, but he had done enough damage to Ramsford, killed enough knights and lesser men, to put the fear of the devil into the young heir. While Anne was grieved by the loss of innocent life among the knights of both keeps, Clifton was very pleased with himself. He had sent Brainard fleeing for his life. He doubted Ayliffe would be bothered again.

Blustering winds brought in the month of November. Under these adverse conditions it was surprising to see a troop approach Ayliffe. Sir Clifton met the group at the gate. He did not dismount, but faced Dylan deFrayne while still astride. "We grant you welcome, my lord. The hall is warm."

"My lady Anne is well?" he asked, a little hesitantly.

"My lady wife is fit; she is not up from child. A son was born four days past."

Clifton's eyes were focused on Dylan's. A half-smile crossed the knight's lips.

"She said you could cipher well, my lord, and by your eyes, you are quick. I am a man of my word; you may see her." And then in a tone of warning, "This once only."

Dylan nodded in resignation. He rode slowly toward the hall, Clifton close beside him. Dylan was amazed that after he was warmed by the fire and given dry clothing, he was ushered to Anne's bedchamber and allowed to enter alone. He actually turned around and looked back at the door that had been quietly closed behind him. Realizing the brief mercy for what it was, he approached the bed.

Anne's eyes were open and she watched him come toward her. While Dylan was being dried and fed, Clifton had told her of his visit. She did not even have to ask her husband a second time; he explained that Dylan would have a few private moments with her because he had given his word on it.

Her son lay beside her, for she had just finished nursing him. Dylan looked down at the babe's contented slumber, then he looked into Anne's eyes.

"My Anne, what has happened to us?" he whispered.

"Two, Dylan," she said softly. "Clifton does not know about Sloan, and this babe he will call his own, for all our sakes."

Dylan sat on the edge of the bed beside her. He reached a trembling finger to touch the brow of his infant son, then took her hand. "And yet he lets me see you? Alone?"

"It was my single request, that you be given the truth. But beware, Dylan, Clifton is not the man Brennan was. He will not abide another visit from you. I belong to him now. And he guards me well."

"I heard about Lord Forbes, long after the fact. I did not know . . ."

"I had to marry. I had to pretend that my dalliance had been with my knight, my guard. Had I refused Clifton's offer, I would have borne you an illegitimate son, and this estate, the estate of my children, would have fallen to Brainard or some henchman of the king's. I did what I had to do."

"I understand. The fault is mine. I did not mean to . . ."

"No look of longing," she murmured. "No stare across the room, no loving glance. Dylan, before Brennan died, he knew. My mother gave the word to Brainard, Brainard delivered it to his father, and I sat in this besieged keep growing fat with your child. I sent my husband to war with the knowledge that I had been unfaithful." She saw Dylan's eyes blink with anguish. "Now, I have given my word to be a faithful wife, and it is a word I shall keep. We have endured enough. We were wrong. It was not wise to have had each other, however briefly, despite our wrong marriages. It would have been easier had we played the game faithfully. There would have been young Sloan, enough for you, and all this would not have transpired. I believe that Brennan might have survived Tewkesbury but for the fact that my sins clouded his vision."

"Nay, Anne, his death was not your doing. It was . . ."

"We will never be sure, Dylan."

He shook his head mournfully. "I had never intended to hurt you as I did, my love. I wished that what we felt would make us strong. I beg forgiveness."

She smiled placidly. She looked at the thin, almost vanished scar on her hand. "I do not regret anything but Brennan's death. That is enough regret for any woman. And I will not let the guilt I feel make me hateful and bitter; I will raise my children faithfully and well. Understand me, Dylan; there will be no more talk of this forever love. That was youth and short vision. It is buried. Go. Find a woman who can return your love. It is not too late for you to breed up a small army. Leave me to raise these young."

She lifted the babe and displayed him. She urged the tiny bundle toward Dylan. She did not weep or tremble. As the child grew in her, she had had many months to think. She knew her heart. If Dylan could not free himself, she would set him free.

Dylan held the babe and she saw his eyes mist.

"Get a wife who will give you children," she said. "You are handsome, young, fit, and strong. Get rid of Raynia; send her home where she longs to be and ask the king to free you of that impetuous bond. You will live to be very old. Do not delay, Dylan. Place no more hopes on our childish dreams. I have been through too much grief for something that cannot be. I love you no more."

"I don't believe you," he said.

"Then you will have pain you do not deserve. It is not my wish that you be unhappy. Better you should go and live your life. We were young, impatient. We created a troubadour's painful song out of war and deprivation. We should have been more prudent. I am more wise now."

"Anne, what do you say?"

"I am done with it, Dylan. I am free of that foolish torment."

"Once we longed to be free of such doomed love, but it would leave neither of us."

"Leave me to raise my children," she whispered. "Let me be a faithful wife to Sir Clifton. He helped me when no one else could."

"You trust him? He is a buck in rut! He is a soldier, a stag! He has sniffed at your skirts since you came here. He saw his chance in your misfortune. Thank God he values you, but I doubt that he has any real love for you. He does not know what real love is. Anne?"

"He is my husband now," she whispered, emphasizing each word. She indicated the babe. "His name is Gage. I promise you, I will bring him to manhood with the greatest of care."

Dylan kissed the tiny head, then raised his eyes and searched Anne's. He saw the hard glint of determination. He had known her first husband and was not oblivious to the size and skills of her second. But Dylan knew his lifelong love better than anyone.

"Listen to me, Anne. I know you do not wish to hear this, but you must. Put these words in the back of your mind for some future day and heed them. I give you my word, as I have in the past, that whenever you say me nay, I am gone fom you. But I love you. I will always love you. When you are in trouble, you must call on me. Do not let Sir Clifton hurt you. Do not let him hurt the children."

"He is a loyal man, Dylan. He —"

"He is a brute! But he values you. Perhaps all will be well, and I will pray for you. But when you need me, you must find me. Remember!"

"I think you are wrong. I think . . ."

"I hope I am wrong. And take this to your heart — when you are lonely and frightened, when you remember these words that you spoke over my son's head, that you loved me no more, remember that I do not believe you. When tears come late in the dark of night because you fear that I took them to heart, that I have somehow forgotten, be at ease. I know you love me still. I will go on with my life knowing that, taking comfort from the unspoken truth. You are a strong woman, my Anne. You have been through much because of me. I would undo your pain and leave you only the joy if I could, but I cannot. Still, I love you. I will love you always. Until I die, I will dream of our someday. Our oath was forever."

She bit her lip. She wanted to say it, but she could not. She had made a decision. By sheer dint of will she would not allow her eyes to moisten. She shook her head. If she opened her mouth she would blurt the truth. Dylan must be free of this, even if she could not escape her own feelings. She was relieved of the burden, for the door to her bedchamber gently opened. Her time was spent.

Dylan rose and, still holding the babe, faced Clifton. He gently kissed the infant's wizened brow and held him close for a moment. Then he passed the child to Clifton. "I thank you, sir. It was my wish that a child of my body come to life, even if he is never to know his true sire. I assure you, I wish him and you well. No good could come of my claim on him now, and I give him to you with good faith."

"You are wise, my lord. No lad should look to the horizon for his father. My wife has suffered enough without bearing the shame of your further attentions."

"Oh, I assure you, Sir Cliff, you will not suffer my presence. I will not bother the good woman." He looked over his shoulder at Anne. "I have been told, and I respect those vows sworn before God. I am a stranger to you now. God keep you." He touched the child once more. "All of you."

The door closed behind Dylan, and Clifton came to stand beside Anne. He handed her the child and smiled down on her, but his eyes were hard. "My word was honored. Now you are mine."

PART III

May 2, 1482

Chapter Seventeen

IN 1478 Dylan deFrayne was named the first Earl of Nowlan. The reasons for this appointment were publicly read and included glorious battle skills exercised in dangerous uprisings all over England, largely in the north and often along the Scottish border. Additionally, service to the king done in secrecy was said to have ultimately effected the downfall of Warwick and the House of Lancaster. DeFrayne also worked at many negotiations with foreign powers, and settled local disputes between barons and gentry, showing his intelligence as well as brawny strength. All the praise was deserved, but only Dylan and King Edward knew there were even more reasons for the appointment.

The king's two brothers, Richard of Gloucester and George of Clarence, married to Neville daughters, argued the division of the enormous estate of Warwick. Dylan remained in the middle of their struggle for longer than he liked. George of Clarence often attacked innocents and frequently went above the law in creating local regulations, taxes, and punishments in his demesne. His vacillating loyalty among various powers did not end with Warwick's death, but continued to disrupt the peace. Finally, in '78, Dylan witnessed the gruesome private execution of George in the tower. He then accepted title and property close to Richard of Gloucester, now the only living brother of the king. The title was his reward. Even though his work for Edward was to be a secret operation, deFrayne became known among the peers as *the keeper of the brothers*.

The greatest change in his fortune, in his restoration, was not in Dylan's title or the acquisition of property. After he accepted the earldom he finally relented and sent Raynia and her maid home to Calais. He could have done so much sooner and regretted that he had not. His happiness peaked when she was gone. He had his mother and Justin, hard work and travel, popularity among the people, and a stable life. Still, he frequently thought how sad it was that between himself and Raynia there had never been a moment of acceptance, of happiness. He had paid a yearly visit to her humble homestead in Calais, often taking Justin with him. This year, after four years of separation, he returned to Calais to bury her. She was only four and thirty.

He looked pensively at the unpretentious mound of dirt that was her grave. "Twice she miscarried, once she delivered a dead child, and for twelve years or more before she died she would have none of me. I wonder if she ever had any happiness in her life." He turned and looked at his eighteen-year-old nephew. "Your father and I married close to the crown while in exile. There was never any question of our purpose; people do what they must. But with your mother and father there was love and happiness." He reflected for a moment. "How does Bess now?"

Justin smiled sympathetically and clamped a hand on Dylan's shoulder. "Mother does well; she is content. You need not worry about her. Visit her; she has a brood of young children and a hardworking husband. Come away from here, Uncle. Let these servants close up this place."

"I'll be along. There is someone I have to see."

He sent Justin to have their horses readied and climbed up the polished wood staircase to the second floor of Raynia's house. It was a peaceful little house, pretty and clean. He tapped lightly on the door that he knew to have been Raynia's bedchamber, but there was no answer. He pushed the door open and found Jeannette standing beside the bed holding up a linen that she had been folding.

For the first time in seventeen years the homely face of the maid did not cause him to wince. He looked at her with compassion. "All is in order, madam," he said. "I will be leaving for the last time. Where do you go?"

"To the convent of Fontevrault, messire," she said quietly.

"Ah, the sisters." He dropped his gaze. "You need not," he said, looking back at her face. "The house is yours if you want it."

He saw the tears gather in her eyes. "The offer is generous," she said in her thick French accent. "I cannot stay here without her."

He smiled at her. "I think I understand." She had loved Raynia; beyond that, Dylan really did not understand anything. "Take whatever you wish, then. I will have it sold. There is a purse for you — your retirement."

"It is unnecessary to —"

" 'Tis done. Raynia would have wished it." Jeannette let her chin slowly drop in a single nod of acquiescence. Her misting eyes had not shed tears once in Dylan's presence. Her grief was as private an affair as her peculiar relationship with his wife had been. He imagined she refused to cry in front of him. "Was she . . . ever happy? A little bit?"

Her eyes gathered a storm of emotion that the maid would not let fall. She nodded her head again, but her lips were pressed hard together and became pink around the edges. The force of grief was strong in her, and Dylan could not tolerate the sight of it. "Thank you," he said. "*Adieu*." And he quickly left the room, the house.

He was anxious to leave this place. Without a word to his patient nephew, he spurred his horse into a brisk gallop back toward the city. He rode two leagues thus before he slowed. He would not think of her again.

Justin was panting when Dylan finally abandoned his hard

speed and brought the horse to an even trot. "Well, Uncle, Calais is full of beautiful wenches."

Dylan chuckled. "Are there any left that you have not sampled?"

"You do me wrong," he insisted. "I was born to uphold a chivalrous code and treat the women with great courtesy." He leaned close as if sharing a secret. "They seem to thrive on courtesy . . . and patience. They like a man . . . a man who has . . . all night."

Dylan threw back his head and roared with laughter. "Do they, now? And you are patient, eh? They like to marry, lad! That is what they like."

"I know a few who have no interest in wedlock."

"Hah, those will either lighten your purse or introduce you to an angry father who is *very* interested in marriage. When do you sleep?"

"You give me more credit than I'm due, Uncle. I sleep more than I would like."

"Some wench is going to see you coming and smell gold, lad. She'll play the game and you'll find her skirts wrapped around your legs and, before you can blink, you'll be singing the vows that will keep you in one bed for a lifetime. Mark me, wenching has its dangers."

"Such a woman will have to be more clever than the ones I have been courting. Now we must get you married."

"Me? Nay. I am content as I am."

"Lord Debarge is old; Lady Debarge is . . ."

Dylan frowned. Elise Debarge was a beautiful young countess, wed to an ancient earl. It was quite obvious that she was bored with her husband. Also obvious was her attraction to Dylan. "All gossip, Justin."

"Her eyes brighten considerably when you enter the room."

"What Elise Debarge is looking for is far more dangerous than marriage. The earl may be old, but his soldiers are young. Now, do I look that foolish?"

"We'll find you a woman who —"

"Justin, don't you think you should leave this discussion alone?"

"You had no marriage with Raynia; you've said so. Your passing fancies are fewer than mine. You're still young; you could have sons."

A melancholy smile appeared on Dylan's face. He looked straight ahead. "I have you, Justin."

"Bah, a nephew? Never mind children, then. A woman," he whispered conspiratorily, "soft and sweet and anxious, eh? Someone to stir your porridge and your blood?"

Dylan laughed. "Do you ever think of anything but women?"

"I have to get you married," he said. "I pant at their skirts and they all look at my older and wiser famous uncle. Once you're out of the way, the court of dames is mine."

"You should spend as much time at work as you do at wenching. You're going to find your favorite part in a snare one of these days, and your chasing will be over. Besides, your grandmother has taken charge of my home and will never allow another woman to gainsay her authority."

"Grandmother is old, Dylan," he said quietly. "I do not want you to be alone forever."

"I am happy, Justin." He clapped the boy on the back. "I will try not to steal all your favorite wenches. I don't mind being alone. In fact, I prefer it."

"It is not healthy for a man to be without a woman for so long. Eventually, you will suffer in this loneliness."

Health, ah! What did the boy know? What I could tell him, Dylan thought. It was most unhealthy being tied in a cask room awaiting execution for almost a fortnight. How was it that now, twenty-two years later, it seemed as though it might have been his happiest time? Neither was exile a healthy state; nor the following years when he lived for a glance of Anne, a quick embrace, a private word. Most of his life, his future, still waited for him at Ayliffe. Waited under Clifton's close, protective hand. Marriage, indeed. There was only one woman; there had always been only one.

Having her had been so close. There had never been an opportunity to tell her about it, of course; they had not spoken in eleven years. It was for the best, he supposed. She had enough grief without adding to it the knowledge that Dylan could have wed her, had he only been there in time. His marriage to Raynia could have been annulled. It would have been a costly and time-consuming ordeal, perhaps not quite complete in time for Gage's birth, but Raynia would have been cooperative. Raynia had denied him his conjugal rights, and Dylan had been close enough to the Archbishop of Canterbury to have had good support.

But . . . by the time Dylan returned to London, his work for the king finally done, Anne had already been there. She was already married to Sir Clifton. Had he suspected she carried Gage, he would have fled from Edward's side the moment he heard of Lord Forbes's death and rushed to her.

In any case, he had hurried to London, hopeful. He knew his beloved had been widowed. He meant to begin the procedure of having his marriage annulled, but the first piece of gossip he met at court was about Lady Forbes's hasty marriage. He even briefly considered pursuing the matter beyond her marriage, but finally good sense won out. She had been through enough because of him. He kept Raynia, then, because he meant never to marry again . . . until he could marry Anne. Had he proceeded with the annulment, he would have faced the clumsy prospect of turning away potential brides.

He had seen her at court in the past eleven years. She looked well kept and in good health. She maintained her dignified bearing. They talked about her most liberally at court, and it had taken a will of iron to keep from defending her. She had sent her old husband off to battle, they whispered, and invited a common soldier to her bed. To look at her one would not think her such a wanton, physical creature; she had a pure look. But the old earl was not cold in his grave before she wed her guard. The little countess, they said, now there was a woman who could not be a day without a man. That was why, it was assumed, Sir Clifton never left her side. The Countess of Ayliffe and her manly consort provided some good gossip.

Dylan knew that Clifton's possessive presence had little to do with passion. He had seen Cliff's brooding frown the first time they were all present at the king's court. Anne did not look at

Dylan, but Clifton did. Thereafter Dylan was careful to have a woman on his arm, especially if he was certain Anne and Clifton were present. He had not felt any lasting attraction in those few, brief flirtations and certainly he was not fooled by Elise Debarge's determination to cuckold her old husband with a younger, more virile man. He hoped, however, that his public display of attention toward other women would pacify Clifton and lessen his jealousy. And he hoped Anne would understand.

I wonder if she knows why I dally with beautiful women, he asked himself often. Does she remember that I promised to always love her? Hardly a promise difficult to keep . . . I cannot be free. She does not love him; her life with him presses down hard on her. Though she is proud and beautiful, I know that dull pain in her eyes as no one else would know it. But, she took Sir Clifton thinking he was her single chance to raise her young — my sons. She has forsaken our love to see our boys tall and good and strong. I could love no other kind of woman.

"You should have a family," Justin said.

"I do have a family, lad. One that I'm quite proud of."

"I mean more than Grandmother and me," Justin said.

Dylan smiled and rode silently on to the center of Calais. They stopped at a crowded alehouse near the wharves. Justin, so much the young man of the world, was quick to find aquaintances and abandoned his uncle, leaving Dylan contentedly alone with his thoughts and his brew.

Dylan was proud of the boy. He'd grown up to be good and strong; playful still, but maturing just the same. He was more interested in bracing an arm with a comrade or chasing a swinging skirt than in policies, politics, land, and fame. But this was as it should be for a young man not yet twenty. There was time enough for seriousness. Dylan was fortunate to be able to bring the boy through adolescence in a peaceful climate. Edward's England had been mostly at rest for eleven years. At four and forty, Dylan knew that to be a rare blessing. He hoped it would continue for a long time.

"My lord, I should like to present a friend of mine." Dylan

looked up into turquoise eyes that reflected his own image. He was momentarily entranced. "Sloan Forbes, late of Ayliffe."

"It is an honor, my lord," the young man said, bowing. "I . . . ah, I have heard so many great things about you. I have, ah, watched you in the tourney." His voice was filled with humble admiration. A score of years plus one; well muscled, handsome, polite. His smile, shy but beautiful, was Anne's smile. His eyes were his sire's.

Perhaps, if we become friends, I can tell him how deeply I loved his mother; perhaps I can convince him that my silence was the better part of my love for him. If he grows to be a man who can feel love at all, he will understand.

"The pleasure is mine, lad. I know Ayliffe; I have not seen the magnificent place in many years. Sit. Call the tapster. Tell me about your home; your family."

"But I am not certain I *wish* to go, madam," Deirdre said. Anne brushed her daughter's beautiful golden hair and looked at the sad, frightened eyes that shone in the mirror. The mirror was framed in gold, sculptured with little flowers. It had been a gift from Brennan when Deirdre was only two.

"You must take the mirror," she said patiently. "Your father would have wished you to use it to keep yourself pretty."

"Madam, I think you ignore me purposely! I have never been away from you!"

"I know, sweeting. But it is necessay. And you will have a wonderful time."

"I have no friends there."

"Not yet, but a good friend of mine will see to you."

"Humph." She pouted. "The queen? The queen has no *friends!* Waiting women and servants and . . ."

"Deirdre, it is decided. You are long past the age. Elizabeth will help find you a suitable husband." She turned her daughter around and lifted her chin. Ah, she was a beauty. And sweet-tempered, if a little spoiled and stubborn, but as smart as both Anne and Brennan combined. She was six and ten now; Sloan had been born to Anne at this age. Deirdre should be settled and away from Ayliffe. Anne feared the way Clifton looked at his stepdaughter, and the way he seemed to avoid the prospect of her marriage. A betrothal, at least, was long overdue.

"Deirdre, you can rely upon Elizabeth," she stressed. "Keep away from the king as much as possible."

"What would I care for a fat old king?" She huffed, turning back to the mirror. Anne sighed and shook her head. That fat old king was only three years older than Anne. And he was a powerful, handsome man. Rumor was, however, that he had become somewhat lazy; a little gluttonous. Anne had not been to court in three years, for Clifton did not like to go. She had heard that in the past few years Edward had become so self-indulgent and decadent that he had begun to use a vomitorium behind his dais so that he could relieve himself and continue gorging and drinking. She was glad Clifton was not often in the king's company. She was not certain what her husband's reaction to such a compulsion might be. Secretly, frightfully, she wondered if Sir Cliff would approve.

"That is just as well. I do not worry that the king would accost you, my sweet, but he has a reputation for making some dreadful marriage plans. For your dower wealth he might find a most unattractive pet of his household for your husband. The queen will do better for you. And . . . I will come before very long; in winter most likely. I promise."

"Come with me now?" she asked, a pleading expression in her eyes. "Please?"

"Nay, darling. You must learn to face some things without your mother."

Clifton walked into Deirdre's bedchamber, unannounced, without knocking. He held scrolled vellum in his hand. "Letters from Sloan," he said with a grunt. He looked at Deirdre. His eyes twinkled briefly, then he frowned. "When do you depart for Westminster?"

"Tomorrow," she answered quietly, a little fright still ringing in her voice.

"Do not speak to any man without the queen's permission. You need not stay long."

Deirdre tried to check eyes with her mother, but Anne was looking at Clifton with an angry curve to her lips. Their disagreement on this issue of Deirdre going to the queen, for a few months up to a year, had been a loud and boisterous one. But Anne had won, at least temporarily. Regarding any decision for Lord Forbes's children, Clifton was forced to use caution.

"Go on, Deirdre. Gather your women to finish your packing." Still she looked at Clifton. Her daughter quietly quit the room.

"That was unnecessary," she said.

"You should read your son's letter, madam. He has interesting news." He handed her the scroll. She looked at him curiously. Since Clifton could not read, he had obviously found some castle scribe to read the letter to him.

Anne read the first page, all episodes common to Sloan's activities, visiting of old friends, companions met along the way. They were always happy, entertaining letters. Her eyes stuck on a sentence and for a moment she could not move on. Sloan had met, personally, the famous Earl of Nowlan. His nephew, Justin DeFrayne, was a friend. And of all amazing coincidences, the earl was staying with Lord Todd in Calais. To his astonishment, this famous knight was one of the gentlest men he had ever encountered, interested in the smallest of news, never gloating, but as strong as any twenty-year-old. He wondered if his mother and Sir Cliff had ever considered requesting that Gage be sent to train as a squire with this awesome and brilliant man.

Dylan, Sloan said with familiarity, had been visiting Calais on sad business; his wife, who had been sickly for a long time, had recently died.

She finished the letter and looked up at Clifton. She shrugged lamely, hoping Clifton would not make much of it. "Sloan, and even Gage, will meet him at some crossroad, Clifton. You could not have thought they would never become acquainted. England is large; the noble court is like a small town."

"You may send Deirdre to court, but you will not join her there."

Anne sighed heavily and sat tiredly on the stool before the dressing table. "Clifton, nothing has changed in that regard.

You will accompany me; you will not let me out of your sight. You know perfectly well that the queen will be angered by my request for Deirdre if I do not even present myself — Elizabeth depends on my friendship. In any case, if Lord deFrayne is in Calais, there is little cause for concern, now, is there?"

His face was a stony visage, his lips pursed. "I do not like the idea of Sloan spending time with him."

She removed her net and began to unwrap her long hair. There were a few silver strands at her temples, but she did not mind. Anne was not vain. "Sloan is pleased to meet any knight of repute. In that regard, he is an ordinary young man."

"His wife is dead now."

Anne did not respond. There was nothing to say. What matter Dylan was free? She was not. And from a discreet distance she had seen beautiful women in his company; Clifton often troubled himself to point them out. She was careful to conceal the pain from Clifton. She had sent Dylan away, and he had gone. Perhaps now he would wed a woman who would give him children, sons he could claim.

"Do you deny that it pleases you?" he blustered.

"Yea, it pleases me," she murmured. "Poor man, to have wasted so many years with a woman who did not love him, did not wish to live with him, would not give him children." She studied her reflection. Did her surge of hope show? "Perhaps he will marry now; someone who gives him heirs."

"You did your part, did you not?"

Anne closed her eyes and tried to remain composed. She took a deep breath. They had been through this often enough before. Clifton's acceptance of his position as her consort had been short-lived. Within just a few years after they were married his possessiveness turned into jealousy. There was very little she could say to dissuade him from such moods and so she said nothing.

"Sloan should not be in his company."

"Clifton, be at ease. Sloan is only in company with a man he has admired from afar. It is a good sign; he will watch Lord deFrayne, listen and try to learn. You once thought Lord deFrayne a good and honorable man; you once admired him. Nothing has really changed."

"Perhaps Sloan will realize —"

"If you let your envy show, he will certainly wonder at the cause. Leave it alone."

"He will not take my boys away from me," Clifton stormed. Anne flinched and blinked her eyes tightly closed despite her effort to remain passive to his thundering. She was not aware that he approached her. He was angry and afraid; outbursts like this had steadily increased over the years. He had been easier to handle when he was younger, when he was confident of his knightly skills. But now his body, which had been his livelihood, was no longer young and willing. He was not as strong as he had been; he did not win every contest among the men as before. He seemed to have little interest in lordship, but when his prowess in contest failed and showed the effects of age, he became even more surly and discontent. He yanked her roughly to her feet. "Sloan is more mine than anyone's! Ayliffe did nothing with the lad — I *trained* him! DeFrayne never knew him!"

Anne trembled. She placed a placating hand on his chest. "Sloan loves you, Clifton. All boys grow up, find heroes, take their fathers for granted . . . but the love does not stop."

"Tell me that you do not care for him anymore," he demanded. "Say that you do not love deFrayne; that you do not hope to see him." She studied the expression in his eyes; something there was verging on panic.

"Clifton, I ended that. You *heard* me! There has been nothing; no word, no message, no inquiry. And by Lord deFrayne's dalliance at court, something you often remind me about, it certainly seems he does not have any further interest in me."

"The truth."

" 'Tis truth I speak."

"You do not always tell me the truth."

"Yea, husband, I do. I know the penalty for lying."

He released her and turned his face from her eyes. At least he was still ashamed of that event. When both her family and Dylan deFrayne had appeared at court, Clifton had suddenly been faced with all three males — Dylan, Sloan, and Gage — and had seen the resemblance in their eyes. He had demanded the truth and she had dodged his questions, unskillfully. He beat her so badly that he had to take her from Westminster.

The tearful truth had emerged. But she swore that only she knew these secret circumstances and that Sloan believed Lord Forbes was his father. Sir Clifton would never breathe that truth. If it ever became known that Sloan was not the earl's son, he would not be the earl's heir. Clifton's only connection to the wealth of Ayliffe came through his marriage to Anne and his rearing of the heirs.

Anne had never been anything but a dutiful wife to Sir Clifton, but that had not saved her from his abuse. When Clifton had humbly begged to be allowed to save her from shame through wedlock, he had been almost reverent. That had quickly changed.

"Clifton, these sons of mine clamor after recognition and praise like all boys. They admire those distant heroes of the court, as all young men do. Young Prince Edward's greatest love may be for his father, but Anthony is his guardian and hero. The boys owe you much; they will not forget you for another. Be at peace on this. Do not torture yourself."

He turned back to her and she saw clearly that there was pain in his eyes. "You never gave me a son of my own."

"'Twas not by choice," she reminded him. She had conceived three times in her life. Even Clifton should know that the problem was not hers. Her monthly blood had now stopped, though she was only seven and thirty. Her time for childbearing was past. Clifton in response played the wenches more liberally. Still, he had not gotten himself a bastard. "Divorce me if you like. Take another."

"You wish it?"

"Nay. I have held my vows sacred. I would have you till death, Clifton, but you must not hurt us. Once," she said softly, "you loved me."

"You never said so to me," he said, a pout replacing his grimace.

She knew she could say so now, but not convincingly. "I

offered what I had, milord, and have been true to it. Once you thought we had more on which to build a union than most people ever had. I depended on your strength and chivalry; to be my husband, you said, would be an honor. I warned you that one day it might not be enough, but you swore that day would never come. And . . . I believed you."

He hung his head shamefacedly.

"You do not wish to send Gage to him?"

"Nay," she said, smiling patiently to hide her disquiet. She had learned to appear unafraid in front of Clifton. He frequently translated fear into guilt. "It is only Sloan's excitement at meeting someone so highly sung; Lord deFrayne would not have requested it. Did he not give his word? Did you not think him an honorable man? Did he *ever* betray his oath to you?"

He did not answer, but simply made to pass her, to leave the room. Anne sighed with relief when he was gone. She went to the window of Deirdre's bower. She looked into the pleasaunce, then at the jeweled tapestry that hung on her bedchamber wall. There was a prickling sensation that ran up her spine. She wondered how much worse Clifton would become simply because Dylan's wife was dead.

Their marriage was eleven years old. In the early days, when she was pregnant and then when Gage was just a baby, Clifton had been respectful and courteous. He seemed satisfied to have her as his wife, to manage the men of Ayliffe on her behalf. Though she had never loved Clifton, she remembered those as gentle days, for she was left to see to her young in the comfort of Ayliffe, and there was a strong man, determined to protect her, at her side.

She could not remember exactly when it began to change, but it was worsening every year. At first Clifton had spells of impatience and discontent, and became angry with her over small things. Before long his unpredictable anger grew into rages. His brow was almost always furrowed, his mouth turned down. She tried to remember his smile and realized she could not. Even as he had gently wooed her into marriage, into his protection, he had been deadly serious.

Their life together was barely tolerable. Clifton was no longer a good teacher for Gage, and he leered at Deirdre. He was so jealous that he had a castle scribe read him every piece of correspondence delivered to her, even letters from Trenton.

Had he finally learned the truth — that Anne was not a goddess to be worshipped, but only a woman? He had the prize, did he finally lament the cost? Or perhaps the luxury of Ayliffe had finally spoiled him.

She shuddered involuntarily. Something eerie seemed to linger at the edge of her intuition. She had not planned to send Deirdre to the queen; that was an impulsive decision. She was beginning to think about a place for Gage to go, but Clifton protested, and since he claimed this boy as his son, his protests were heard. He was determined to raise the boy alone, and he was hard on him. Anne saw that Clifton's regard for Gage was much as Marcella's had been toward her. He looked at the boy, remembered the circumstances of his conception and birth, and these rankled. And there was little she could do about it. Sloan was still away and would stay at least through the winter, perhaps much longer if Calais proved a profitable place for a young knight, which pleased Anne. She wanted to settle her children. There was a nagging feeling that bothered her.

Once she thought she had conquered her greatest problems. She had said good bye to Dylan, had exchanged vows with Sir Cliff, and set about raising her children. But it had been unraveling almost since the day it began. The unreasonable envy in Clifton's eyes warned her. She knew the days ahead were going to be even harder.

Anne had begun to worry that Clifton would never relent and allow her to go to London to see about Deirdre, but he was forced to reconsider when a summons arrived from Richard, the Duke of Gloucester. It was fall and the harvest was in, and Gloucester demanded Clifton's arms of Ayliffe for a coup in Scotland. The duke offered a modest barony in exchange, but the summons was most firm; Clifton was not allowed to defer with gold or soldiers in his stead. In eleven years, this was the first demand that Clifton could not escape. Additionally, Gloucester summoned the countess to the queen's service.

"We will send word that you are ill," Clifton had said.

Anne, though afraid of a beating or at least a tongue lashing, braved the outburst. "My daughter is there, my lord, and I have promised both Deirdre and the queen that I will winter at the palace. It is better that you take me there than to have me find an escort and travel alone after you are gone. It is important that I see to my daughter, and I will."

Clifton knew that on the issue of her children, Anne would brave his worst temper. He grasped her by the upper arms, gave her a shaking, and warned her that if he heard any tales about her behavior while he was away, she would be severely punished. Then, cleverly, Clifton made plans to leave Gage at Ayliffe so that Anne would think about his future should any temptation present itself. He knew Anne well. She would not chance her son's well-being.

For the first few weeks at court, Anne and Clifton stayed at Westminster, but Deirdre was not with them. Deirdre was with other maids of like circumstance, waiting on the queen, and secretly — or so the maids thought — looking over the men. Anne was not surprised to see that Deirdre was happy. But there was a new quietness about Deirdre that Anne did not quite understand; a secret smile, a twinkling eye, a lighter step.

Also at court were Lord deFrayne and his mother, but Anne did not chance the slightest word to either of them. She did see that the most talked about, and indeed, the most beautiful woman at court was frequently on his arm. Once, Clifton turned Anne toward Dylan and whispered in her ear, "Do you see, madam? I know that he is here, and if you even speak one word to him, I will hear of it." Anne looked at Dylan and saw him kiss Elise Debarge's neck. The pain bit her deep, but she kept it from her eyes as best she could and replied to her husband, "I believe the earl is otherwise engaged and does not seek conversation with any other." Later, that same evening, when Clifton was engaged in a contest of strength, bracing arms with another knight at a table, she stole another look at Dylan and his current mistress. But Dylan did not fondle the lady; he gazed at Anne. Her glance was quick, for Anne trembled and had to look away. To tremble or weep in Clifton's presence was dangerous. But the look haunted her.

It was a full ten days before her husband left Westminster with Gloucester. Anne let all the emotion flood from her then, when Clifton was far away and could not question her. To have Dylan love another was almost as painful as the thought that he might wait for her and be lonely for the rest of his life. She tried to remember the exact tilt of Dylan's head, the glint in his eyes. Did he love another now, finally? It was a look of parting, she told herself. She had told him she loved him no more. In eleven years she might have glanced at him eleven times. Nothing could endure as long as that. There was no point in keeping the flame of hope alive; Clifton was not ancient or doddering and he was secure in his possession.

In the following days she turned her attention to Deirdre, almost hoping Dylan had likewise joined the duke's campaign to Scotland. She was not sure she could bear even another look.

Deirdre had only been with the court for a few months, but she had thrived during that time, and Anne knew she had been right to get her daughter away from Clifton and Ayliffe. Deirdre had changed; she had grown into a woman. In November an especially festive celebration following a noble wedding was held at Westminster, hosted by the queen's company. There were plentiful food, drink, music, games, and dancing. The young people enjoyed it more than their elders. She had not seen Dylan nor Lady Daphne in the room, and was happily watching the performance of a dance.

Deirdre was led to the floor by a handsome young courtier, and Anne lifted a brow, smiling, actually hoping. Deirdre danced with skill, something she had obviously learned at court. She was a magnificent beauty — lithe, graceful, stunningly attractive with her golden hair, her warm brown eyes, and pink lips. Her eyes were focused on the young man with a look that Anne suddenly realized was not only adoring, but familiar.

All at once the music seemed distant and Anne's head was

filled with other sounds, sounds that were not in the room. There were voices from her past, stories told about her at court, whispers, music that had no real melody, wind and the crashing of the sea against the rock. Her vision began to blur slightly. Then, beyond Deirdre in the distance, amidst the gallery of observers, she saw Dylan. There was no Elise Debarge on his arm tonight. Not far from him stood Daphne. She was transfixed by the imaginary triangle the three of them seemed to form around the dancing couple — all three of them watching with sad, pained eyes. Her head pounded with the voices, the sounds, the music. Her hands trembled with sudden vision. She asked herself, why, why, why.

"Madam, I should like to present Sir Justin deFrayne," Deirdre said, smiling.

Again and again it happened. First with Daphne and Ferris, then with Anne and Dylan, and now — Deirdre.

"Madam? Mother?"

"Ah," she sighed, shaking herself. "A pleasure, sir knight," she said, extending a hand to be kissed. Deirdre looked at her mother in bemusement and then, shaking her head patiently, pulled her young escort away from Anne, going again to the dance.

She felt a hand on her elbow. She turned her own tearing, bewildered eyes to find Daphne looking at her with sympathy. "There is only one way to finally stop it, my dear," she said, her soft voice still clear and youthful, though Daphne was nearly seventy. The dowager was stately still and, though of small build, she emanated a feeling of strength and power. Anne could not respond, but only looked at the older woman in shock, amazement. "I don't know why it keeps happening, over and over again. Perhaps it is only because it has been so long forbidden. Who can say?"

"But . . . Deirdre does not know —"

Daphne turned Anne so that they looked at the young couple together. Deirdre and Justin laughed, touched cautiously, looked deeply into each other's eyes. Among the observers on the other side of the room, Dylan also watched them. He did not attempt to approach Anne, although he surely must know that Clifton was not present.

"If this goes on, forbidden as it has been," Daphne said, "have you any idea of the terrible possibilities we face? Aye, we all thought we were the first, and most forlorn . . . but look. One day, will brothers and sisters fall in love? Had Dylan had a daughter, would Sloan love her?"

Anne's head jerked in Daphne's direction. She *knew!* But Daphne did not respond to Anne's shock.

"Perhaps it will be Deirdre's child, or her grandchild. Whatever this is, whatever pulls these opposing families together, seems to be forever sealed with the secrets of greater powers, but it happens over and over again. End it, dear Anne. Let them have each other."

Anne listened, but her eyes were locked into Dylan's, though the distance was great. There was a faint smile on his lips, but hers were slightly parted in wonder, awe. How does this happen?

"My husband," she said, her voice trembling like a young girl's. "He will never allow . . ."

"Sometimes we must take grave risks. Perhaps there is a greater plan."

Anne looked back to the young couple, and beyond them.

"He will not approach you," Daphne said. "I am to tell you that if you need his help, only send word. He is at your call."

Help, Anne thought. Not love . . . he did not tell his mother to pass the word that she should call only if she needed his love. Oh, and she needed love as never before. After all the hard years with Clifton, all the loneliness, all the regret. But it was help he offered . . . because she struggled alone to protect his sons. Dylan was still a man of honor, though undoubtedly he had finally overcome their youthful covenant.

She turned toward the older woman then, regaining her former composure and determination. "Oh, madam, not again," she said passionately.

"My dear Anne, not only again, but it appears until the end

of time." Daphne laughed lightly. "Do you doubt that they will find a way? Do we give thanks, or curse the gods? Or . . . do we simply not question these strange miracles?"

"Madam, there is *nothing* I can do! Sir Cliff will surely be driven to madness by this!"

Daphne frowned and squeezed Anne's hand. "Do be cautious, my sweet child. I could not bear to see you hurt."

Chapter Eighteen

SIR CLIFTON returned from the Scottish campaign in an exhilarated mood. During his years of hovering protectively over Anne, he had personally avoided every major royal call to arms by sending soldiers in his stead. In the midst of his melancholy, while he suffered the feeling that his fighting days were fast fleeing, Gloucester demanded his support. Once the choice was taken from Clifton, he found new promise in revisiting the field. He had done well, laid waste to every town en route to Edinburgh, and was highly sung as a glorious warrior. He was created the baron of Wressel, and though it was not much, and far to the north for better access to the Scottish border, he was full of his good fortune. Additionally, a court that had snubbed him when they did not ignore him completely now sang his praises. England was always and forever impressed with men who could fight battles and win. The young duke, the king's brother, favored Clifton.

Clifton did not wish to retire to Ayliffe. The quiet of the country did not appeal to him now. He had business in the north with Gloucester, and business at Westminster with the king. Dylan deFrayne was not present, and Clifton was free to enjoy himself. Anne watched her husband warily. An interest in politics, in playing these courtly games, was a side of Clifton she had never before seen. For the first time since they had married, he wished to remain with the court for the holiday festivities. "And what of Wressel? Are there lands, keeps?" she asked.

"There is a property, the keep is little more than a fortification; thick walls that can hold a thousand men, but no luxuries whatever. I would not put a family there. But, it would do as a property for Gage."

"Need you be there?" she asked.

He laughed. "Nay, madam, my work is to provide armies, amass lands. Richard depends on me now; he wishes more of me. I will transfer some of Ayliffe's men to Wressel, for now."

"For . . . now?"

"Perhaps I should call Sloan home. I will need him." He laughed again. "He will need me."

She frowned slightly. Ambition did not seem to fit well on Clifton. But his mood was so high, his excitement so fierce, she said nothing. It was the first time they had ever been away from Ayliffe that he did not scan the crowds for a glimpse of Dylan deFrayne. Clifton had not even asked her his usual questions; it was almost as if his jealousy was forgotten because he had some recognition from the royal family. Taking this as a good sign, she brought up the subject of Deirdre.

"My daughter has been courted by a young man of some considerable worth and repute, my lord," she said cautiously. Clifton raised a brow and waited. "Sir Justin deFrayne."

His eyes hardened and he held silent for a long time, staring at her. He knew nothing about Justin, as far as Anne knew, but he knew that Dylan had no sons he could claim. "Nay," he said finally. "No deFraynes."

"Your quarrel has never been with —"

"Nay!"

Anne looked down into her lap, feeling a familiar tightening in her stomach. Silence as thick as fog hung between them. When Clifton did speak, it was of other things.

"Ayliffe does not need so many; we will move a number of

men to the demesne that the earl settled upon Sloan. He should begin to command them soon. When I must call on Sloan's arms, he should be ready. He is old enough . . . and quite soon I will be commanding both my boys and their arms.

"I commanded a sizable troop when I was little older than Sloan," he went on. "At Ayliffe, do you remember? I was already saddled with that whiny bastard, Brainard. Ha! Brainard, the slimy lizard. We do not often hear tales of his doings — you may thank me for that. His banishment from Ayliffe could not have been supported so well by anyone else."

She wanted to ask him if he had ever considered what would happen if she died, but she held her tongue. Brainard's title was, thus far, secure under King Edward. Brainard would return to Ayliffe one day, possibly with royal support for his claim, to do the like to Clifton. Anne, alone, but for Brainard himself, held the secret that Brainard was not a legitimate heir. And she held it for Sloan's sake. She thought that Clifton was oblivious to the greater complications of his life, but she was wrong.

"Soon, when the moment is right, I will have a long talk with Richard about Ayliffe's heir. Brainard has not been within the wall in many years, and he proved himself a traitor during the Warwick uprisings. Sloan would be better placed as the next earl. I think it can be fixed so."

Her husband rattled on about his plans. He would wait upon the king for a while, send a letter to Sloan to bring him home from Calais, take Gage with him as he installed his forces around various family holdings in England — all holdings that belonged to Anne and her children, with the exception of this new prize of Wressel.

She poured wine while he talked and carried a goblet to him. He took it from her, his eyes lively as he figured his plans aloud, pausing only to take a gulp. She used his pause, perhaps unwisely.

"Deirdre is my daughter. I will wed her where I feel Lord Forbes would have wished."

He stared at her for a long moment, his eyes darkening with anger. She did not even see him raise his large hand, but he slapped her fast and hard across the face, causing her to drop her own goblet of blood-red wine and reel backward.

"*No deFraynes*," he stormed. "Not now, not ever!"

Christmas passed as Clifton hung close to the court. Gloucester had retired to Yorkshire for the winter, the king's son was with Anthony, Lord Rivers, at Ludlow Castle, Dylan had taken Justin out of harm's way to Nowlan, and Clifton had the king as much to himself as he ever might. Anne penned all the many letters that Clifton wished to send to the Duke of Gloucester and others. Although she found her husband's politics inexperienced and clumsy, she finally knew that the only thing worse than Clifton's jealousy was his ambition. Once she had suffered because he was overly possessive; now she would suffer because he had many plans to elevate himself.

"If Richard Woodville can be elevated to the post of Lord Rivers through his daughter's marriage, and if Anthony, only a simple knight himself, can assume his father's title and become the governor of Ludlow; if young Grey can become the Marquis of Dorset, I can in like assume a higher station through my guardianship of Ayliffe, and the marriage of Deirdre, and perhaps even Sloan and Gage."

Clifton failed, in his dissertation, to name the important connection the Woodvilles had to this fast-rising wealth and power. They were the queen's family. She did not bother to tell him it mattered not to anyone, least of all the king and Richard of Gloucester, whom Deirdre wed. While Anne lived, Clifton commanded ten thousand Ayliffe men.

"King Edward loved Lord Forbes. . . . I do not know if we should expect him to expel the heir —"

"Lord Forbes has been dead a long time. Did you think I would be content to be your lackey forever? Nay, we will see this done my way, and you will not argue."

Over the winter Clifton had slowly developed an intense infatuation with the court and began copying their habits. Whereas he had once served the king at a great distance, now he wished to be a close vassal. While her husband enjoyed Edward's heavy tables and full casks of drink, Anne went to Elizabeth.

"The feud between the families is alive again in my husband," Anne told the queen. "He hates all deFraynes, though he is pledged to King Edward, and the deFraynes have a strong reputation for loyalty to the king. He should welcome such an association, but he forbids it."

"Your husband." Elizabeth huffed. "He has lately become quite a figure in the king's company." Elizabeth curled her lips slightly, obvious in her distaste. "I had thought to help you by approving your request to wed the knight, but now I wonder. I liked him better before we became acquainted. How can you curb his passion for a title?"

"I cannot, Your Majesty. Clifton listens to me least of all. But for Deirdre I would have young deFrayne, despite my husband's protests. DeFrayne is rich and strong . . . and loyal to the crown."

"Humph, it says something of your husband's own loyalty that he will not approve the marriage for you. I think he puts his own desires ahead of the realm."

"If approval does not come by your hand, Your Majesty, I cannot see them wed."

"My hand?" The queen laughed ruefully. "And what will *his* hand deal you, my lady?"

"Perhaps the king . . ."

"If Shore's wife puts his majesty in a soft mood, I will have a royal seal delivered to you, sanctioning the marriage." Mistress Jane Shore was the king's mistress, and Anne almost smiled to think that Elizabeth was clever enough to control her own jealousy and use the situation to an advantage. "I would prefer to have one of the Ayliffe heirs settled with a deFrayne than to see my husband bequeath more power to Sir Clifton. Deirdre's dowry is fat; with one of the king's best vassals putting it to use, my son's future in this realm is more secure. DeFrayne it shall be."

Anne received the document bearing the royal seal within a fortnight. Justin deFrayne was not in London, and Anne did not tell poor Deirdre, but had to let the brokenhearted lass endure the belief that she was forbidden to have her chosen knight. Anne had to bide her time past the new year and into early spring, waiting for an opportunity to take Deirdre to Justin. Clifton was busy at court and would not leave Westminster.

After returning from a hunting trip in March, King Edward fell ill. On April 9, 1483, he died. He was only forty years old, but he had lived a life of drink, gluttony, and general decadence for at least the last five years. To Clifton, who felt he had only just discovered life in his own decadence and ambition, the death came hard.

To Anne, the death came harder still, for she had not seen her daughter wed in time.

"I must ride to Gloucester," Clifton informed Anne. "He is the protector of the princes and I need to be his ally now. Time is short."

"Why, Clifton?" she asked. "The princes are young; Richard will be their guardian for a long time."

"Time is short for *me*," he said angrily. "I am older than Edward; I do not wish to die as a simple knight."

"But you're not only a knight — you're a baron with full title."

He spat into the fire. "Wressel is nothing. I have been your guard and consort for over ten years; what am I to do if you die before I have altered the inheritance of Ayliffe? Retire to *Wressel?*"

His eyes glittered, and for a man so large his fidgeting seemed odd. Anne swallowed hard. Worse than his ambition was his impatience. He was filled with ludicrous plans. He hoped to have Brainard disinherited, himself named as the earl, and Sloan as the heir. Clifton's heir.

"Ayliffe," he said. "I must have Ayliffe."

"But Sloan is Lord Forbes's heir. . . . If Brainard is disinherited, Sloan might take Ayliffe now."

"Nay, madam, that will have to change. But you need not worry; God willing, Ayliffe will one day fall to your sons through us. If there is no interference in their loyalty to me, that is."

As she watched him, she could see the plans formulate in his mind. Between him and Ayliffe there was only Brainard, if Clifton could sway some higher power to let him own that title. And between his affection for her sons and their loyalty to him, there was only Dylan.

She watched in sheer wonder as Edward's death and the events that followed plummeted them all into a debacle worse than the decade before, when Warwick had temporarily captured the power he coveted. This time, however, there was no king hovering offshore to land with armies and right any wrongs. This time the heir to the throne was a twelve-year-old boy.

Richard of Gloucester did not attend the burial of his brother, but intercepted Anthony Woodville and Prince Edward en route to London. Anthony, Earl Rivers, and the other escorts were taken as prisoners, and the little prince was brought to the Tower for his protection. Elizabeth fled into sanctuary in Westminster with her other children, where Anne visited her secretly whenever possible. By June Clifton was among the eight boatloads of soldiers who went with Richard and Cardinal Bourchier, the Archbishop of Canterbury, to the sanctuary to take Elizabeth's other son, ten-year-old Richard, into custody with his brother.

By the end of June Earl Rivers had been executed without a trial, along with some of Edward's other supporters. The little princes had not been allowed out of the Tower, and in churches throughout the city sermons were read about King Edward's invalid marriage to Elizabeth. It was bandied about that Edward had previously pledged himself to Eleanor Butler and given her a child; the troth-plight was considered no less binding than marriage, and Edward's sons were declared bastards. It was a favorite route to power. Yet again the conspiracy rose about legitimate versus illegitimate birth.

Richard crowned himself. Among his faithful followers was Clifton, Lord Wressel.

Queen Elizabeth, whom Anne had always found stronger than any other woman, wept copiously. "If only a mother could be allowed to see to her children. They should never take our children from us."

Anne thought of her own — Sloan still out of the country, Gage at Ayliffe, and Deirdre still with her at Westminster. Her letter, dated before the death of Edward, which sanctioned the marriage of Deirdre to Sir Justin deFrayne, was no longer valid. But within a week of Richard's coronation, Anne was sent word from Trenton that Marcella was dead. Anne hid the letter and began making plans for a conspiracy that might anger Clifton enough to kill her.

Richard's coronation at Westminster was on the sixth day of July in 1483, but it was late August before Clifton was summoned to ride with Richard as an escort back to York. Anne asked permission to take Deirdre back to Ayliffe. Clifton left her a twenty-man escort, some silver, and approved her decision. He did not wish to look after a family. Richard needed him.

"Perhaps when I join you at Ayliffe in the spring, I will be your lord," he said pompously.

"I have always named you my lord and husband, Clifton," she said.

"Do not even pretend you would be pleased, madam. I know you better than you think. Dare not interfere; that is my only warning."

When Clifton was gone, while Anne and Deirdre were packing, she crossed a few open palms with silver, sent messengers, bribed a priest, and calmly advised her escorts that she had just received word of her mother's death and must settle Deirdre at Heathwick before returning to Ayliffe. Any one of them, she advised, who worried at Sir Clifton's reaction to a change in plans, need not accompany her. She offered to hire escorts from London.

"You are the Countess of Ayliffe," said one. "It is by your order that we serve Sir Clifton." All twenty agreed to accompany her to Heathwick. It was the first time since she married Clifton that she had tested his orders for his men, and she was exhilarated to find they were *her* men. It calmed her considerably during her dangerous plan.

Deirdre, thinking only that they traveled to her dower demesne to settle her with her uncle Trenton, was downcast as they traveled. But when they entered the Heathwick gates and she saw Justin, her eyes swelled with tears of joy. She stifled a gasp of surprise, and a trembling hand rose to her lips. "Oh, Mother," she murmured, "thank you." And then, lifting her skirts, she ran into Justin's open arms.

There was more than one familiar face within the Heathwick courtyard. Dylan, who had been advised to send his nephew to Deirdre's holding, had delivered him. He stood beside Sir Trenton Gifford in front of the hall, looking at her across the courtyard. He was too far away for Anne to read his eyes. She glanced at her daughter as Deirdre embraced and kissed her knight. The young couple stood looking at each other with the caressing eyes of lovers long parted. Daphne had been correct. They could not have been kept apart for long. She looked back at Dylan. What about us? she wanted to ask.

Anne's reunion with Dylan was sedate. He bowed from the waist and she curtsied. She embraced Trenton, grateful that the reunion with her brother gave an excuse for her sentimental tears. They walked into the hall together, Anne between these two knights who were once enemies.

"This took great courage, Anne," Dylan said. "I was afraid you would not be able to succeed."

"I have not had success yet," she said, laughing nervously. When they were all seated before a warm hearth and the servants were out of earshot, she began to explain what must take place. "What we shall witness at Heathwick shall be called a celebration of a reunion. I obtained a royal sanction for their marriage from King Edward and Queen Elizabeth." Trenton leaned forward in surprise. "That's right, before the king died and Richard crowned himself. I placed a few careful pieces of silver with a priest in London who will swear that he called the banns and performed the wedding last February. Trenton, I hope your priest will perform a secret ceremony now to make the matter right. Later, your castlefolk may help them celebrate with a late wedding feast, but we must all get used to the idea that they were wed before the king died."

Dylan smiled. "God's blood, but you're clever!"

Anne shuddered. "We had best get these young people wedded and bedded before Sir Clifton finds out what I've done. All the cleverness in the world will not hold his anger at bay for long."

"Where is the hearty knight now?" Trenton asked.

"With King Richard in York."

"At the bastard's right hand," Trenton grumbled. He paused to await the service of three goblets of dark red wine delivered by a castle maid.

"You do not support this reign?" Anne asked in a whisper when the maid had gone.

"Few do, Anne," Trenton said. "Dylan and I have had several hours in which to discuss this atrocity. Richard still thinks Dylan his loyal servant, but there are many close to the king who are dissenters. It is for the princes that we hold back." Trenton glanced around. "Buckingham is not for Richard. If need be, he will lead a rebellion."

"Clifton is at the king's right hand."

"I am at his left," Dylan said. "For now."

"I saw you at the coronation," Anne nearly gasped. "You . . ."

"I carried his robes away from the archbishop, yes. Where did you expect me to be?"

"Oh, Dylan, again? This is dangerous work!"

"Aye," Dylan said. "When has it been otherwise?" He lifted his goblet toward Trenton. "There are good and brave people to work together on this conspiracy."

Trenton returned the salute, and Anne was suddenly filled with happiness. "You are allies now," she murmured.

"We have been allies for a long time, Anne," Trenton said. "It has been a spoken alliance for only a short time, but it was formed when I brought our mother here, to Heathwick. It was then that I understood and finally knew whom to blame." He looked away in discomfort. "You will take our mother's chamber while you're here. All of her things, her letters and clothes and jewels, will need to be dispersed. Read some of the letters, Anne."

"And now you engage in a dangerous conspiracy," she whispered to her brother. She could not bear to think that some rebellion against the king might cost her both Trenton and Dylan. "Be careful," she said, knowing better than to try to change the minds of either of them.

"What of Ayliffe, Anne?" Trenton asked.

"Clifton's labor is to convince Richard to defer Brainard's title to him. Under the order of widowhood, given me by Lord Forbes before his death, Brainard could not inherit the earldom while I live. Clifton hopes to share title with me and bequeath it to Sloan." She shrugged her shoulders. "Perhaps he will succeed."

"You must stay here then," Trenton said. "Ayliffe is not worth the cost of your life, and I do not believe Clifton values you."

Anne smiled at her brother. "Gage is at Ayliffe, Trenton."

"We could fetch him. . . ."

"I must await Sloan," she said. Before Trenton could respond, she shook her head. "Nay, I will not abandon my children. Most especially to Clifton. When they are settled away from Ayliffe, then I will consider such a move." She glanced at Dylan, and seeing his proud smile, her eyes became misty. She had to tear her eyes away, but too late, for Trenton had seen the exchange. He stood.

"If you will excuse me, I should visit the priest and set the cookery to work on a feast. We will have this done in a few hours." He leaned down and kissed his sister's cheek. "Convince her to stay here, Dylan," he said before leaving.

A long silence separated them after Trenton left the room. They looked at each other. He was the first to break the silence. "A dozen years ago it would not have taken us this long to be in each other's arms."

"That was a long time ago, Dylan. Other arms welcome you now. You are free to marry. You should do so."

"Would it help your case with Sir Cliff if I married?" he asked. "My Anne . . ."

"We have children in trouble," she said quickly, avoiding the subject of his many women. "Our problems are much larger than you think. Sir Clifton is close to the king and he is jealous of you, Dylan. I know very well what he intends. Unless our new king compensates him mightily, giving him the earldom, there are a great many people he must eliminate to obtain it. He will surely go first to Brainard so that he can assume the title through the failure of heir, through me. Then you will be confronted, and the reasons are clear only to Clifton. I believe he would like never again to see you in the same room with Sloan and Gage."

Dylan leaned his elbows on spread knees, sighed, and looked down at the floor. "I can almost understand," he said solemnly.

She went on, "I imagine I will be the last to go." She laughed ruefully. "Clifton may even allow me old age; I have long been a property he has been proud to own."

She continued, "But it is becoming terrible, Dylan. In the beginning Clifton was true to his word, content to stand at my side and oversee Ayliffe. But in the end you were right about him. I should have seen it when you did; I could have prevented much hardship. I should have abandoned Ayliffe and fled into sanctuary with Trenton. Undoubtedly the children would be safer were they not tied to that inheritance. It took a dozen years but suddenly Clifton realized what he wanted. It was not I; it was my power over Ayliffe. He asked me, quite recently, if I really thought he would be content to be my lackey forever. You may believe this; his ambition is far more dangerous to me and my children than his jealous guardianship ever was. Dylan," she said quietly, her eyes regretful, "he knows about Sloan. He forced me to admit the truth."

Dylan visibly winced as if in pain. She could tell it was all becoming clear to him then.

"I could not help it, Dylan, please believe that. I tried to protect my son . . . our son."

"Of course," he murmured. "I met the boy. He resembles me to some degree."

"As Gage resembles Sloan." She shook her head. "It has all caught up with us at last. Now we must see to the children. If they are to get their due, I must put their welfare ahead of my own, ahead of yours."

"Yes," he quietly agreed.

"If I am to help the boys, you must take responsibility for Deirdre, with Trenton. Send some of your own here to fortify Heathwick, if necessary. After today, there is nothing more I can do for my daughter. Deirdre must be kept safe from Clifton. I will go back to Ayliffe and do what I can for my sons."

"Anne, it is foolish to go back there now."

"Don't you see I have no choice? If I don't return, Clifton can work against me through my sons. He still has much influence over Sloan; Sloan has not seen Clifton in a long time. He would only remember his faithful teacher and would be hard pressed to believe that Clifton misuses his power. And Gage needs me."

"Have you any idea what Clifton might do to you, to Gage, if he becomes angry?"

She smiled confidently. "Until he manages to convince his king to bestow some honor on him, Clifton cannot really hurt me. He controls my soldiers for me, true, but they are still mine. Ayliffe is the only place I am truly safe, for many are still loyal to me there. Here, behind Deirdre's wall, Clifton could bring a force of thousands to liberate me . . . he could accuse my brother or you of holding me hostage . . . but at Ayliffe, I can still gainsay his authority, as long as I am careful never to act in treason against King Richard. Nay, Dylan, Ayliffe is still safer than any path of flight."

Dylan leaned forward, closer to her. "Let me help you, Anne. Let me get Gage to a safehouse. You would be safe there as well; letters could be written to Sloan. . . ."

Help. She almost choked at the sound. "I know you wish to see your sons safe, Dylan, but it is better if I go to Ayliffe and see to that myself. You need not concern yourself for now. If I need more help, I will get word to you somehow."

"I want you safe! I want you —"

"You have other women whose safety should be your concern. You —"

"Other women?" he questioned. She was afraid to look at his eyes. "The women you saw me with at court? Women convenient to keep Sir Clifton's jealous fits from harming you?" She looked back at him, her heart pounding.

"Don't . . . ," she quietly entreated.

"*Don't?* Anne, tell me your heart! Tell me now!"

"You ask too much . . . my children. . . . I do not hold you to foolish promises made when you were a lad, foolish . . ."

"And what of promises made as a *man?* What of promises made when I held my second son and I swore that I would never believe you loved me no more?"

She looked into his penetrating gaze, speechless. She looked hard. Was it still there? After all they had been through? She opened her mouth to speak, to shout, I love you still; I need you more than ever! Give me hope, love!

The door to the hall opened and a castlemaid peeked in. "Ma'am? Milady? 'Is lordship says come to the chapel when ye can, ma'am. 'E says come."

Anne recovered herself with some difficulty. "Thank you. We're coming." She shook her head and stood, still trembling.

Dylan touched her arm tentatively. "My Anne . . ."

"Let us get these children wedded and bedded, my lord," she said, her voice shaking. "We'll have time to sort out whatever difficulties remain after this weighty chore is done."

His deep turquoise gaze held her. He gave her arm a slight squeeze. "Rest assured, madam," he promised.

Anne could not suppress the longing in her own breast as she stood witness with Dylan to the quick ceremony in the church. Later, at the feast in the hall, they were attended by castlefolk, knights and archers. There had been no time to plan a celebration, but that did not dim the happiness of the bride. A few pigs and calves were slaughtered, wine and ale were liberally served, and finally, as nightfall was upon them, Anne helped her daughter prepare for the nuptial bed. Deirdre was beset by all the sentimental tears of a young bride, and Anne found it difficult to play the part of the stronger, wiser matron. She knew exactly what her daughter was feeling.

"This is not the kind of wedding your father would have wished you to have," Anne said with sentimental sadness.

Deirdre paused in her undressing and looked into her mother's eyes. "He would have approved of my husband, wouldn't he, Mother?" she asked.

Her eyes glazed with unshed tears. *If you were my daughter, I would want you to have a man such as Dylan deFrayne.* What more approval could Brennan give? She nodded. "He was a good man, Deirdre. He loved you more than anything. And he was more than wise; he was compassionate and forgiving. Yea, he would hold your happiness above all other considerations. Even now, I believe he smiles on you." She looked down for a moment, then raised her eyes again to her daughter's face. "Deirdre, I was not a perfect wife to your father, but please believe me — I did love him. I loved him deeply."

"Why does Sir Cliff wish me ill?" she asked, as if she had not heard Anne's near confession.

"He is a hard man to please," Anne said solemnly, averting her gaze. Because of me, she almost said. It was on her lips. She could not explain all the reasons, some jealousy, some greed, some simple overindulgence. But she knew he had become dangerous. "Do not worry about Sir Cliff now; let us prepare you for your husband."

As she saw her daughter readied for Justin, Anne was driven back in time. Small snatches of memories blended with her daughter's present happiness. She longed to tell Deirdre how her marriage to Justin finally played out a legacy of love, but she knew it was not the right time.

When Justin arrived in the small chamber amidst shouts from the men in the hall below, Anne felt a brief temptation to play the mother, to warn him to be only good to her all her life, to love her gently, to protect her for the rest of their lives together. The look in the young man's eyes stilled her tongue, for he was much as Dylan had been at two and twenty; ready, eager, and brave. And Deirdre loved him.

Trenton had directed Anne to her mother's chamber for the night and she stood nearby when he told Dylan where to take his rest. The celebrating went on in the hall below. In the chamber Anne used, Marcella's belongings were stacked in chests and bundles in a corner. There was no one else to see to these personal effects; Trenton had done nothing about the jewels, letters, and gowns. Anne thought the time as good as any and began sorting through Marcella's things to try to direct her mind away from her daughter's bedding and her own envy.

She gave the gowns a cursory look; some castlewomen would be delighted to share them. The jewels could go to Deirdre, for they were undoubtedly purchased with the allotment Brennan had provided for Heathwick.

Then came the letters. Anne was astounded to see a large trunk filled to the top with bundles. Marcella's letter writing had always been remarkable in its amount, but she had no idea that so many people actually responded to her. She picked up a bundle, untied it, glanced through a long page of dull history written by another dowager countess from Yorkshire. She sifted through many, just reading the date and the name of the correspondent; the most recent letter was over ten years old. With a bored sigh, she read.

Soon she was kneeling on the floor beside the trunk, a candle beside her, reading passages from page after withered page. Her cheeks grew flushed; her heart pounded. Through the subtle remarks written to Marcella by her acquaintances it became clear that Marcella had never really held tight her secret about Anne. All through Anne's years of marriage to Brennan Forbes, Marcella had dropped innuendo and gossip about Anne . . . until Trenton took custody and censored her. "I had thought C. of Ayliffe so demure and shy," one correspondent wrote, "but it is clear she deceives as you say." "I saw him, the one you say she slipped past Lord Forbes, and perhaps you are right; perhaps he got sired on the wrong side of the sheets." "She fools him now, but not for long. Do you dare name the sire? Is it the king?" And finally, "I would not breathe a word, my dear, for I could not bear to be the cause of your banishment by your selfish daughter."

It came as little comfort that most of the correspondence was from old women with much in common with Marcella. It appeared that her mother had written to most of England, accusing Anne of infidelity, and naming Sloan a bastard. Her mighty secret, confining her all those years with Brennan, was hardly a secret at all. How many knew? How different would things have been had Brennan actually learned the truth, as he had earlier claimed, and confronted her before the tryst that got her Gage? Had she not been full of Dylan's child, she never would have wed Clifton. Had she only known how early Marcella loosed her tongue. How many wondered? How many believed they knew? If there had been whisperings in Ayliffe, Jane would have dutifully reported them. Anne almost laughed, for in the end her mother had proved smarter. From the grave, Marcella could still do damage to her.

The noise in the hall below began to quiet. The candle burned low. Anne found the treasured letter, carefully wrapped, that had been written to Lord Gifford from Lord deFrayne. She carefully placed it aside to save: the letter that began their feud. She found several letters from her father to her mother, but one that caught her attention was not addressed to Marcella. Tears came to her eyes. The letter was dated January 12, 1435, ten years before Anne was even born. Though Daphne deFrayne was already married and a mother, Ferris tried to explain his own marriage, and his admission of unfaltering love. He wished his love well; he hoped she would find contentment. He hoped he would. She could only wonder why her mother had it. Ferris must have thought better of sending it, or Marcella had somehow intercepted it.

Over the years this attraction and collision between various deFraynes and Giffords had grown and waned, only to arise again and again. Did Daphne know of Ferris's undying love? Did she know how he suffered in his marriage to Marcella? Had Daphne likewise suffered in her wedded ties? Was it really only Lord deFrayne and Marcella who kept the feud alive because of jealousy?

And now, of course, Clifton had taken up the hatred. He had no real quarrel with Dylan. Even when she was pregnant with Dylan's child, Clifton had been aware of her circumstances. All he had demanded was loyalty, and she had not tested that oath once, not with so much as a glance. But as her sons grew tall and strong, Clifton had become more and more jealous that they were not of his loins. He often raged, accusing Anne of wanting Dylan still. When he learned that she had spent a few days at Heathwick with Dylan in residence, he would never believe she had been faithful. He would very likely beat her senseless regardless of her actions.

She dressed herself for bed and, taking only a candle, ventured down the cool, unlit gallery. The celebrating below was barely surviving the effects of drink and night. She did not knock, but slowly pushed the door open. Dylan leaned against the wall beside the hearth, staring into the flames, and then he slowly turned to look at her.

"Your nephew is settled with his bride," she said, her voice trembling.

Dylan stood straight, his eyes roving over her. "Two years ago he thought of nothing but wenching. I warned him some vixen would make him sing the vows from his aching heart." He smiled at her. "Would that I could sing them. Someday, then."

She dropped her gaze. "Did you know I would come?" she asked in a whisper.

"Some things, it seems, are more powerful than we are." She looked up into his smiling eyes and slowly entered the room, closing the door behind her. "Come, my Anne," he said, opening his arms. "Let me love you again."

They were not the same people they had once been, Anne reminded herself. The bodies that strained together now were older, not the young, well-muscled, firm bodies of their youth. Even their fears were tempered after having survived so many secret meetings. There seemed no hurry; they had lingered at the doorway of danger so many times before. But when Dylan's hand touched her flesh, she became alive in the same way. Passion was not only for the very young. Passion could endure.

Here, in Dylan's arms, she could even afford to think of the good years she had had. All things considered, she had been fortunate. Three children were born healthy and strong, smart and determined. Dylan, who had always been taken away from her at the worst possible times, had always returned. She had never really forgotten, never was able to truly convince herself that he would take her advice and forget their love. The time was too precious for sleep. She curled up close to him, her head on his shoulder, her leg resting over his.

"I will be a grandmother within a year. An old woman —"

"Hah," he said in a breath, brushing her back down to her buttocks in one long, slow caress. "Your body is as I remember it; no older by a day."

"Even though I worried about the consequences, I did as you instructed. In the late nights, if I felt afraid and alone, I remembered that you would always love me. It gave me comfort."

"As did I, my Anne."

"But I sent you away with a denial."

"Aye. How else could you survive? I knew, just the same."

"And never doubted? Never?"

"Sometimes I feared that our time would never come. But doubt you? Nay. How could I?"

"Oh Dylan, the barriers only become larger. Once it was our parents — now it is our children. And Clifton — he will be an adversary to remember."

"Don't go back to him," he urged.

"Abandon my sons? Nay, my love, that I will never do. Even this will pass."

"I will wait, in that case."

"You may be a very old man before . . ."

"Hush," he cautioned. "With you in my arms, I am forever young. There are troubles enough to keep us talking through the night, but my mind is turned to other things."

"I feel no older than in the cask room," she murmured.

"Nor I. But once I was driven by lust, and now, though my desire does not wane, I long for the comfort of the true substance of love. I would have long hours of quiet with you, walks along a country road, perhaps, with no troubles to discuss, no plans to hatch. My Anne, I love you as never before. Each year that we are apart it grows stronger, deeper. Do you lament your lost youth? Not I. 'Tis better, what we have now. Though we never had our day, never had the sanctity of marriage and public affection that we longed for, we have had each other just the same, and all I ever wished was to grow old with you. I was with you before and after our children. I was given the gift of watching you grow round with Deirdre, and though she was not mine, I felt more a part of you then than at any other time. And even now, while our youngsters test the boundless joys of love's pleasures, I suspect our own passion rivals theirs. Aye, my love, my Anne, little has changed. I am still your slave. I would die for your love. And . . . I will wait for you. Forever."

She turned her head slightly and kissed his lips lightly. The kiss grew deep and his hands moved again. He covered her body with kisses, stroked her thighs, her hips, pulled her hard against him and moved into her again. Just as the first time with Dylan, this felt natural and right. Their bodies together were like a rhythmic song, never a note out of tune.

Anne did not question it any longer. There was something eternal that happened between a man and a woman when there was deep love, when it was right. Dylan touched her just as she was meant to be touched, making her body rejoice. And it was the same for him; her touch caused him an agony of pleasure. Whether their mood was desperate and clutching, or easy and slow, the rapture was incomparable.

What can be done? she asked herself, relaxed again in the aftermath of love. How will my sons love me, an adulteress? How will my daughter accept me? How do we finally make right a love that was forbidden from the beginning? The answer kept coming back — it has endured through so much, it cannot be wrong.

"Dylan, do I shame my children with my sins, or do I cause them more pain in attempting to live in such deceit? Should they be protected from the slander that will surely come? Or, should they *know* their father? Sloan is grown now," she whispered.

"Aye. A good man; it makes me proud just to see him from a distance. You did well with him, Anne. Thank you."

"The choice of futures is his, Dylan. I can not mother him any longer."

He squeezed her closer. "Deirdre is married now," he said. "And Sir Clifton is no longer a good teacher for Gage."

"It will be difficult, Dylan," she said, her voice soft and almost distant.

"It has never been easy, my love. Tell me what you want."

"Come for him. Quickly and secretly. As soon as possible."

Chapter Nineteen

ANNE, with Jane and the small escort troop, finally returned to Ayliffe in the fall when the crops were in and the animals were being stabled. King Edward had been dead only six months, but for England and the countryside it had been a confusing time. Her people seemed glad enough to see her finally return, but their questions were all about Richard, how he had become King, and what had become of the princes. She fended off the questions as well as she could, making no real commitment for herself, but stressed that Sir Clifton had won a barony for himself and was hard for Richard's cause. Many eyebrows were raised above surprised mouths. She thought perhaps she had been wrong to call her best and most loyal people simpleminded. She wondered if they had long ago known Clifton's true colors.

Word came from Clifton that Richard had put down Buckingham's rebellion swiftly with the help of his supporters, and Buckingham and others were executed. Anne felt her heart lurch, but there was no mention of Dylan or Trenton as a part of that conspiracy against the king. Another messenger came; Clifton was staying at Westminster for Christmas. He did not wish to look after a family now. He was busy with his king. Anne breathed a sigh of relief. The longer Clifton was absent, the better for her.

Christmas was a lavish affair at Westminster, and word of it was brought to Ayliffe by traveling merchants, always the best route for news. It was said that Richard was enjoying the pomp and expensive possessions that had belonged to his brother. Despite the poor weather and the bad conditions of the roads, Richard continued his progress through England in January. Clifton's messengers with his word were frequent, and rested horsemen, archers, and knights were sent to replenish him at his command. There was no word of Dylan, and on a warm April morning in 1484 Clifton finally returned to Ayliffe. He returned in a high temper. He felt betrayal deeply.

"Where is she? What have you done with her?"

Anne was seated in the common hall on a large stuffed settle. There were only a few servants in the room, and only two knights of Ayliffe were present with their squires. At the sound of his booming voice uncertain frowns crossed the faces of those present and brought more of the curious to the doorways and stairs.

Clifton was travel-weary, dirty, and, Anne suspected, drunk. He looked unwell and had gained a great deal of weight over the winter. His tunic was stretched to its limits and he wore no armor. He displayed the badges of Ayliffe and the boar for Richard on his broad chest.

"Who, my lord?"

" 'Who, my lord?' " he mimicked. "Your daughter, madam! Deirdre!"

"Countess Heathwick," she confirmed. "I took her to her dower demesne, my lord. With Edward dead and Elizabeth in sanctuary, there was no purpose in leaving her alone at Westminster."

He approached her in a few quick, long strides and slapped her so hard across the face that she tumbled from the settle, her lip cut and her face instantly beginning to swell. Gage was halfway down the stairs and stopped in a state of shock. He had been the recipient of such a blow a few times, but he had never before seen his mother so abused. The two knights who previously might have left the room stood, but did not interfere.

"You've wed her to deFrayne," he thundered. "Against my wishes!"

Anne looked up at his towering form, gingerly touching the bruise on her cheek. She knew she stood on trembling ground on this issue. Some decisions were her right; some were not. She could gainsay Clifton in the marriages of her two eldest children, and the management of the Ayliffe estates, but in her position as his wife, the mother of the son he claimed, she was the subordinate. "She is my daughter, milord," she said quietly. "It was my obligation to see her wed where the queen willed it."

"The queen is Anne Neville, Queen Anne."

"Deirdre was wed secretly, in London, before King Edward's death. And yea, against your wishes, but with the sanction of the king and queen. There is a royal seal."

"She has been married for a year?" he asked, stunned.

"Aye," Anne returned skillfully.

"You *lie*," he screamed, jerking her to her feet and giving her a violent shake that she thought might break all her bones. "You played me false! I *forbade* you to wed her to a deFrayne! Do you expect me to believe you hid a marriage that took place in London? That you lied to me, all these many months?"

This time the men in the room were not so slow; both of them rushed toward Clifton, pulling him back from his attack. Gage came running the rest of the way down the stairs, but as he ran to his mother, his frightened eyes were focused warily on Clifton.

Gage, at the age of thirteen, was a large boy and equal in height to his mother, and he helped her to sit again on the settle. Clifton's face was twisted with his impotent rage; he was held most securely from behind. It brought to mind another time, long ago, when Clifton held a man who would attack her. Tears of pain and regret came to her eyes.

"I meant you no disrespect, my lord, but I had no choice. I could not tell you the truth sooner for fear you would interfere.

I meant only to settle my daughter. It is a good match; one Lord Forbes would have approved."

"Hah! The very notion makes me laugh! Forbes, approving a deFrayne!"

"By his own lips, Clifton. I swear."

"Unhand me," he ground out to the guards.

"You do not strike the Lady Anne, milord?"

"I am her *husband*," he said in a threatening tone.

Anne bolstered herself. "Clifton, use caution, I beg you. Do not abuse this dominion you have over me, for all our sakes." And then in a quieter voice she added, "Let my husband loose."

"Dominion?" he laughed cruelly, shaking off the men's slackened grips. "Not yet, but soon." He shook himself free of the guards and took a step backward, showing that he would not strike her again. Still, the guards did not leave.

"He told me to use patience," Clifton babbled. "After all I have done, he told me not to be greedy, but to be *patient!* You knew I wished for Deirdre's marriage to put me closer to the king's generous hand. Richard's son is dead, did you know it? Edward of Middleham, dead as a youth. An heir for an heir!" He began to laugh cruelly.

Anne's heart was in her throat. Richard's son, dead? An heir for an heir? Did Clifton admit that the princes were dead? He had done some dreadful errand for Richard; had he killed children to secure the crown?

"Clifton, what do you say?"

"He promised me I would have Ayliffe one day, but he delays. He prompted Parliament to pass new laws of property. Property cannot be transferred while prisoners await trial. Now, I am to wait. I *gave* him Brainard!"

Anne rose in spite of herself. "What?" she asked, confused, stunned.

"The rebellion is put down. Richard is king; Richard will be king. We marched from Devon to London. We put down the rebels, capturing, killing, and sending them fleeing. Ha! Your daughter's husband, his uncle — deFraynes unwisely chose the wrong side. They are gone, madam. Expect no support from that quarter."

Gone? Her mind asked the question, but her voice did not dare. Gone where? To flight? To death? Poor Deirdre. She could not even have her mother's consolation now.

"We took Brainard from his old Welsh Ramsford and liberated the keep for the king's men; Buckingham was killed, but Brainard is in the Tower. Alive. He could have been so easily killed; I should have killed him when I had the chance."

Anne did not see but sensed the men who stood behind her looking at each other. Many remembered the days when Brennan ruled Ayliffe with Anne faithfully at his side; they remembered Brainard. Anne's rule was not hard to abide when Brennan was gone and Brainard was sent away, and they were faithful to their lady. With Clifton, the people had continued to thrive through the peaceful years of Edward's reign. But Clifton had lately outdone even Brainard in his cruelty. The men of Ayliffe, bidden to protect the magnificent castle and towns, would not know whether they would do better by having Brainard or Clifton.

Her instincts told her not to discuss political matters with him, especially finding him in this enraged and unkempt manner, but she foolishly sought answers. While Clifton paced back and forth like a caged beast, Anne questioned him. "Did the king tell you why he chose to preserve Brainard's life? Was Brainard bidden to the rebellion, or was it only Ramsford keep that Richard wanted?"

"He uses my strong arm to possess the crown, to hold it against usurpers, with promises of great rewards, and all he gives me is Wressel. The Ayliffe heir was in hand and could have been finished; there is no need for him to live. How can I have Ayliffe if he lives? And Richard has promised me. He *promised* me!"

Anne almost breathed a sigh of relief. So Brainard was still the heir; Richard had not yet given Clifton his coveted title.

"Brainard has not bothered us for many years. He has been quiet at Ramsford," she said softly.

"He betrayed me," Clifton said, and she knew that he spoke of Richard, his king. "And even you betray me. You swore your loyalty to me, but the first time ever that I denied you something, you defied me and went your own way. Does everyone betray me?" He stepped closer to Anne, Gage still sitting on the settle, partly behind his mother's skirts, which earned him even more scorn. "Do you call yourself a man, you sniveling baby, hiding behind your mother?"

"Leave the boy alone, Clifton. You confuse and frighten us all with this anger. Brainard's capture was none of our doing."

He whirled away, running a hand through his overlong hair. Anne wondered about his presence when he was with the king. Did he allow himself to become fat and dirty even with Richard, or was this only the effect of the hard ride, the long campaign?

"No one here means to betray you, milord," she said to his back. She watched anxiously as he drew himself a full cup of wine and slugged most of it down too quickly, dribbles running down over his chin. He closed his eyes briefly, as if the brew calmed him. Then he smiled, and his eyes shone with mischief. "You delivered Deirdre to Heathwick?" he asked. She slowly nodded. "To accept her property?"

"And to join the husband she had been denied."

"Was he there?"

Anne closed her eyes tightly, thinking. "Lord deFrayne delivered his nephew," she finally replied.

"You are a whore," he said in a strained whisper. Gage shot to his feet, anger burning in his blue eyes. Anne held an arm across Gage's middle, forbidding him to take so much as a step.

"Everyone knows it," Clifton went on. "You are the most interesting gossip at court. They talk about you even in front of me, as if it does not burn me deep. But then," he laughed, "they call me the culprit to draw you away from your near-dead old husband." Anne closed her eyes hard. It was fast becoming too late to save Clifton from himself. She almost hoped he would spill it all out, publicly, taking the burden from her. She had heard whisperings all her life. She had read the letters at Heathwick. She had no idea how many secrets she actually held. She heard her husband chuckle wickedly, and she opened her eyes to look at him. She did not see the young, strong, faithful man who offered to keep her safe with marriage, but an obese, indulgent, obsessive fool. He bowed from the waist. "But of course they all say 'twas me to tinker with the old lord's woman. It was my pleasure, *chérie.*"

"Clifton, you must —"

"Do not tell me what I *must* do! You are a mere woman, and my wife. And as mistress of this keep you might distract the men from my command sometimes, so long as you do not interfere with King Richard's rule, but as *my wife* you will not gainsay my authority. You will not defy me again. You are my servant, my chattel, and you need be punished. Punished!"

Anne stiffened but held her chin up, keeping her bearing proud. "And for what crime am I to do penance, milord? For seeing my daughter wed?"

"For adultery," he grumbled.

"There has been none of that," she lied, knowing he could not prove it. She had stayed in Heathwick with Deirdre only four days and no one knew for certain that she went to Dylan. It had been much as it was in that time so long ago, at Ayliffe, when they exchanged but a few polite sentences by day in the company of other Heathwick residents, though by the dark of night she crept to his room. Only three nights in all. She prayed no one would betray her in that, even through conjecture or suspicion. Even her body served her in this secret, for she knew she was past childbearing.

" 'Tis an old adultery, for which you were rewarded with a good marriage, when you should have paid dearly. You were unfaithful to the Earl of Ayliffe, and he was killed before you could atone. I will consider the matter."

She should have known he would not expose the boys' true sire; that would put a wedge between himself and Ayliffe.

He refilled his cup, swilled the brew quickly, and slammed the silver chalice on the table top.

"Do not leave the hall, madam. I will return. Consider yourself prisoner for now."

I have been a prisoner all these many years, she thought in despair. However, before, his hold had been tight only to keep her close and watched so that he might own her completely. Now he wished to destroy her. She placed her arm around Gage's shoulders as she watched Clifton leave the hall and go to his men and his horses in the courtyard.

"Madam, what has happened to Father?" Gage asked.

"Try to keep a healthy distance from him, Gage," she whispered. "I fear he is unwell." She turned to the guards behind her. "You find me at my weakest, sirs. I fear I need locks on my chamber door and sentries without. But be cautious that you mind Ayliffe for me, and mind me for Clifton. Do you understand?"

"But my lady . . . ," one man began.

"His authority over me is absolute. His authority over Ayliffe does not exist until such a time as the king endorses him. Pray God, Richard is not hasty."

"You support Richard as king?" the other man asked.

Anne smiled briefly, causing her mouth to hurt. "It is bad enough to be punished as an adulteress; pray do not lure me into any punishment for treason. Richard is crowned. Parliament endorsed him. That much is done."

The men looked at each other again, scowling blackly, then left the hall to carry out her instructions.

Anne turned to her son and grasped his shoulders, carefully brushing her lips against both his cheeks. She saw him struggle not to cry, and she pitied him for the effort it took to behave like a man. Gage knew the family story, the one Clifton wished him to know — that he was sired on the wrong side of the bed, but born into a legal marriage.

"You must trust me, Gage, for Clifton loves no one today, and this is not your fault. You must not leave Ayliffe with your father, even if it means that you go into hiding. 'Tis a large house; there are many places to hide. Stay much out of sight until this passes. I do not think he will stay here long. He is too ambitious to have Ayliffe to remain here, even to dally with these punishments."

"When did this happen, madam? How? Why does he love us no more?"

She smiled sympathetically. One day he would know the truth, and she hoped he would delight in the news. There was a father who had never stopped loving and wanting him. And she would never abandon him.

"It is impossible to know," she sighed. "I did defy him with Deirdre's marriage, but I saw love in the maid's eyes and I could not deny her. And deFrayne is a good and powerful man; he adores her. Perhaps my husband's anger in that is justified."

"If he touches you again . . ."

"Nay, my love, my son. This business is between Clifton and me and has little to do with you. A man's treatment of his wife is his own cross to bear. Do not interfere. Take a lesson from this. You will marry one day."

"But if he hurts you?"

"I am strong, Gage. He cannot hurt me that badly."

"I don't know what to do. Sloan needs to be here to protect you. Tell me what to do, Mother."

She smiled at him; she was so proud of him. "If you will only trust me, and love me, I think we will mend even this, given time."

Bolts were placed on the inside of Lady Anne's chamber. The lady kept much out of sight throughout the afternoon. Gage was seen by two knights as he stole to the donjon to avoid his father. In late afternoon Clifton called together a group of three dozen knights to the hall to drink with him. They came warily, only one or two of them eager to imbibe. Then he called for his wife, and someone was sent to fetch her.

Clifton lounged in the chair on the dais he had occupied in the hall since his marriage to the countess. He was drunk and well fed, and his eyes glazed over. Anne descended to the common hall, surprised at first by the size of the gathering, but when she noticed Clifton's strange behavior, she reasoned he had some plan. She hoped that Gage had taken her advice.

"Ah, madam, you look lovely . . . lovely," he said. "You have always been proud of your beauty, have you not, Lady Anne?"

She dropped her gaze to the floor, unwilling to parley with him.

"Answer me," he snapped.

"Nay, milord. I do not think myself vain."

Clifton struggled against his growing paunch to sit up straight. He leaned an elbow on his knee, his chin on his fist, and stared at her through reddened eyes. He belched loudly, and she cringed. She had never been so ashamed. That she did not love him was not at issue. He had destroyed himself. There was nothing left of the pride that had burned so brightly in his eyes when he was a young man. She pitied him; she hated him.

"Do you deny you have defied me?"

She stiffened her spine and held her head with dignity. "I deny it, milord," she said softly.

"Louder. For these men."

"Please, milord, I . . ."

"You defied me. True?"

"Nay, my lord husband. I did not follow your wishes in my daughter's marriage, but I did not defy you. 'Twas my decision alone, with the queen."

"Never mind that," he slurred, sitting back in his chair, his belly swollen with food and drink. "Did you not deliver your daughter, Deirdre, to her dower estates?"

"Is this a trial, my lord?" she asked.

"Answer!" he shouted.

"I did. I delivered her to her grandmother's burial, her dower estate, and her husband."

"And was Lord deFrayne at Heathwick?"

"Aye, my lord. He did escort his nephew, Sir Justin."

"Aha!" The cry was victorious, followed by laughter, rude and almost shrewish for a man of his size. "Did you join him in bed, madam?"

"Nay, milord. I was well guarded."

From the corner of her eye she saw one of the men who had accompanied her on that journey turn away from the scene of questioning. She had no idea how much her people gossiped about her. Clifton had never mentioned Dylan deFrayne, especially in conjunction with her sons, a silence that she surmised was never to protect her, but to keep himself some dignity as her husband. Perhaps the knights whispered; perhaps many wondered. Perhaps the luscious gossip from letters written by bored, bitter old dowagers had traveled even this far.

She tried to catch the actions and expressions of all of them, but she failed to do so. In her heart she knew that Clifton was ready to expose her now, to name her sons bastards.

Clifton's voice came softly. "You loved him once, many years ago," he said, his voice barely a whisper.

She glanced around the room, her cheeks showing the fire of shame. She was terrified that he had hit his mark, that he would not cease until he saw her stoned. Would he speak the truth before them all? He could do it; he knew it all.

She tried to look into Clifton's eyes, but his gaze wavered as if he could not focus. "Many, many years ago, my lord. I was five and ten and our parents forbade us. But I beg you —"

"Do you remember Jane Shore, madam?"

The king's mistress was unforgettable. The way Edward had flaunted her was permanently etched in Anne's memory, and Richard's treatment of her later also could not be forgotten. Richard punished her publicly for whoredom. But the poor girl was truly an innocent whore, if ever there was such a thing. Jane Shore had been merely a loose, frivolous woman who delighted in her affair with the king. But she had never presumed on power, not ever. She had not dressed herself more ornately than the queen, nor had she spun conspiracies based on her position of power. She had simply shared her body, first with Edward, then with others. She had been a powerless, fleshly trollop. She had never been as dangerous as many virtuous women Anne had known over the years.

"Of course, my lord," she finally answered.

"Well," he said, spreading the word out loudly and with a breath. "If I strike you, these men will come to doubt me, for they are smitten with you." He chuckled. "They do not know you, of course. They do not see you as you are. You are selfish, hoarding your fortune and your children by Forbes. You delight in keeping me without title here. But they cannot deprive me of fair punishment of my wife."

"For what am I being punished, my lord?"

"For causing me to worry. For spending days in the same hall with your previous lover. And, of course, you were never punished for what you did to Forbes. You are only a whore, but few of us know it."

She dared not look around, but then neither did Clifton. Clifton hung on to the old lie that Gage was sired by him. She wondered why; he was surely drunk enough to tell all.

"You wish I would leave, don't you, madam? I will not. Food and drink are plentiful here. These men will deliver me a wench from the village to warm my bed now that you are locked in yon chamber. And I am still your husband." He looked at her long and hard. "Take off your dress."

Her eyes widened in disbelief. "My lord?"

"The punishment did well enough for Shore's wife; it will do for you. You may take your walk through the streets of Ayliffe at dusk, your feet bare and your body likewise. These hearty knights will spread the word among the townspeople. The sun will set . . ." He broke off in the middle of his well-planned sentence as it briefly eluded him. Unless the wine took the better of his head soon, she would have no recourse.

"You will carry a candle, as Shore's wife did. To your shame, madam. Mayhap you rule your castle well, but you serve your husband ill." He laughed suddenly, and just as suddenly he recovered his former surly disposition. "Take off your dress."

"Do you punish me for my sins against my former husband?" she asked softly.

"Yea, that and other discomforts."

" 'Tis not your right —"

"I make it my right. Do as I say."

She briefly considered defying Clifton, but feared goading him into disclaiming her sons. Better to take his punishment, unjustly levied against her. "Do you plan to have me walk through the villages in my thin kirtle, as Mistress Shore was made to walk through London?"

"Nay," he replied, leaning back and smiling. "I think you do not need a kirtle."

"My lord, you cannot —"

"*You* spelled out the confines of our marriage, madam, as I have been oft reminded. Over your body, I have dominion. Over these estates, the dominion is yours, for now at least. You need to be taught a lesson. Your people will learn of my might from this, I reckon. *The dress!*"

At his command, Anne braved a look around the room. She took quick note of a variety of expressions and postures. She was not allowed much time to survey her people, but she caught a few eyes cast to their boots, a few castlewomen hanging back in the doorways with pain in their eyes. She saw Jane, horrified anger shining in her eyes, a few scowling mouths, some disturbed frowns, questioning or frightened twists to lips; she did not see anyone enjoying the scene.

Faith, she told herself. Strength and faith were her only tools. She had been at Ayliffe for twenty-three years; since she was barely sixteen. She had made mistakes, but she had been true to her oath to keep the place well. If her people doubted her or did not respect her, it was their careful secret. They had always treated her well; few had ever defied her. Clifton was clumsy and drunk. He did not know what he was doing. In his effort to gain power and control, he could be yielding the last of it.

"Mistress Jane," she called. The servant came forward of the knights with a furious grimace on her lips. "My fastenings," Anne instructed, pulling her unbound hair over one shoulder.

"My lady, you cannot allow . . ."

"The fastenings, Jane. My husband has commanded me in this; and in this I fear to defy him."

She could feel the fingers of her old friend and servant tremble as she unfastened the dress. The dress was finally dropped around her ankles. Anne kept her eyes focused on Clifton, but his eyelids dropped now and then. She hoped he would fall into a drunken slumber soon. She wondered at the feelings of the men who surrounded her now. Were they too curious to avert their eyes? Would someone slay Clifton in the dark of night for this cruelty?

"Are my sins so serious that I am not allowed a kirtle?" she asked softly.

"You are insolent," he barked. "Nay, no kirtle. To the flesh, for you are not a good wife."

Anne could no longer look around the room. She prayed. She felt Jane retreat to safety.

"Do not forget, my lord," she said. "Alert the villeins that the Countess of Ayliffe does penance."

"Aye," he shouted, throwing an arm wide to the room in general. "Announce my lady to the streets of Ayliffe!"

"And a candle? As with Mistress Shore?"

"Mistress Jane," he bellowed. "Bring the lady a candle."

He waited while people hesitated. Looking directly at Clifton and not daring to look around, she quietly said, "My lord addresses his wife; do as he orders."

Slowly, but finally, a long taper arrived before her, but Jane could not meet her eyes. Anne felt sympathy for her friend. This was the first woman to attend her, to notice the young breeding in her. Her body was different now, heavier, sagging in places where once she was firm. She had given birth to large babies and there were sweet, memorable months of nursing them. Hers was not a girl's body, but a woman's. She wondered if this punishment was likely to hurt some of the onlookers more than her. She heard the door to the hall open and she bravely turned to see who went. It was Sir Gravis, a seasoned knight who had been at Ayliffe since Brainard was a baby.

"Sir Gravis," she hailed. "Do be certain that all the village is informed."

He did not turn to look at her, but she saw his lips quiver in what might have been a tempted smile. Clifton, swollen on his mission, did not notice. "Rest assured, my lady," Sir Gravis replied.

He is one, Anne thought. There were ten thousand here; it was difficult to know, precisely, who would side with her over Clifton. She counted on Gravis.

"The kirtle?" she asked.

"Keep it, then," he grumbled. "You are no worse than the strumpet Shore."

Slowly she let out a sigh of relief, but the kirtle was sheer. He had not allowed her much.

"The shoes, madam. Your feet will be bare."

She kicked off her shoes. Her hair was thinner than it had been in her youth, though it was still long. It did not cover her well. Two panels of dark hair hung over her shoulders to cover her small breasts, the back covering her posterior, but she was shamefully exposed and her cheeks were on fire, despite her determination.

"Walk," he instructed, gloating in his dominance.

She turned from all those gathered in the hall, leaving them all at Clifton's mercy, and left the hall. She sensed that the courtyard was nearly abandoned, but pride would not yet allow her to lift her gaze to be sure. She heard distant shuffling and whispering as she moved down the road from the central hall, through the inner bailey, under the portcullis, toward the church, into the village. The sun was making its downward path. It would take two hours to traverse this one road. She took a deep breath and tried to stop her shaking. She watched her feet, but even so the jagged pebbles cut them. It never even occurred to her to try to cheat the punishment, although Clifton did not follow her and she might safely stop walking, wait out the time, and return to the hall. But she opted to let the people see that she could be commanded, even mistreated, by her husband.

Ah, Sir Cliff, she thought. Once you would have let my shoe be wet by your blood to keep me safe and honored, and now you have cast off the last piece of dignity either of us could have claimed. For what? For Ayliffe? You divide our people, perhaps not in your favor. For Richard? Perhaps he will be king long past our deaths, but to what end do you do this?

[356]

And a boy who calls you father, who once would have ridden into hell to free you, will now abandon you as you torture his mother. In your last days of life, do you mean to prove your strength? There is more strength, my lord, in yielding twine than in brittle metal. Beware.

After she passed through the portcullis, she dared to look around. A smile of vain pride graced her lips. The doors to the village huts were shut tight; light did not protrude from their windows. She scanned the mighty Ayliffe wall. Gravis had done his chore well. She saw only backs of the men by the dusk light of the cressets. No one looked on her shameful walk. And if anyone looked, she wished to know who. Of ten thousand men, ten thousand more women and children, she did not meet more than a dozen mocking stares, and she knew each of those by name. So she walked. And walked. She was paying her penance to Clifton, collecting her reward from her people.

There was a face in the donjon she could not see. It would have ripped her heart from her if she had. Gage wept bitterly at the single candlelight moving slowly through the village below him. He knew her feet would be bloodied from the walk; her spirit possibly broken. He could not fathom the perversity that would cause a man to do such a thing to his own wife. He swore to himself that he would never let Clifton abuse his mother again.

The sun had long since set when Anne returned to the main hall. As she entered she was surrounded by quiet; the room was vacant of spectators and her husband was left sprawled in drunken slumber in his mighty chair. Her feet were cut and bleeding and her candle had burned to a nub.

She slowly climbed the stairs, tears from the pain coursing her cheeks. Cliff, oh Cliff, you have lost them, all of them, she thought. The men who guarded her door did not raise their eyes to behold her in her shame, but one leaned aside to open her chamber door. Jane ran to her, embracing her and crying.

"Be brave, my Jane," she consoled her. "Tend my feet and bring me food. Do not cry. It is too late for all that."

* * *

The sun was high up when he roused. At first he did not know the hour, but by squinting through the window into the inner bailey and judging the progress of the village, the condition of the common room, he suspected he had been left in his chair until almost noon. His skin prickled, his eyes burned, and he dashed from the hall, through the long, dim gallery, to the rear of the keep. There he threw open the door and vomited.

Clifton's insides were wrenched with pain. He had killed a goodly cask, he reminded himself. He cursed his age; when he was young he'd never shown nor felt the effects of too much wine. It had never made him drunk; it had never delayed him from early rising, nor from a full, vigorous day. It was a curse to become old. He was seven and forty. He believed he would die soon. He hoped he would die on his horse with a bloody weapon in his hand, but he was sore afraid he would simply fail to wake up from one of those bad nights.

He swayed slightly as he made his way back through the gallery to the common room. He drew a cold draft of ale to clear his head, but instead the room swayed more, and he left the half-filled tankard on the table. He trudged up the stairs, and at the top the twin chambers stood, two guards with crossed halberds standing before Anne's door. Something tickled his memory. She had done something that angered him, but he could not remember what it was.

"I would like to see my wife," he said.

The guards regarded him with caution, then uncrossed halberds, and one tapped lightly, then pushed the door open. Clifton noticed with some confusion that the men did not look into the room. He stood in the frame of the door, looking at his wife.

Anne was reclined on the day bed, her feet propped up and wrapped in sheepskin. Her hair was caught in the back in a single ribbon, giving her face full exposure. Her eyes were hard, and she frowned. He nearly winced at the blue swelling under one eye and at her lips, one half of her mouth thick because of a cut. He vaguely remembered that he had wanted to kill her, but he could not remember what she had done.

"Do you wish something, milord?" she asked, her speech poor because of the condition of her lip.

"I . . . ah, you are . . ." He broke off. A glimmer of memory that was long and far removed by years caused a sudden anger to rise in him. He remembered her beauty, her quiet strength, her dignity. He remembered when he had watched her distantly, when he had seen her run into Lord Forbes's arms, kiss his old withered cheeks, and welcome him. And the sight of the earl's gentle hand at her back, walking with her, had filled him with envy. She had loved Forbes though he was old. Why did she not love him in his deteriorating old age? Perhaps he should beat her.

Perhaps he had, he thought. His memory failed him.

"I will stay in my chamber until I am healed," she said. "Unless you forbid it."

"Nay," he said. "Do as you will. Your feet?" he questioned.

"Cut by stones in the road, my lord. My walk, milord," she reminded him. "Like the walk Shore's wife took for King Richard."

He stiffened slightly. He glanced warily at the guards by her door. He could not remember, but the men would. He was suddenly filled with remorse, but not for what he supposed he must have done to Anne. If he had acted foolishly, as he had fairly commonly in the past years, he would pay the price by having lost some respect. Though he did not speak of it to anyone, he knew that very thing had happened with his king, his king who was going to reward him.

He gave Anne a nod and departed. He went to the lord's chamber and dismissed the patient squire. He fell onto the bed, face down. I will have to be more careful, he told himself. I will have to force myself to remember things, and walk about this place with caution. It will take time, but I will regain these men. They were mine once. They will be mine again.

"An accident could befall him, milady," Jane whispered.

"My God, do not even think it," Anne returned passionately. "Clifton has done the worst that can be done to me. His own men already watch him carefully and keep me as far from his quick and mighty hand as they can. But Jane, my dear, if I am widowed and hold Ayliffe alone, with Brainard sitting as a prisoner in London, what would *Richard* do? Which one of his henchmen would be given a countess?"

"Clifton might kill you," Jane warned.

"Nay, he will not. But the next man, one with full title, might. Oh, Jane, Clifton is too stupid to be any more dangerous than this. I will suffer, true. There will be pain, true. But do you not see? King Richard has the best of it all now. He has the heir to this rich demesne in his custody, ready to be killed at the best possible moment, and Clifton, Lord Wressel, doing the king's will with ten thousand good, strong men. Richard surely knows that Clifton is loyal in hopes of one day earning this valuable property. Believe this, if Clifton dies, so will Brainard, and you will see your lady wed again, this time well into Richard's power."

"And what are we to do, madam? Watch this abuse? Stand silent through his rages?"

"Keep him well fed and his cup full, my faithful one. He cannot do much damage so encumbered. And when you deem it safe, bring me Sir Gravis."

Chapter Twenty

SOMEDAY, THEN.

Dylan's words haunted Anne while rumors assaulted her from outside the castle walls. Sometimes she thought herself so foolish, a woman of two score years, pining for a man. Other times, she thought it was the only sane hope she had. Their love had endured, despite tragedy and heartache. But the someday they had so often spoken of she knew might never come. Each year it seemed not closer, but farther away.

Clifton Warner had not left her alone for a year. From the April evening in 1484 when she had walked through Ayliffe doing penance until the following April, Clifton left the castle towns only on short errands of hunting and riding. But merchants, monks, and peasants from neighboring villages passed their way often, spreading tales that were very likely embellished along the road.

Armies were amassing in far corners of the countryside. Rebels were rising, raising arms. Henry Tudor had landed, and his name was whispered as a future king, but with caution and secrecy. Queen Anne, who had always been a sickly woman, fell ill at Christmas and died in March. There was talk of Richard's marriage to his niece, Elizabeth, Edward's daughter. In the small rebellions that dotted the realm, another name was often mentioned. Dylan deFrayne.

There were many names cautiously spread, but when she heard Dylan's name Anne's ears burned. There was a royal order issued for his capture and execution, but he still, according to rumor, rode fearlessly through England, through even Yorkshire with a small troop of no more than fifty men, gathering dissenters and calling for rebellion. He accused Richard of murdering the heirs; the princes had not been seen in well over a year. The deFrayne estates of Nowlan, Ewele, and Creighton were confiscated by the crown and held in attainder. Dylan was on the road again, not fleeing for his life this time, but riding with a cause. If he were captured, his life would be short. Anne heard nothing of Heathwick, but with Dylan, Anne's son-in-law rode; she had had no word of Deirdre for almost a year. She was not even certain her beloved daughter was alive. The only encouraging sign was that word of death always traveled faster than word of safe flight.

Clifton, surly and often depressed, stayed close to Ayliffe and was careful of his behavior. He must have sensed the waning support of the knights, for he had not beaten her again, something for which she was most grateful. When travelers passed through their hall, he listened as intently as she to the stories, and sometimes she saw his eyes twinkle hopefully and meet hers when word came of the king's resolve to capture and kill the treasonous deFrayne. Once he said, "Perhaps I shall find him, and capture him. Surely that would endear me to Richard and hasten his promised rewards." Such a statement would have frightened her a great deal more if Clifton had retained half of his youthful skills, or even his ability for combat-sharp planning. Fortunately, Clifton was mostly drunken bluster. It had proven unnecessary to prompt him toward food and drink. He kept his own mug filled.

It was with a great deal of pain that she watched young Gage practicing with the knights in the courtyard. He had grown tall over the year, and his skills were good, but hatred shone in his eyes, and it hurt Anne to see it. Clifton deserved the boy's scorn, but she had never hoped for this. She was sorely afraid that it might somehow fall to Gage, one day, to kill the man he had called father.

As she walked from mass to the hall on an early April morning, Clifton came upon her and grasped her by the arm, thrusting letters in front of her. "From Sloan," he snorted. "Read them." She began to walk away from him, not in defiance, but toward the main hall, where they might take a chair and read, but he snatched her up short. "Read them now. Here."

She sighed at his impatience. There was no way to read Clifton's moods anymore, for they altered swiftly, swinging high to low. She unrolled the vellum and read. Her eyes grew wide with horror.

"Madam, my Mother, and Sir Clifton," she read, her hands beginning to tremble. "At your call, I am come home and will arrive by the first day of June, or perhaps sooner. Your request will be met and I am ready to lead arms with you against the rebels. It pains me to know that those men I have admired and would have called friends would in treason oppose our king. One of them I would have welcomed as my brother. As a man of duty and by my code, however, I am bound to protect the realm with you. For Ayliffe and for England. Long live King Richard.

"Your son and loyal servant, Sloan."

Clifton smiled and his glittering eyes bore down on Anne.

"What have you done, Clifton?" He was silent and superior. "Will you tell me?" she asked again.

"I called him home. I wrote him letters."

"You cannot write, Clifton. Who did this for you?"

"What matter who? 'Tis done. Did you think I had no loyal vassals here? Come, Anne, surely you know that among so many, some are still mine. I go to London. I will be home for Sloan, however. And when I return, all that will stand between my inheritance of Ayliffe and Sloan's will be the truth. We shall see."

"You had letters written to him, calling him to arms against

Dylan and Justin deFrayne, on behalf of the king?" she asked, amazed at Clifton's cleverness. She would not have guessed he was smart enough to develop such a scheme. Clifton would use Sloan's loyalty to help him find and kill Dylan . . . and Justin. Unless she told her eldest son the truth, thereby letting Ayliffe fall as it might. "Do you really think that Ayliffe means that much to me?" she whispered. "To Sloan?"

"Do not forget Gage, my lady. When Sloan is home, we three shall do the king's work," he said. Then he turned and left her standing alone in the yard. She watched him stalk away. She followed him numbly away from the hall, toward the outer bailey. She could see that in the courtyard there were already about twenty horsed knights, and his destrier was held for him by a page.

"My lord, where do you go? And why?"

"To Westminster," he said blandly. "I await Richard's instructions."

"Has he sent word? Does he call for Ayliffe's men?"

"Do not concern yourself, my lady wife," he replied curtly, not looking at her, but swinging himself clumsily into the saddle.

She held his boot, half afraid he might kick her. "Clifton, do you go to harm Brainard? Please, do not!"

His destrier pranced and he glared down at her. "Get out of my way, Anne. Make ready for your son's return."

The bridge had already been lowered for Clifton's departure, plans for which had been arranged without her knowledge. Some servants within her household must have worked with him. None of the knights had warned her that her husband was taking a journey to London. No scribe had confessed to writing letters on Clifton's behalf. How many other good vassals did he have? For a year she had existed with the hope that in a critical moment, the people of Ayliffe would defend *her*, and abandon Clifton. Suddenly, the only ones she was sure of were Jane and Sir Gravis.

There was a great deal of shouting and cursing all around her, for another bothersome band of traveling vagabonds had approached the gate in hopes of trade. Planting and clearing had begun, and peasants from neighboring villages, who had been forced to use the grain they saved through winter for food, ventured to richer keeps and castles in an effort to trade for seed for the planting. They blocked the bridge for Clifton's departure with their carts and baggage. They were a scraggly bunch leading a cart of caged hens, a small wagon of what might be sheep's wool, and a third small litter of leather goods fashioned through the long winter.

In Clifton's impatience to depart, the largest cart was toppled into the moat and the hens' cages went crashing into the water. The would-be merchants, probably only farmers, scrambled to save their birds, undoubtedly their most prized articles, and Anne watched Clifton brutally kick an old man hunched over, who led a mule. The donkey backed away, the man fell, and their goods were scattered across the bridge, half in and half out of Ayliffe's mighty gate. The knights rode through them without caution or courtesy. Clifton's troop departed thus, leaving a grand mess and a good deal of bellowing and squawking behind them.

Anne glanced toward the gate to meet Gravis's eyes. She shook her head. Anne was usually a compassionate woman and would normally have taken pity on the poor group, offering to right any wrongs with coin, or in this case, whatever seed they needed, but she was in no such mood. She suspected Clifton's trip to London meant serious business with King Richard, to secure Brainard's execution or kill the heir himself. And soon she would be faced with her sons. Her choices would be cruel ones — to tell them the truth about their common sire, leaving them both without claims to Ayliffe and at Clifton's mercy, or to hold fast the lie and chance Dylan's death, perhaps at the hands of one of his own children.

"Will the lady of the keep see our wares?"

"I have no time," she returned brusquely. "You may trade in the village, but make yourselves swift."

"The hens have gone bad, I fear, but the leather is undamaged." She looked into the old man's eyes and felt sorry for him. She reached into her pouch and pulled out some coins.

"For your damage," she said shortly, putting a few pieces of silver in the old man's hand. She saw that one of his arms was withered and useless and his back was badly bent. He smiled gratefully, and toothlessly. "You can purchase what you need with this. Hurry with this mess; we cannot leave the gate open to vandals. Be quick."

"Look at our leatherwork, my lady, I pray you."

"Leave me be," she whispered, looking over the scraggly group again. Two women younger than she, dressed in pitiful rags and looking frail and hungry, lifted their skirts to wade into the moat to retrieve floating cages. A young boy, equally thin and gaunt, used a long pole to try to pull them toward the shore. Another old man struggled with his donkey, now refusing to move either into or out of the keep. The village people had already started to gather around the small cart laden with trinkets and leather goods.

"A new pouch for your keys, my lady? A new girdle or strap?"

"Nay," she said, turning to leave them and their mess alone. She wanted to get away from the confusion so she could think. She took quick strides toward the hall, her mind churning.

Her first frantic thought was that Sloan or Gage might kill their real father, but an even worse fear startled her — would Dylan be forced to end the lives of his sons to save himself? He would not, she decided. He would die, himself, first.

But if she told her sons the truth, that they were both of Dylan's blood, how would it affect their lives? Sloan had once admired Dylan, and Gage hungered for a father's love. But, bastards must make their own way; adulteresses lived at the mercy of their betters. Dylan was too far away, in too much danger, to help her now. And following her admission, would Clifton kill her? Would he pursue Dylan alone, out of jealousy? She had long since ceased to know what her husband really wanted.

She was unsure what to do about Sloan, but Gage was too young to be a part of this, too young to hear the truth while still living in Clifton's house, too young to go with Clifton in pursuit of Dylan. She would have to spirit him away somehow. She could wait no longer.

"My lady," Sir Gravis said from behind her. She turned impatiently to see what he wanted. "The leather goods, my lady. Have a look."

She jerked her eyes to that direction, both annoyed and confused. A man in a wide-brimmed hat was showing his wares to village women, while behind him the rest of his group was trying to put order back into their modest entourage. She checked eyes with Gravis. She did not understand, but lifted her skirts to walk swiftly toward the cart. The village women made room for her, retreating from the cart slightly. The man slowly lifted his eyes, his wide-brimmed hat rising. Dylan! His eyes caused her heart to lurch in an excited and terrified spasm. How many times had those same eyes glittered from under a peasant's hat, from behind the trunk of a tree, from a dark corridor? She looked slowly in the direction of Clifton's departure, but saw only the dust from the knights' horses. Still, she could not speak to him, for she did not know for certain who could be trusted. A word whispered in Clifton's ear by a village wench might be enough to tip the cart against her.

"What do you recommend, sir?" she asked.

His eyes sparkled. His lips parted briefly in a dazzling smile that was quick, and quickly gone.

"This purse of doe's hide should please her ladyship," he said quietly.

She shifted her eyes in the direction of the rest of his ragged group. "What does your family require of Ayliffe?" she asked.

"Only silver, my lady, if our goods please you. We will travel on to Huntingdon to buy seed. We farm near Huntingdon."

A farm near Huntingdon, she thought frantically. She had heard that Dylan traveled fearlessly in Richard's own country, stirring up trouble, rounding up rebels. He would be in Huntingdon.

"Will you leave by the afternoon light?" she asked, her voice quiet but courteous.

"Aye, my lady. We do not look as fleet as we are." Then, in a whisper, "Send him to me. . . . Anne!"

She picked up the doeskin pouch and noted that there was something inside. "How much, then?"

He shrugged. "Whatever you deem as fair, my lady."

She took a silver from her own pouch and laid it in his hand. Her fingers wanted to linger and she paused over his palm for a long moment. She bit her lip in indecision, then softly, "Deirdre?"

Another fleeting smile was his answer, and quickly he dropped his gaze to look into his hand, as if examining the coin. "This will do. My thanks, my lady. Visit Huntingdon yourself one day soon; a good city, certes!"

"Perhaps one day, but I cannot soon. I await the return of my eldest son. But the best of luck to you in trade."

"You are generous, my lady. Long life to you." He bowed away from her, keeping his eyes respectfully downcast.

The temptation was to linger, watch him for a while, or just remain near enough to assure herself that he was alive and well. She knew better than to indulge and she spun away, resuming her brisk walk toward the hall. Will this never end? she asked herself. The sound of his whispering voice, his eyes, his mere presence filled her with both hope and doom. She could find a way to send Gage to him, but when could *she* finally go with him, give up the lying and the penalties of loving him? Would she ever be free to escape to him? So intent was she with these deep thoughts, she nearly ran full speed into Sir Gravis's broad chest. She looked around the hall almost fearfully before whispering to her vassal. "How did you *know?*"

"One among them was not a peasant, although he kept his bearing low. There are whisperings, madam. Some of us remember days long past, other secret men, from the time of Warwick's short reign."

"What do my people think they know?" she asked. She had divulged nothing of a personal nature to Gravis, but only asked him for his help, when and if she needed it.

The large knight only shrugged in reply. "People are fond of guessing. I will only say that I never thought you were smitten with Sir Cliff, I thought you loved the old lord. We all knew, though, that the knight wanted you. In your presence he was a chivalrous knight — but among his own kind his more selfish passions were known. "I heard the old man urge you to the leather monger's cart. And?"

"Whom do I trust? If you betray me, it is surely over," she said uncertainly, knowing she had no choice now. She did not want to doubt Gravis, but then she had doubted no one before today. "Will you take my son to Huntingdon, Sir Gravis? By moonlight? In secret?"

"You have but to ask it of me, my lady."

Gage was more than a little reluctant to leave her, especially without any explanation. But the explaining would have to be done by another. And sending him away by night, with only Gravis to ride with him, to be left with a band of rebels, was the hardest thing she had ever done, although Gage was a large, healthy young man. She knew that henceforth he would ride with his natural father, on whose head there was a handsome reward.

In her doeskin pouch there was a crude coastal map. Only four cities were lettered, and Anne did not know how to read the directions. She guessed at the location shown by dotted lines, no doubt meant to be travel lines, but she nearly wept for all the good it would do her. She did not understand what it meant, where it was, or what Dylan intended her to do with it. Was this where he would take their son?

Equally terrified of Dylan venturing back to Ayliffe for any reason, she did not mention the map or her lack of understanding to anyone. She sent Gage off with simple instructions. "Say only that I await my eldest son," she told him. "And trust me, my love, that I send you to the best possible place."

Gravis returned to Ayliffe alone, passing the word to her secretly that he had left Gage in the grateful hands of the nameless leathermonger. She was not certain whether or not

Gravis knew who Dylan was, for these things were better left unspoken.

"The man told me to help you with the drawing, my lady. I know the route. It is a safe house for you; one Clifton will never find."

Anne smiled gratefully at Gravis. "You have been here a long time. Sometimes, I forget that." She took the doeskin pouch from her belt and passed it to Gravis. "Do you think it will ever be possible to leave here?" she asked him.

He smiled at her. "Before today I thought it more possible to leave than to have a place to go."

"And do you think you can take me there, when it is safe?"

"If God spares us from Sir Cliff, my lady. I say go now, while he is away."

"Nay," she said solemnly. "There is one more son. None of mine has ever been favored; no one has ever been neglected."

"Dangerous work, this," he grumbled. "But . . . I cannot work for Sir Clifton . . . and I cannot pledge to King Richard. Whom I will finally pledge to, I can only guess."

"Will you stand fast by me?"

"Yea, I do. You were steadfast in loyalty to the only noble I ever knew who wanted good for his vassals. This place cannot endure under Sir Cliff or Brainard. This I do for you . . . and Ayliffe."

Her eyes misted at the memory. She touched Sir Gravis's arm. "I did the best I could," she whispered. "I am sorry it was not good enough."

"Your best was better than that of many others, my lady. Do not weaken now."

She strained her eyes each day for the sight of Clifton's returning troop, quizzed each traveler that passed through their gates about the happenings in London and around the country, and prayed earnestly to be delivered through this terrifying time. It was the last week in May when the banner approached and Clifton was home. With him, Sloan.

The reunion was strained, for Clifton let it be known instantly that his plans had grown while he was on the road to London.

When Sloan crossed the channel from Calais, Clifton met him and took him to Westminster to wait upon King Richard. Sloan talked excitedly about his visit with the king, about his pledged arms to the cause to wipe out rebels, for Clifton had had Sloan's ear to himself for days. And Sloan was taken with the troubled young king and his serious household company of courtiers.

As she listened to Sloan, even though she feared she had lost him, she could not help but study him with her eyes. He was fully a man now. At four and twenty he was handsome and tall. He had mentioned no woman yet and had no plans to marry. He had traveled with a few English nobles into France, partaking of small battles here and there, securing some prizes of which he was quite proud. Now, home in England, he was eager to make his mark, build his wealth and reputation. She almost smiled, for he was rather pompous; a typical, immortal young knight. She wondered what principles really drove him. She wondered if the virtues she had taught him of honor, honesty, and compassion were lost to his youth, or if those qualities would rise in him again.

Oh Dylan, he is strong and able, and ours. Yet we do not know which way the winds of fate will blow him. Will he be your son or your slayer?

"You have been well tutored about these villains who would snatch the crown," she said. "What of Brainard, then?"

"Brainard," Sloan scoffed. "We did a piece of business there, Sir Cliff and I. After a long list of promises made to the king, he has secured a date for Brainard's execution. I shall stand heir to Ayliffe for my father's memory. Brainard dies next week."

"So soon," Anne said in a breath. What Clifton could not do, Sloan would. Richard might have thought it chancy to give Ayliffe to Clifton, but it must have appeared quite safe to give all of Ayliffe's fighting men, all this land, and these thick walls to the dedicated young nobleman she had raised. She almost smiled again, but the worst was surely yet to come. She watched Clifton wander about the hall and fetch himself a cup of wine. He was decently dressed, for once, and did not stagger in a drunken lurch. He must have paid attention to his indulgences and manners to have managed to retain Sloan's respect for this long. Anne had hoped that her son would see Clifton's true colors. Sloan had not been with Clifton for three years.

"It will seem rude to leave you so soon, but I must stand witness to Brainard's death. Therefore, we return to Westminster right away."

"And then?" she asked, letting her eyes close briefly, as she spun a silent prayer.

"Northwest, where it is rumored Tudor gathers forces with the help of deFrayne. Madam, do you see the opportunity in this?" he asked excitedly. "To put down a rebellion will win me much favor in Richard's kingdom, but beyond that, to support the king is my sworn obligation."

"You swore once to Edward. What of his heirs?"

"They are safe and hidden. To give them freedom would only encourage the Woodvilles to begin a new campaign to restore them."

"Do you believe that, Sloan?" she asked gently.

He looked at her now with cold eyes combined with a wrinkled brow. She remembered distinctly where she had left it with Dylan. Sloan was a man now. The choice of futures was his.

"What else?" her son asked. "They cannot be freed, of course. What troubles you, madam? I thought you would be pleased for me."

She shook her head. There were close to a dozen knights in the room, and when she had considered this black day, she thought of a secret conference. Now she realized that it was better thus. There should be witnesses.

"Edward's heirs have not been seen alive in almost two years. There are plenty of Tower guards who would have seen them, if they yet live."

"They are not in London, madam," Sloan said with a laugh, as if his mother was not nearly as adept at politics as he was himself.

"They are dead, Sloan. Surely it will be proven one day soon. Ask Sir Cliff. He knows."

Sloan looked at Clifton, but the burly man simply turned back to the full flagon to refill his cup. He shook his head and shrugged, as if he knew nothing.

"He knows," Anne insisted. "One night over a year ago when he delivered the news that Richard's son had died, Clifton said 'an heir for an heir' before a room full of knights. Sloan, my husband has an evil plan that will use you badly. He took you to the king not to provide your best opportunity, but to insure your demise."

"Sir Cliff?" Sloan laughed. At the same time, there was the sound of the full flagon of wine tipping off the table and spilling to the floor. Anne was startled and she looked fearfully toward Clifton. His face grew red and his eyes smoldered.

"Do not shame yourself with lies to protect your daughter's husband, madam. Do not spread useless tales here."

"What is it?" Sloan asked. He looked between Clifton and his mother, shaking his head and giving a short, nervous laugh. "What is amiss here? Do you quarrel over the keeping of the boys? What matter? Richard is —"

"Clifton wishes to have you chase down Dylan deFrayne and kill him . . . because Dylan deFrayne is your father."

Anne kept her eyes focused on Clifton. He had looked at her from over his shoulder, but slowly he turned to face her. His mouth was set firm, and the silence in the room was as hot as fire. There was not so much as a movement among the few knights present.

"She lies, Sloan. She wishes to keep you from joining me on this campaign. She wishes to protect deFraynes . . . for Deirdre."

Slowly she turned her eyes back to her son. His face had paled and his eyes were glittering with shock and disbelief.

"I once pledged myself to Dylan deFrayne. We were very young and filled with hope then, but Lancaster and York went hard against each other and there was war. I came to Lord Forbes already with child. Lord Forbes knew you were not of his loins, and claimed you anyway.

"Much later, Lord deFrayne came to Ayliffe. He was a spy in Edward's camp and pretended to be close to George of Clarence and Warwick; he liberated this castle from Lancaster for Edward. Yet another time I pledged to him, this time in sin, and he gave me Gage. To save me from my shame, and to keep me safe from a bad union of marriage to a greedy stranger, Sir Clifton wed me. Sir Clifton knew who sired Gage. He has always known. Later, by way of his fist, my husband brought forth the truth about you. Once it was enough for him to be my husband, Sloan. Enough to train you and Gage. But no more. Ask him what he wants now. He means to have Ayliffe, and revenge."

"Lies," Clifton shouted, banging his fist on the table.

Sloan looked at Clifton, whose hard eyes were focused on Anne, and then back at his mother. He was speechless.

"Brainard must die," Anne said, "for Clifton to have what he wants. Then? Perhaps my death, for defiance of some sort? I tell you this so that you will not trust him and be tricked into killing your own father."

"Nay," Clifton rumbled. "The old earl would not go to her bed and she craved a man! 'Twas me she used for her pleasures. 'Twas I who sired the boy, Gage! And wed her when she was widowed, to have my son and stay with you. She is wanton! She cannot be long without a man."

Sloan glanced uncertainly at the faces around the common room. No one met his eyes. Only his mother would look at him.

"I loved Lord Forbes," she said. "I regret that I hurt him. But I tell you this, and 'tis truth I speak, truth that can be borne out by at least one witness — Lord Forbes knew I was unfaithful, he knew that I had loved Dylan deFrayne since girlhood, he knew about you and Gage, and he forgave me. He could have punished me, cast me out, divorced me, or even killed me, but he did not. Clifton, who has never had the right to make me pay for those sins, has punished me mightily. Even now, he would use you to mete out his revenge."

Sloan watched his mother's eyes and knew she spoke the truth. He glanced at Clifton, and back to Anne again. His lips parted in a rueful smile, but all that left him was a gust of air. "How could you?" he finally said to her, shaking his head.

She faced him bravely, her hands clasped in front of her and her chin held high.

"How could I tell the truth, Sloan? Or, how could I love Dylan deFrayne? Perhaps you should ask how I endured the terrible partings, the forbidden love I had for your father. Or perhaps you should question how I survived Clifton's beatings, his drunken stupors, his wild rages, or the night he forced me to parade almost naked through the streets of Ayliffe to atone for my sins, though they never were against him." Clifton took a step toward her, his face red and his fists clenched. "Nay!" she shouted at him, holding up a hand. "Do not slay me before Brainard dies, my lord, or you will hang for treason. It is within the rights of these witnesses to take you, for I am the countess here, and you are my husband."

She looked back at her son. One of the knights seated at the long trestle table near the door stood, as if ready, but Anne was uncertain whom this man would defend.

"You could not tell these tales in privacy?" Sloan asked angrily.

"Nay, I could not. The time for whispering has long since passed, Sloan. There is bad business afoot, and the choice is yours. Ayliffe does not really belong to any of us, unless it belongs to Deirdre. It does not belong to you any more than to Clifton. And what deFrayne does is for England, for a crown that was wrongfully taken. I bid you remember that deFrayne's part for Edward was to watch the greedy brothers, and if anyone knows King Richard's true colors, it is Dylan. If he is certain that Richard is wrongfully king, I believe him.

"Clifton would use you to his own ends. No matter what he says. His plan is not for Richard, not for the king, but for himself. And these truths need to be heard by witnesses, for you may be certain that my husband will be quick now. Your life is in as much danger as mine. And I will not let you ride toward your own father with murder in your heart."

"Why do you tell me this?" he asked, his voice barely a whisper. "Would it not be better that I have never known?"

"Now that you know the truth, anything you choose to do will be by your own will."

Sloan shook his head and paced nervously, trying to make sense of it all. When he paused before his mother, his eyes were angry and pinkened by the strain it took to keep from crying. "You are nothing but a whore," he whispered to her, baring his teeth.

Her hand flew with a natural motion as she slapped his face. Her eyes blazed with fury. It was not the name he had placed to her; she could not even deny that slur.

"It matters not what you think of me," she nearly shouted at him. "But you will hear this, my little lad. Your sire protected you for the sake of your reputation and inheritance, out of love for *you*, though he longed to know you, to call you son. And Lord Forbes, my husband, kept you safe and well and rich, out of love for *you*. And I suffered through terror, and pain, and even beatings that might have rendered me maimed, for love of *you*. God kept us all safe to see you grown, nurtured, taught. Many times we could have fled, but we always held fast to Ayliffe, for *you*.

"Do what you will," she said. "Call me by whatever terrible name you think I deserve. Even Ayliffe is not worth more lies and Clifton's trickery; you have the truth now. If in anger you abandon us all, or even if you choose Clifton's plans to cover the truth, Sloan, you know whence you came, and there will be no excuses for you." She took a deep breath. "If you hunt down your own father, a man you once knew and admired, you will at least know what terrible sin you commit. And . . ." She glanced at Clifton. "Gage is already with him."

"*What!*" Clifton thundered. "What have you done?" He came toward her in a fury, his hands outstretched toward her throat as if he would choke her on the spot. She did not back away or even flinch. She wished to know the truth.

Sloan stepped between them, his back to Anne, facing Clifton. Clifton stopped almost instantly. There would be no tussle. "Nay," Sloan said almost solemnly. "Perhaps she is not good, but she is my mother. You will not abuse her. It is no longer your right." He turned around and faced his mother. "And it is unnecessary. I will not live as the bastard son of a rebel."

"Think hard on it, Sloan," she said.

"Oh yea," he said, his eyes tearing despite his struggle to maintain control. "It should never have happened thus, madam. You should never have passed me off as another man's son; you should have borne me rightly, naming the sire. Now you and Clifton have left me dirty work to do." He sighed heavily. "I will bring Gage home."

Her lips trembled, but she clenched her hands together so tightly that her nails bit into her flesh. She remained silent, looking into his eyes, praying he would change his mind.

"Don't you beg me to spare deFrayne, Mother?"

"Nay," she whispered. "If you wish to kill him, you will find easy success. He will not raise a sword against you, Sloan. He loves you. His silence was for you."

"He is England's rebel now; alive, he can say me his son. His illegitimate son."

"You are who you are, whether he lives or dies."

"I think I hate you, madam," Sloan whispered. He looked at her long and hard and then, whirling away, quit the hall.

Anne stared at Clifton for a moment and then with eyes downcast, slowly ventured toward the stair. She was one step up when she heard a shuffle and the clang of crossed halberds, causing her to stiffen her spine and pause.

"Do you protect her from me? Even now?" she heard her husband ask. She sensed that the knights prevented him from following her.

"Yea, milord. Even now," one quietly replied.

It was hard to meet the eyes of her villeins, for Anne was certain that the word had spread rapidly through Ayliffe. That the Countess of Ayliffe had preserved for another noble a forbidden love that defied two marriages and shamed her children made for a scandalous story. In the three quiet days since her son had left Ayliffe, she kept to her rooms and forbade Jane to repeat what the residents were saying about her.

Then Clifton came to her chamber. He was allowed to enter by her bower guards and, once within, he dismissed Jane. The servant looked at him warily. "There is no need to worry, mistress. We only converse, my wife and I."

When they were alone he leaned wearily against the hearth wall, staring into the glowing embers. When he finally turned, Anne saw something rare in his eyes. He was sober and controlled. "What has happened?" he asked solemnly. "All I wanted was you."

"Then why?" she replied. "Why seek more of Ayliffe? Why pursue revenge on Dylan, through his own son? Surely you knew I could not let you do that."

"You could never love me," he said.

"I gave you all I promised to give you," she replied. "I was loyal, I stood firm beside you; I never strayed. Am I the fool, Sir Cliff, that I did not see that one day all those things you said would keep you happy would fail to be enough for you? Would title to Ayliffe succor you where I could not? Would Dylan's death please you where I failed? Would Sloan's pain give you pleasure?" She shook her head. "Ours was not a perfect marriage, Sir Cliff, but we might have survived it better. Do you pretend that it was love you wished from me? Would you even *know* it if I loved you? 'Twas the brew you loved, the fat table and wenches. Was that how you proposed to gain my undying *love*? From your drunken rages? From your fist?"

"I did love you," he said sincerely, with a pleading look in his eyes. "It was not my desire to hurt you, but to force you to love me. You are wise and scholarly, Anne. Why do you not see that you've made me a desperate man?"

"And what could I have done, Clifton? I tried my hardest . . . until it was too late."

He looked down into the embers again. One hand was pressed against the wall and the other was planted on his hip. Both hands shook.

"Richard has called my promised arms to Westminster. I am leaving to answer his call. Those left at Ayliffe will let you escape, if you can do so without causing a great stir. I suggest you flee. I do not want to hurt you more, but if you are still here when Richard has finally put down the rebellion, I cannot swear that I will be a kind husband. Sometimes it happens to me without my desire. Hide well."

He went to her chamber door without looking at her again.

"There were some years, Sir Cliff, that were not painful," she said quietly. "I respected your strength, your devotion to my sons. I thank you for that. I am sorry that we failed each other so badly in the end. In my memory, I will try to keep only those first, good years."

She saw him nod after a moment. Then he was gone.

Chapter Twenty-One

CLIFTON WARNER went to London to attend an execution, but the king vacillated; he postponed Brainard's execution, waiting for Sloan. Clifton knew with certainty, for the first time, that Richard was not inclined to reward him. All would pass over him en route to Sloan, who was young, smart, and sober.

Clifton had abandoned his indulgences on the day Sloan left Ayliffe, at first from absolute necessity. He did not wish to be caught sleeping off a heavy and intoxicating meal when some conspiracy was blooming. He did not fully trust the villeins at Ayliffe, and later he wondered about the men he took with him to Westminster. It was fear that kept him sober and without wenches.

Later, it was penance he did. The demons of envy, jealousy, and greed had overpowered him and caused him to try to crush the only person he had ever loved.

The date of Brainard's execution came and went. Richard was busy with spies, soldiers, supporters, and plans. The king meant to wipe out the rebels and maintain control of his kingdom, and he would do nothing to the Ayliffe heir without the next heir in place. And Sloan, who had left home with an oath that he would not live as Dylan's illegitimate son, had not been heard from. In frustration, Clifton went to the Tower.

Brainard was not an important political prisoner, and so he was allowed a room, locked from the outside, but without guards posted. The dozen or so that guarded the corridor where he passed had seen Clifton enter, but his presence in Westminster and the Tower was common and no one questioned him. A ring of keys that he had lifted from the cookery served him well, and on the fifth try he found one that opened Brainard's door.

He stood just inside and waited for Brainard to look up. It irked Clifton instantly that Brainard sat at a writing desk; his room was appointed too richly for a prisoner. He had a bed, a chest, a table, which he used for eating and writing, a stool, and a generous stack of papers, grooming articles, bowl and pitcher.

But Clifton was pleased to see that Brainard was pale and thin. He was not doing well in the Tower. His pallor spoke of no sunlight, and the stench in the room was hideous. Dark circles hung under the man's eyes, and his hair was falling out; he had a round bald head and long locks of reddish-gray hair to his shoulders. His clothing, once rich and ornate, was now old and threadbare, and his shoes were falling apart. But he smiled at Clifton.

"My teacher," Brainard said ruefully. "It has always been between us, hasn't it, Sir Cliff? Betimes I thought she was my enemy, or her brat, Sloan. But in the end it was you."

Clifton said nothing. He closed the door quietly, not bothering to lock it, and faced Brainard.

"Did she send you?"

"Nay. No one sent me."

Brainard laughed. "Not even the *king*? What of my execution, then? I had marked off the days; what is amiss? Or, my question should be, why must I die? What was it I did? Oh, of course, I lived. That's it, isn't it? I lived long enough to be a threat to Ayliffe."

"Nay," Clifton said, his voice rumbling like a distant thunderstorm. "You are no threat. Ayliffe has already been awarded. Sloan takes Ayliffe."

Brainard shook his head, and a sadness crept into his eyes. "I do not know why you have betrayed me," Brainard said. "Once, we were friends. Once, I looked up to you."

Clifton laughed. "When was that? You were no more than six years old and named me your lackey. You slept me in the stable to protect your harnesses and shields. Even she did not do that to me."

"Oh? She treated you so well, then?"

"Aye," Clifton replied simply, recalling that even as he had struck her and her guards had held him from killing her, she had addressed him as a wife should, as "my lord."

"Now seems a strange time to come here to gloat. I am imprisoned. Why bother?"

"For her," Clifton said.

"And . . . was she worth it, Cliff?" he asked quietly.

Clifton's eyes watered, but he ground his teeth, causing his jaw muscles to tense. "All she wanted was to be left in peace. All she ever asked was that no harm come to her or her children."

"Her children by deFrayne," Brainard flung with an ugly grimace.

"You would have hurt her, no matter the sire of her children. You hated her the first moment she arrived in your home. I was there and I remember."

Brainard began to laugh nervously. "If you do me any harm on her behalf, Sir Cliff, you are a fool. She will not thank you for it. Ayliffe is rich; there is room enough —"

He broke off suddenly when Clifton turned back toward the door. He hung the ring of keys on the nail by the door, and one of his hands crept under his short tunic as he approached Brainard. Brainard stood and kept the narrow table between them. In a swift motion Clifton drew the thick, sharp knife from his belt and plunged it, underhand, into Brainard's midsection. The younger man's eyes widened in shock, but the assault was so fast that he had not even raised his hands against Clifton. His palms were still pressed to the table, and a stream of blood began to run on the parchment on which he had been writing. A cough escaped Brainard, then another as his knees gave out and he began to sink behind the table.

Clifton held fast to the knife as the victim fell, and finally held the bloody weapon in his hand. Brainard was still, his hands grasping his opened gut. Clifton walked around the small table and crouched, wiping the bloodied knife on Brainard's shirt. He slowly stood, looking down at his first student. Brainard looked like an old man now, bald, pale, lifeless. His eyes were open; he died with the shock of betrayal etched on his face.

"You never understood," Clifton said. "Aye, she was worth it. She asked nothing of me but what I offered. And she would belong to me still, had I not betrayed her."

He replaced his knife in his belt, grabbed the keys, and departed, locking the chamber door. Brainard would be found when his next meal was delivered. Clifton left the Tower to go back to Westminster, but he left by the back stair. He dropped the borrowed keys in a barrel in the courtyard when no one was about.

She would never have asked it of him. She never wished for any man's death. Sloan was the rightful heir to Ayliffe, if not through birthright, then through his training and knowledge. Clifton was not certain, though, that he could keep himself from hurting Anne again. He was most unsure of his demon. Every moment the devil struggled in him, wishing for his day again. But at least Brainard could not be freed now to assault them.

He hoped battle would come soon. He could not endure the waiting.

One could almost feel the unrest in the rising of the dawn, in the sunset. Anne and Jane took ship with Gravis, for the land route through most of the breadth of England was far too dangerous. She left her people without a leader for the first time since her marriage to Brennan Forbes. She said good-bye to very few, for she did not know who was still loyal to her. And she did not know who owned Ayliffe. By now it could be Clifton, or Sloan, or even Brainard. She advised the castellan to open the gate at his own discretion.

"You take very little," Gravis had commented when he saw her modest baggage.

She had taken only simple clothing, some of the jewels that were hers from Brennan, some silver to see them through. Beyond the safe house to which Dylan had directed her, she had no idea where she would be welcome. Ayliffe would be at the fulcrum of a devastating struggle, and she knew better than to move toward Richard's court. There were few acquaintances who would open their homes to her, especially after the gossip about her and her children had circulated. She thought about Elizabeth, still in sanctuary. The queen, now called Dame Grey since her marriage to Edward had been declared void, would welcome her. But Anne did not dare chance London.

"I am leaving all this behind, Sir Gravis. A woman needs very little for retirement."

Anne had always felt her heart tug sentimentally when she traveled away from Ayliffe, for she had always loved her home. She had felt safe there, even through the brutal last years with Clifton. But this departure was different. She would never return. If her son succeeded in gaining the estate, he would not welcome her as the dowager. Clifton would only die there, fat and encumbered. Brainard? He might send out bands of soldiers in search of her. Surely he would hope to find her and make her pay. Anne thought of her hideaway and knew even that would be temporary. Perhaps she would eventually have to go to the continent and find a cloister of forgiving nuns. But first, she must learn of the fate of her children — Deirdre and Gage.

They traveled three days to Harwich by palfrey, pulling one cart for the slight baggage. They boarded a ship at Harwich that was bound for Calais. In the foreign city Anne disembarked with Sir Gravis to find the best vessel to carry them back to England and around the southern coast. She finally found a merchant trader that would land at Portsmouth. That portion of the journey was the most terrifying, since the king's ships occupied the Channel. Anne and Jane hid in the bowels of the ship for three days. At Portsmouth Sir Gravis was able to find a boat that would take them on to Plymouth, but the ship was not in good repair and was blown off course in a summer squall, leaving them aboard, tossed about mercilessly, for over a week.

It was during this portion of the voyage that Anne decided to confide in Sir Gravis. But Gravis declined to hear her confessions. He had heard enough, he said, in her conversation with Sloan. And he had known for quite a while that he had delivered Gage to Dylan deFrayne. It was not solely out of loyalty to Lady Anne that he had offered to do so much. In part, Gravis was motivated by an enduring respect for Lord deFrayne; he hoped deFrayne would liberate Ayliffe once again. But Anne was not so sure. She was left to assume that Sloan searched for Dylan and meant to kill him.

By the time Gravis was able to get a local fisherman to pilot a small craft from Plymouth into the deep inlet in which the safe house was supposed to be located, they were exhausted and famished. Anne had expected that it would be a long while before they could rectify most of their ills, since she expected a vacant house. She was reduced to tears of relief and happiness, however, when she met the residents already there.

The caretaker was the first to meet Sir Gravis and inquire who they were. Next was Sir Markham, who had been bidden by Dylan to keep the women safe. And within the comfortable house Anne found Daphne and Deirdre. There were shrieking, embracing, and many tears among all the women when they were reunited, and it was a long while before they could even settle into the many questions and answers that had to pass between them.

Once Anne and Jane were fed and clean, the four women settled before a hearth fire with goblets of sweet wine. The house on the coast was cold, though it was July, and they burned wood year-round. For the first time in years, Anne felt as though she were secure and at home. Her first question was whether there was a midwife to attend Deirdre, who had blossomed full on Justin's child and would have her lying-in soon.

"With Justin following a rebellion . . . ," Anne began.

"Did I not tell you that they would find a way?" Daphne laughed. "At least you had the good sense to get them wed in time."

"At least you are not as young as I was," Anne reminisced. "I was barely sixteen when Sloan came, and frightened. You are nearly a score. Ah, how my children grow old before my eyes."

"I'm afraid it is up to us to deliver my great-grandchild. Praise the saints, I am still alive to see it come," Daphne said with laughter in her voice. "At least there is more than me now."

"Deirdre, you are well? No problems?"

"None, madam, but that there is no word from Justin or his uncle. We do not know where the men are, nor what they do. Sir Markham travels weekly by horse to Plymouth to buy supplies from the merchants he knows, and there is nothing yet. I am afraid for my husband, but not for his child."

"And your brothers," Anne said quietly.

"My brothers? Sloan is in Calais, and Gage . . ."

Anne shook her head. "An explanation is long overdue." She quietly excused herself and returned a moment later with a large tapestry bag for keeping sewing supplies. Resting it in her lap, her hands on it, she took a deep breath and began to tell her story. Oddly, she did not tremble. Deirdre, in love with her husband and full on his child, would not abandon her now.

"My sweeting, it is Dylan deFrayne I have been most loyal to all these years. He is the father of my sons, your brothers. It was not my wish to defy two husbands, to hurt my sons with the truth, nor to have you ashamed of me. I loved him because I could not make the love stop. Somehow, we always found each other. And now . . . I sent Gage to Dylan to keep him safe from Clifton. And before Sloan left Ayliffe, he knew the truth. He hates me for it."

Deirdre smiled at her mother. "I know, madam. I think I know all of it. Daphne had to explain to me why her son would go to such lengths to help you. I am not ashamed of you. I could never be that."

Anne checked eyes with Daphne. Daphne shrugged. "There is a great deal of time to think and talk here, as you will soon learn."

"I should thank you, but first tell me how long you have known."

Daphne laughed lightly, too old now to blush over these scandalous trials. "I saw that light in Dylan's eyes when he was a boy. It was the same glow that I had seen in another young knight's eyes — your father's. But Ferris Gifford and I were never to have our day. I was wed to Lord deFrayne before I could even think of running away with my chosen knight. Thenceforth, I gave all my energy to bringing up my sons. My life was not sad, dear Anne, but mostly good. I am only sorry that Ferris suffered so.

"When I saw that same glow in young Justin's eyes, I knew we had to rise above that old feud. We cannot continue to torture our children with an old, futile hatred. Bless you, dear, for wisely delivering your daughter out of Ayliffe to my grandson."

"Deirdre," Anne said solemnly, "I did love Lord Forbes. I did try my best. And he adored you."

Deirdre nodded, her eyes becoming misty, more in sympathy for her mother's painful confession than any feelings of loss of her own. She had been only a little girl when her father died. She was a married woman now. She could not imagine never being in Justin's arms again. "I . . . think I know, madam, what you must have felt."

"And Heathwick?" Anne asked.

"Trenton is there, but the place is full of Richard's army. There is attainder on all the deFraynes from having it."

"We may be attaindered from Ayliffe soon," she sighed. "It will surely be closed to me." She looked around the modest, pretty house. "We may have lost everything but life. Yet, if I could stay here all my days, I would be content." She opened her cloth case and retrieved an old, yellowed parchment. The ink had faded badly, but she passed it to Daphne.

The older woman held it away from her eyes, straining to

read the ancient writing. Finally, she looked up at Anne, her eyes round and surprised. "Is this what I think it is?" she asked.

"The letter from Lord deFrayne to Lord Gifford. Can you make out the writing?"

She smiled suddenly. "My eyes fail me these days, but one thing is clear. I had not thought to see it ended this way." She rose to leave the room, carrying the letter with her. When she returned she had more than one parchment, the second one in two pieces from having been folded for many years. "I should have guessed we were of like minds, Anne. I, too, saved the precious letter." She passed the pages to Anne. "The dates are at the top."

Anne squinted to make them out. The letter written to the Earl of Heathwick by Lord Gifford of Raedelle was dated October 1, 1399. It explained that Henry of Bolingbroke was in London, Richard II was in the Tower, and Parliament had read Bolingbroke's claim to the throne. Gifford offered to lay down the arms that had been raised in defense of Richard for amnesty. The request was somewhat humbled and called on his old friend for compassion. Gifford had already lost many in defense of Richard.

The other letter, Anne's possession, written by the Earl of Heathwick, said very nearly the same thing, if just a bit more pompously, since his side had found the seat of power. DeFrayne called for Gifford's surrender, but offered both friendship and safety for fealty to Henry. It was dated October 2.

"The first could not have been received," she began. Daphne slowly shook her head. "Then who is to say —?"

"Exactly, my dear Anne. Had we compared the letters fifty or sixty years ago, we would have found the error. The couriers must have passed each other; the two small bands of knights and archers met each other too soon, midway between Heathwick and Raedelle. They may not have even known they fought each other. The battle that ended the lives of the Earl of Heathwick and the Earl of Raedelle was said to have happened on the fifth day of October, eight days before Henry's coronation . . . only three days after Lord deFrayne wrote his offer to Lord

Gifford. The two earls may not have even received their respective offers." She shrugged her shoulders. "There were no survivors. Who is to say there was not a third force of arms that did them all in, carrying away their own dead with them, removing their presence from the field? We will never know — there was war all over England then. Those of Raedelle were attaindered and lost their high rank because of their loyalty to Richard."

"It was all a mistake," Anne said in a breath. Tears came to her eyes and she blinked hard. "None of it should have ever happened."

"Later, I think, there were other reasons why they fought. After the deaths of Gifford and deFrayne there were other skirmishes. Each family sent out little troops to lie in wait for the opposition. But this was the beginning," Daphne said, pointing to the old letters. "And that was nothing more than a mistake. God's pity on us."

Jane and Deirdre were both silent and alert as Anne and Daphne recounted the years and the battles they could remember between the families. Anne told Daphne how she had met Dylan and how they had put down the feud together in that first meeting Finally, Anne pulled another letter from her satchel and gave it to Daphne.

"I don't know why my father attempted a letter to you, since the date indicates you were already wed to Lord deFrayne. And perhaps this is one of the reasons my mother hated you so . . . for I found it with her belongings after she was dead. But this was for you. You should finally have it."

Daphne's hands trembled slightly as she accepted the old letter. Tears came to her eyes, but she smiled bittersweetly. "He was a good and kind man," she said softly. "I think he suffered much more than I did. Did you know, Anne," she began, her voice cracking from emotion, "that it was your father who delivered me a tabard bearing Ayliffe's badges, that I might have my son rescued?" Daphne nodded affirmatively before Anne could even respond. "Just before he died." And then, rising, she very quietly asked to be excused. Daphne took the old letter out of the room. Anne suspected she wanted privacy for the reading, and for her memories.

"What will happen now, Mother?" Deirdre asked.

"Now?" Anne replied in kind. "There is nothing to do now but wait. I believe Sloan rides toward his own father with a hurt, angry vengeance. My youngest child has been delivered to his sire, and my husband is driven with a sick vengeance of his own, although in a moment of rare mercy he did allow me to escape. If I could end it all by tossing these mistaken letters into the fire, I would do so. But," she said with a sigh, "I'm afraid it will not be that easy for us." She reached into Deirdre's lap, giving her hand a squeeze. "I will pray for Justin, my love. You are young and deserve to have happiness."

For herself, Anne would ask for nothing.

There was no chapel, nor a priest to hear Anne's prayers, but she found that both the wilderness beyond the house and the beach offered her a sense of serenity that aided her prayers of thanks, of repentance, and even her requests. There were few duties in the small house, all of which the caretaker's wife and Jane could manage quite well. Sir Gravis and Sir Markham hunted, or traveled to Plymouth for news, so Anne was often able to enjoy the solitude and beauty of her surroundings. It was the first time in twenty-six years that she did not have to worry about the care and feeding of multitudes.

At this stage in her life there was very little she wanted for herself. She would be grateful just to know that her sons were safe and well. If she could hold her grandchild in her arms, her most ardent prayers would be answered. She prayed Dylan would survive the unrest in England, but she asked for no more, even on his behalf. They had been through so much, she would be content to know that they had repaid the saints by uniting Deirdre and Justin. She hoped Sloan would one day overcome his anger and his hatred of her, but she wasted little time praying for that. She had given Sloan all she had to give; she had taken him from her breast and nurtured him into manhood with the

[390]

greatest of care. If he clung to useless hostility now, it was his burden.

For her husbands, both of them, she prayed that they would finally find peace. Brennan, after death, for his goodness and forgiveness, for the love he gave her when she was less than deserving. Clifton, in the remainder of his life, for those early days, as she had promised, because of his loyalty to her. She hoped Clifton could somehow overcome the madness that threatened to consume him.

The first month in the safe house brought Anne renewed health, for the quiet and peaceful place allowed her to empty her heart of hurts, pray for forgiveness, and give thanks for the many times she had been rescued. The second month brought cooler breezes and a new strength of spirit. She was two score plus one and felt many years younger. There were good years left to her; at least a score. Brennan had been far older when she wedded him, and even that shy girl of sixteen had found youthful vigor in her mature mate. Whether her days would be played out here, or abroad in some convent or sanctuary, she could look back over her life and feel with certainty that it had all been worth it. She had no regrets. She was only a woman, and her failings were no more than her virtues.

The leaves were beginning to fade when Deirdre went to childbed. The young woman had been courageous in wait for the birth, but was stricken with terror when the pains began, for there was neither physician nor midwife to attend her. She cried pitiously for Justin, still fearful he would not live to see his child. She cried for herself, for there was no one to nurse the babe if she died. It took all of Anne's and Daphne's strength to see her through the birth.

Deirdre labored through one afternoon and the whole night, finally bringing forth a son at dawn through frightful screams of pain. She was held down, and it was Anne's own hands that brought her grandson from her daughter's womb. The infant was large and squalling, pink and healthy.

"He is alive?" Deirdre breathlessly asked. "Whole?"

Anne's tears coursed down her cheeks. She was reminded of

Sloan's difficult birth, his large size. She remembered holding him to her breast, thankful to have that part of Dylan, though she might never again have him. Did Sloan find his father? she wondered. Did he ever know how he had been loved?

"Alive. Strong. Beautiful." She wrapped the babe in a linen towel and passed him to Deirdre. She felt her hands trembling. She knew Deirdre would be all right, but she wondered about her other children. A mother, she learned, never stops fearing for her children, even when they have grown and left her.

Daphne's hand was on Anne's shoulder. "Leave Deirdre with me, Anne. She will sleep soon. It's all right."

She has seen my tears before, Anne thought, and has always understood. That my own mother never knew my joys or sorrows always pained me deeply, but that the gift of this woman's love is mine, has always been mine, has ever eased the pain. "Thank you," she whispered.

Anne removed the apron, soiled from the birth, and descended from Deirdre's room. She looked at the inlet first, seeing the glitter of a rising sun move on the water, and then she opened the door to the front of the house to join the forest for the dawn. Each morning here was like a birth as the animals came alive, made their early morning noises, and the sea fog began to lift from the land. She could smell the fish, the dew on the trees and flowers, and the thick moss from the nearby marshes. It was good and clean.

The clearing before the house was small. She sat on a favored stump left by the caretaker last spring and let the chilling morning refresh her. Deirdre had done well.

Suddenly, the chirping ceased and she was aware of another sound. She heard the rustling of brush, but the morning fog was still dense and she could see only the trunks of the trees at the clearing's edge. The marshes and woods around this place were plentiful with boar and deer, food for their table, and she stood, thinking she might have to make a dash for the front door if a beast of the forest threatened. Sir Markham and Sir Gravis were not yet evident this early morn, but the door was stout and would keep even the meanest beast at bay.

But the beast was not of the four-legged type. Through the brush that blocked the road, bushes that had purposely been left in place to keep the passages concealed, Anne saw the two booted feet. Her heart thumped at the sight; her first thought was that they could not be rousted and arrested by the king's men on the morning of Deirdre's birthing. Then the man broke through and she saw the weary traveler emerge, his visor up and his tabard covered by a heavy cloak. Her lips issued a voiceless prayer. He led his horse and was followed by another man, still astride, likewise dressed for warmth. A third. Tears blurred her eyes.

Dylan left his mount while the others stayed astride behind him. He approached her slowly, limping slightly. There was a contrite smile on his lips, a smile of sorrow and joy. In his eyes there were also tears. He paused a few paces in front of her.

"The battle was done in Bosworth Field," he quietly told her. "Richard fell to Henry Tudor's own sword. So did Clifton Warner fall in the fighting."

Her hand rose shakily toward him, as if she would touch his chest to be assured he was alive. "My sons?" she asked in a fearful whisper.

Dylan stepped closer, a limping step, and took her trembling hand in both of his. "Your family is come home, my love," he whispered. "All of them."

She looked past him and saw there were three riders moving closer to dismount, slowly penetrating the fog. She could not yet see their faces, but by their silhouettes she assumed it was Justin, Gage, and even Sloan. She looked at Dylan again. Dylan tilted his head and smiled. "It appears he grew into a man who could feel love . . . for eventually he seemed to understand. Not well, but well enough to accept a father's pain, plight, and commitment."

Anne advanced, leaning against him and touching his beard and roughened cheeks with both hands. She sobbed his name and required his strength to keep her upright. "Do not leave me, Dylan. Do not leave me again."

"Nay, my Anne," he whispered. "Never again."